OCR gateway

GCSE separate sciences

Authors

Graham Bone

Simon Broadley

Sue Hocking

Mark Matthews

Jim Newall

Angela Saunders

Nigel Saunders

Contents

ST BENEDICT'S SCHOOL
BEETONS WAY
BURY ST EDMUNDS
IP32 6RH

How to use this book

Welcome to the continuation of your Gateway GCSE courses in Biology, Chemistry, and Physics. This book has been specially written by experienced teachers and examiners to match the 2011 specification.

On these two pages you can see the types of pages you will find in this book, and the features on them. Everything in the book is designed to provide you with the support you need to help you prepare for your examinations and achieve your best.

Module openers

Specification matching grid: This shows you how the pages in the module match to the exam specifications, so you can track your progress through the module as you learn.

Why study this module: Here you can read about the reasons why the science you're about to learn is relevant to your everyday life.

You should remember: This list is a summary of the things you've already learnt that will come up again in this module. Check through them in advance and see if there is anything that you need to recap on before you get started.

Opener image: Every module starts with a picture and information on a new or interesting piece of science that relates to what you're about to learn.

Main pages

Learning objectives: You can use these objectives to understand what you need to learn to prepare for your exams. Higher Tier only objectives appear in pink text.

Key words: These are the terms you need to understand for your exams. You can look for these words in the text in bold or check the glossary to see what they mean.

Questions: Use the questions on each spread to test yourself on what you've just read.

Higher Tier content: Anything marked in pink is for students taking the Higher Tier paper only. As you go through you can look at this material and attempt it to help you understand what is expected for the Higher Tier.

Worked examples: These help you understand how to use an equation or to work through a calculation. You can check back whenever you use the calculation in your work.

4

Summary and exam-style questions

Every summary question at the end of a spread includes an indication of how hard it is. You can track your own progress by seeing which of the questions you can answer easily, and which you have difficulty with.

When you reach the end of a module you can use the exam-style questions to test how well you know what you've just learnt. Each question has a grade band next to it, so you can see what you need to do for the grade you are aiming for.

Grades G–E
Grades D–C
Grades B–A*

Revision checklist:
This is a summary of the main ideas in the module. You can use it as a starting point for revision, to check that you know about the big ideas covered.

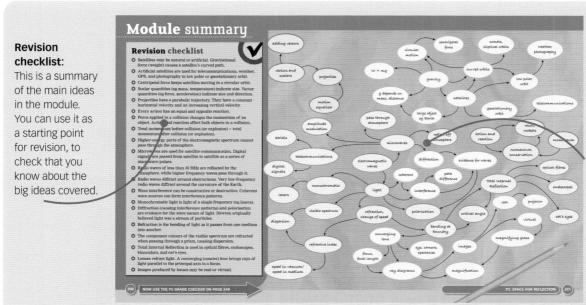

Visual summary:
Another way to start revision is to use a visual summary, linking ideas together in groups so you can see how one topic relates to another. You can use this page as a start for your own summary.

Upgrade:
Upgrade takes you through an exam question in a step-by-step way, showing you why different answers get different grades. Using the tips on the page you can make sure you achieve your best by understanding what each question needs.

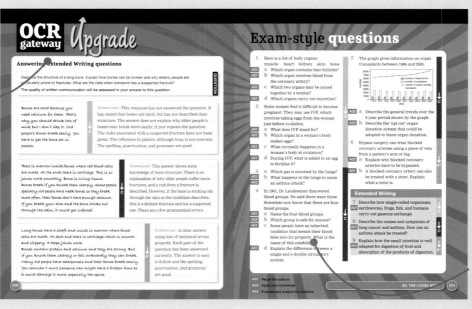

Exam-style questions:
Using these questions you can practice your exam skills, and make sure you're ready for the real thing. Each question has a grade band next to it, so you can understand what level you are working at and focus on where you need to improve to get your target grade.

Matching your course

The modules in this book have been written to match the specification so that you can take three separate GCSEs in science.

In the diagram below you can see that the modules can be used to progress from **GCSE Science B** and **GCSE Additional Science B** to **GCSE Biology B**, **GCSE Chemistry B**, and **GCSE Physics B** courses.

	GCSE Biology	GCSE Chemistry	GCSE Physics
GCSE Science	B1	C1	P1
	B2	C2	P2
GCSE Additional Science	B3	C3	P3
	B4	C4	P4
	B5	**C5**	**P5**
	B6	**C6**	**P6**

GCSE Biology B, GCSE Chemistry B, and GCSE Physics B

The content in the modules of this book covers all the things you need to know to be able to progress from taking two GCSEs in Science and Additional Science to taking three separate GCSEs in each of Biology, Chemistry, and Physics.

Understanding exam questions

The list below explains some of the common words you will see used in exam questions.

Calculate

Work out a number. You can use your calculator to help you. You may need to use an equation. The question will say if your working must be shown. (Hint: don't confuse with 'Estimate' or 'Predict')

Compare

Write about the similarities and differences between two things.

Describe

Write a detailed answer that covers what happens, when it happens, and where it happens. Talk about facts and characteristics. (Hint: don't confuse with 'Explain')

Discuss

Write about the issues related to a topic. You may need to talk about the opposing sides of a debate, and you may need to show the difference between ideas, opinions, and facts.

Estimate

Suggest an approximate (rough) value, without performing a full calculation or an accurate measurement. Don't just guess – use your knowledge of science to suggest a realistic value. (Hint: don't confuse with 'Calculate' and 'Predict')

Explain

Write a detailed answer that covers how and why a thing happens. Talk about mechanisms and reasons. (Hint: don't confuse with 'Describe')

Evaluate

You will be given some facts, data or other information. Write about the data or facts and provide your own conclusion or opinion on them.

Justify

Give some evidence or write down an explanation to tell the examiner why you gave an answer.

Outline

Give only the key facts of the topic. You may need to set out the steps of a procedure or process – make sure you write down the steps in the correct order.

Predict

Look at some data and suggest a realistic value or outcome. You may use a calculation to help. Don't guess – look at trends in the data and use your knowledge of science. (Hint: don't confuse with 'Calculate' or 'Estimate')

Show

Write down the details, steps or calculations needed to prove an answer that you have been given.

Suggest

Think about what you've learnt and apply it to a new situation or a context. You may not know the answer. Use what you have learnt to suggest sensible answers to the question.

Write down

Give a short answer, without a supporting argument.

Top tips

Always read exam questions carefully, even if you recognise the word used. Look at the information in the question and the number of answer lines to see how much detail the examiner is looking for.

You can use bullet points or a diagram if it helps your answer.

If a number needs units you should include them, unless the units are already given on the answer line.

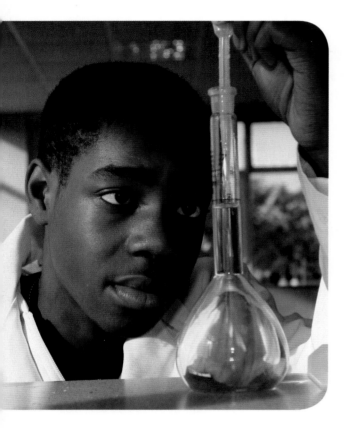

As part of the assessment for your GCSE Biology B, Chemistry B, and Physics B courses you will undertake Controlled Assessment tasks. This section of the book includes information designed to help you understand what Controlled Assessment is, how to prepare for it, and how it will contribute towards your final mark.

Understanding Controlled Assessment
What is Controlled Assessment?

Controlled Assessment has taken the place of coursework for the new 2011 GCSE Sciences specifications. The main difference between coursework and Controlled Assessment is that you will be supervised by your teacher when you carry out some of your Controlled Assessment task.

What will I have to do during my Controlled Assessment?

The Controlled Assessment task is designed to see how well you can:

- plan practical ways to answer scientific questions
- plan practical ways to test hypotheses
- think of appropriate ways to collect data
- assess and manage risks during practical work
- collect, analyse, and interpret your own data
- research, analyse, and interpret data collected by other people
- draw conclusions based on your evidence
- evaluate your method
- evaluate your data.

How do I prepare for my Controlled Assessment?

Throughout your course you will learn how to carry out investigations in a scientific way, and how to analyse and compare data properly. These skills will be covered in all the activities you work on during the course.

In addition, the scientific knowledge and understanding that you develop throughout the course will help you as you analyse information and draw your own conclusions.

How will my Controlled Assessment be structured?

Your Controlled Assessment is a task divided into three parts. You will be introduced to each part of the task by your teacher before you start.

What are the three parts of the Controlled Assessment?

Your Controlled Assessment task will be made up of three parts. These three parts make up an investigation, with each part looking at a different part of the scientific process.

	What skills will be covered in each part?
Part 1	Research and collecting secondary data
Part 2	Planning and collecting primary data
Part 3	Analysis and evaluation

Do I get marks for the way I write?

Yes. In two of the three parts of the Controlled Assessment you will see a pencil symbol (✐). This symbol is also found on your exam papers in questions where marks are given for the way you write.

These marks are awarded for quality of written communication. When your work is marked you will be assessed on:

* how easy your work is to read
* how accurate your spelling, punctuation, and grammar are
* how clear your meaning is
* whether you have presented information in a way that suits the task
* whether you have used a suitable structure and style of writing.

Part 1 – Research and collecting secondary data

At the beginning of your task your teacher will introduce Part 1. They will tell you:

* how much time you have – for Part 1 this should be about 2 hours, either in class or during your homework time
* what the task is about
* about the material you will use in Part 1 of the task
* the conditions you will work under
* your deadline.

The first part of your Controlled Assessment is all about research. You should use the stimulus material for Part 1 to learn about the topic of the task and then start your own research. Whatever you find during your research can be used during later parts of the Controlled Assessment.

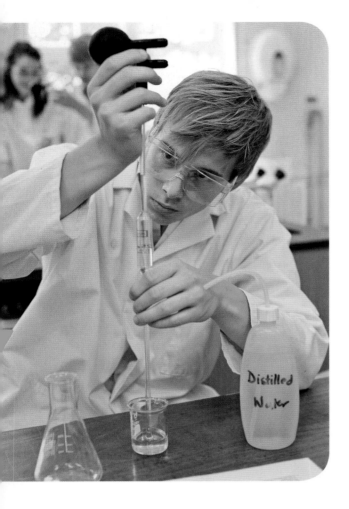

Sources, references, and plagiarism

For your research you can use a variety of sources including fieldwork, the Internet, resources from the library, audio, video, and others. Your teacher will be able to give you advice on whether a particular type of source is suitable or not.

For every piece of material you find during your research you must make sure you keep a record of where you found it, and who produced it originally. This is called referencing, and without it you might be accused of trying to pass other people's work off as your own. This is known as plagiarism.

Writing up your research

At the end of Part 1 of the Controlled Assessment you will need to write up your own individual explanation of the method you have used. This should include information on how you carried out your own research and collected your research data.

This write up will be collected in by your teacher and kept. You will get it back when it is time for you to take Part 3.

Part 2 – Planning and collecting primary data

Following Part 1 of your Controlled Assessment task your teacher will introduce Part 2. They will tell you:

- how much time you have – for Part 2 this should be about 1 hour for planning and 1 hour an experiment
- what the task is about
- about the material you will use in Part 2 of the task
- the conditions you will work under
- your deadline.

Part 2 of the Controlled Assessment is all about planning and carrying out an experiment. You will be given a hypothesis for the Controlled Assessment task. Once you have the hypothesis you will need to plan and carry out your experiment in order to test it.

Risk assessment

Part of your planning will need to include a risk assessment for your experiment. To get the maximum number of marks, you will need to make sure you have:

- evaluated all significant risks
- made reasoned judgements to come up with appropriate responses to reduce the risks you identified

- manage all of the risks during the task, making sure that you don't have any accidents and that there is no need for your teacher to come and help you.

Working in groups and writing up alone

You will be allowed to work in groups of no more than three people to develop your plan and carry out the experiment. Even though this work will be done in groups, you need to make sure you have your own individual records of your plan and results.

This write up will be collected in by your teacher and kept. You will get it back when it is time for you to take Part 3.

Part 3 – Analysis and evaluation

Following Part 2 of your Controlled Assessment task your teacher will introduce Part 3. They will tell you:

- how much time you have – for Part 3 this should be about 2 hours
- what the task is about
- about the answer booklet you will use in Part 3
- the conditions you will work under.

Part 3 of the Controlled Assessment is all about analysing and evaluating the work you carried out in Parts 1 and 2. Your teacher will give you access to the work you produced and handed in for Parts 1 and 2.

For Part 3 you will work under controlled conditions, in a similar way to an exam. It is important that for this part of the task you work alone, without any help from anyone else and without using anyone else's work from Parts 1 and 2.

The Part 3 answer booklet

For Part 3 you will do your work in an answer booklet provided for you. The questions provided for you to respond to in the answer booklet are designed to guide you through this final part of the Controlled Assessment. Using the questions you will need to:

- evaluate your data
- evaluate the methods you used to collect your data
- take any opportunities you have for using mathematical skills and producing useful graphs
- draw a conclusion
- justify your conclusion.

B5

The living body

Why study this module?

In this module you will find out about the changes in your body as you grow up and change from a child into an adult. You will find out about menstruation and fertility, and how fertility can be controlled or assisted. You will learn about the stages of human life, such as adolescence. Today adolescence is extended, as many young people want a university education so are not ready to begin a fully independent life until they are in their mid twenties.

However, more of us are living longer. 'Spare-part surgery' is increasingly possible, and you will learn about organ transplants and mechanical devices that can help heart or kidney function.

You will also learn about some of your body systems and life processes, such as your skeleton, digestive system, respiratory system, circulatory system, and excretory processes.

You should remember

1. You are made of cells organised into tissues, organs, and systems – such as the reproductive system, circulatory system, and respiratory system.

2. Your joints and antagonistic muscles enable you to move.

3. The male and female reproductive systems.

4. Puberty and the menstrual cycle.

In 2009, UK Biobank was launched. This is a major UK medical research initiative around 500 000 UK citizens aged 40–69 are taking part. They give blood, saliva, and urine samples that will be frozen and stored. Their DNA will be analysed. The participants also take tests to assess their mental faculties and answer questions about their lifestyle. As time passes, data about the participants' illnesses will be correlated with their genetic and biological data. Hopefully this information, along with the data from the Human Genome Project, will inform medical scientists about how our genes and lifestyle influence our health and life expectancy. This will help produce better treatments and medicines for people in the future. Within your lifetime, it will probably be standard medical practice for everyone to be able to have their genome sequenced.

Key words

cartilage, bone

A Name three functions of skeletons.

▲ The great white shark, *Carcharodon carcharias*. Its skeleton is made of cartilage.

Exam tip | **OCR**

✔ Remember that bone is living tissue. It needs a blood supply to bring oxygen and nutrients to the cells for their respiration.

The functions of skeletons

Skeletons provide

- support
- protection
- a framework for muscle attachment to allow movement.

Types of skeleton

Some animals do not have a hard skeleton

Many invertebrate animals do not have a skeleton. Those that live in water can become quite large because the water buoys them up. Earthworms are supported by the pressure of the fluid inside their body. The fluid presses outwards against their muscular body wall.

Insects have an external skeleton

Insects, along with spiders and crustaceans (lobsters, crabs, and prawns), have an external skeleton made of chitin. This gives a protective outer covering which supports the animal. It also gives a framework for muscle attachment. These animals all have jointed legs and their skeleton, muscles, and joints allow them to move. However, this hard covering can restrict growth. The animals have to shed their old skeleton at intervals and grow before the new skeleton hardens.

Some animals have an internal skeleton

Fish, amphibians, reptiles, birds, and mammals, including humans, have an internal skeleton. In some fish such as sharks, dogfish, rays, and skates, the skeleton is made solely of **cartilage** (gristle).

Your skeleton is made of **bone**, but there are places where there is still cartilage, such as:

- the tip of your nose
- your ear lobes
- at the ends of your long bones, such as limb bones and ribs.

Bone and cartilage are both living tissues. They have blood vessels and nerves and they can grow with the body. The internal skeleton forms a framework. Joints and muscles allow it to move. The many small bones of the spine give great flexibility.

More about bone

While you were growing in the womb, your skeleton was first made of cartilage, which is mainly protein. From about 6 weeks, minerals are deposited into the cartilage. These are mainly calcium phosphate. The cartilage becomes ossified – is turned into bone. Children have more cartilage at the ends of their bones than adults, because they are still growing. Forensic scientists can tell the age of a person from the skeleton, according to how much cartilage is still present. Both cartilage and bone can be infected by pathogens.

Paramedics have to be careful not to move a person who has a suspected bone fracture. Moving someone with a broken backbone could injure their spinal cord.

> **B** Why do children need to drink milk or eat cheese to make their bones strong?

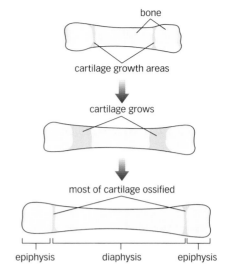

▲ How a bone gets bigger

The structure of a long bone

You can see from the diagram that the head of the long bone is covered with smooth cartilage. The outer part of the shaft is hardened bone. It can withstand compression. The shaft is fairly hollow. This makes the bone lighter than solid bones, but still strong. In the centre of the shaft are the bone marrow and blood vessels. Some fat is stored here, and new blood cells are made.

Bones can break

Bones are very strong, but if you knock them they can fracture (break). There are different types of fracture:

- Green stick – the bone is bent but not broken. Children with rickets are prone to this.
- Simple fracture – the bone is broken but the skin is intact.
- Compound fracture – also called an open fracture; the broken ends of the bone stick out through the skin.

Doctors use X-rays to look at the damage done to a broken bone before treating it.

Older people who have osteoporosis (soft bones) are more susceptible to fractures, which may happen in a fall.

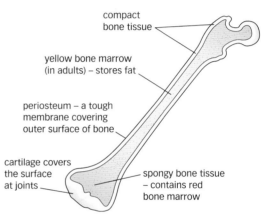

▲ The structure of a long bone

Questions

1 List and describe three types of bone fracture.

2 Find out how long a broken limb has to be immobilised in plaster.

3 Explain how the embryo skeleton changes from being cartilage into bone.

4 Why do you think there is a higher incidence of osteoporosis in Scandinavia?

Learning objectives

After studying this topic, you should be able to:

- ✔ understand how joints and muscles allow bones to move
- ✔ identify the main bones of the arm
- ✔ know that the biceps and triceps work antagonistically to bend or straighten the arm

Key words

tendon, synovial joint, ligament

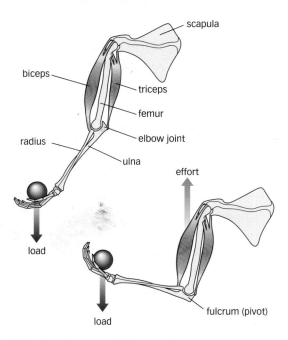

▲ How the arm works as a lever

A Explain how your arm muscles allow you to bend and straighten your arm.

B What are antagonistic muscles?

The human arm

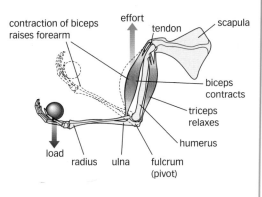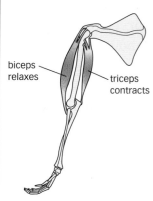

▲ The main bones and muscles of the human arm when bent and extended

When you bend your arm:

- Your biceps muscle contracts and your triceps muscle relaxes.
- As your biceps contracts, the **tendon** that joins it to the radius does not stretch.
- So it pulls the radius upwards and your arm bends.

When you straighten your arm:

- Your triceps muscle contracts and your biceps relaxes.
- The tendon from the triceps pulls on the ulna.
- Your arm straightens.

When a pair of muscles acts together in this way, one contracting and the other relaxing, we say they are antagonistic.

Levers

When the arm bends and straightens it acts as a lever:

- The elbow is the pivot point (fulcrum).
- The hand moves through a larger distance than the muscles.
- The muscles exert a larger force than the load that the hand lifts.

Joints

The contracting muscles provide the force to move your bones. However, you could not move if you did not have joints in your skeleton. Joints are where the end of one bone meets another bone. There are different types of joint.

Fixed joints

Your skull is made of many bones and they join together by fixed joints. At birth, babies have a cartilage patch on top of their skull, so that the bones of the skull can be squeezed as the baby passes down the birth canal. When these joints in the skull are fused, the skull protects the brain well.

Synovial joints

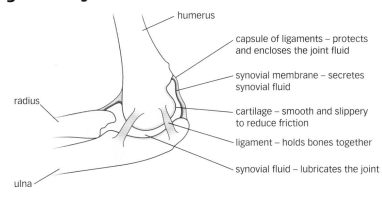

humerus

capsule of ligaments – protects and encloses the joint fluid

synovial membrane – secretes synovial fluid

radius

cartilage – smooth and slippery to reduce friction

ligament – holds bones together

synovial fluid – lubricates the joint

ulna

▲ A **synovial joint**

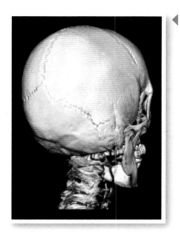

◀ Human skull showing the seams between the different bones

Joints that are freely movable are also called synovial joints. Synovial joints are well adapted to allow smooth, almost friction-free movement:
- The ends of the two articulating (moving) bones are covered in smooth, slippery cartilage.
- The whole joint is enclosed in a capsule.
- Lining the inside of the capsule is a synovial membrane.
- This membrane secretes (makes) synovial fluid.
- Synovial fluid lubricates the joint.

Ligaments join the two bones of a synovial joint together. They stretch and allow movement.

Examples of synovial joints are:

Hinge joints

At your elbow you have a hinge joint. It allows movement in one plane. This allows you to bend and straighten your arm and to also lift heavy weights. Your knee joint is also a hinge joint. You can bend and straighten your leg to walk, but it can also lock into place to bear your weight.

Ball and socket joints

Shoulder and hip joints are ball and socket joints. At these joints you can rotate the limb bones.

Did you know…?

By the time you are seven years old, your head has reached full size.

Questions

1 Where do you have fixed joints?

2 Name two places in your body where you have hinge joints.

3 Name two places in your body where you have ball and socket joints.

4 Explain why tendons are not stretchy.

5 What are synovial joints?

6 Describe the functions of the following structures in a joint: (a) synovial membrane (b) synovial fluid (c) cartilage (d) ligaments.

7 When you lift a heavy book, your biceps muscle exerts more force than the weight of the book. However, it enables you to lift the book through a large distance. Explain how it does this.

E

C

A*

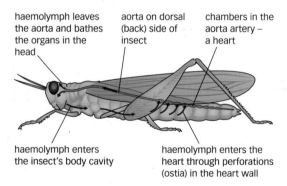

haemolymph leaves the aorta and bathes the organs in the head

aorta on dorsal (back) side of insect

chambers in the aorta artery – a heart

haemolymph enters the insect's body cavity

haemolymph enters the heart through perforations (ostia) in the heart wall

▲ An insect's circulatory system. It is an open system because the blood is not always in vessels.

A Explain why single-celled organisms do not need a circulatory system.

B Why is an insect circulatory system described as an open system?

Single-celled organisms

Small organisms such as amoebae do not need a circulatory system. They have a large surface area compared with their volume. They are surrounded by the water they live in. Dissolved oxygen diffuses from this water into the cell through the cell membrane. Waste material can diffuse out of the cell. There is no need for a special transport system.

Larger animals need a circulatory system because diffusion alone cannot efficiently transport substances to and from their cells. They need blood to do this.

Open systems: insects

Insects have an open circulatory system. They do not have arteries or veins, but their blood flows freely through their body cavity.

The blood makes direct contact with the organs and tissues. Blood travels in the aorta from the heart up to the head. It bathes the organs and muscles of the head and then trickles back through the body cavity. It passes over the gut and gets back into the heart through small holes.

Insect blood does not carry oxygen, because the insect's breathing tubes deliver oxygen directly to the tissues. Their watery, greenish yellow blood carries amino acids, sugars, and ions. There are some white cells to ingest pathogens.

Closed systems: vertebrates

Vertebrates have a closed circulatory system. The blood is contained in **blood vessels** – arteries, veins, and capillaries.

Fish

The blood circulates once around the body, from the **heart** to
- the gills, where it collects oxygen and unloads carbon dioxide
- the body organs and tissues.

The fish heart is a single pump consisting of two chambers.

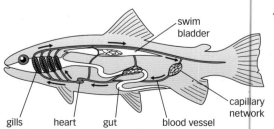

swim bladder

gills   heart   gut   blood vessel

capillary network

◄ The circulatory system in a fish. Because the blood passes through the heart only once on each circuit around the body, the heart needs only two chambers.

Humans

Humans and other mammals have a double circulatory system. There are two circuits from the heart.

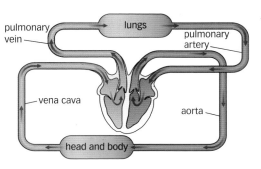

◀ The double circulatory system of humans

Blood passes
- from the heart to the body organs and tissues
- back to the heart
- to the lungs to remove carbon dioxide and collect oxygen
- back to the heart before being pumped out to the body again.

Because the blood makes two circuits from the heart, the heart needs four chambers. It is a double pump. Blood in a double circulatory system is under high pressure and so it transports materials more quickly around the body.

Galen and Harvey

In the second century AD, Galen, a Roman physician (doctor) of Greek origin, dissected monkeys and pigs. He noticed that blood in veins was darker than blood in arteries. He mistakenly thought that the liver made blood and pumped it in the veins to the organs, which consumed it. Galen's ideas influenced medicine for well over 1000 years. In the sixteenth century, Leonardo da Vinci studied anatomy and made drawings showing how blood passed through the heart chambers, and how the heart valves worked.

In the seventeenth century, William Harvey, a doctor at St Bartholomew's hospital in London, published a book showing how blood circulates in the body, from the heart and back again, and to and from the lungs. He realised that the pulse in arteries was linked to the contraction of the left ventricle of the heart. He discovered that veins have valves to prevent backflow. He postulated that there were capillaries, but did not see them as he did not have a microscope.

Did you know...?

The circulatory system consists of the cardiovascular system (heart and blood vessels), which is a closed system, and the lymph system. Lymph fluid is not always in vessels – the lymph system is an open system.

Exam tip — OCR

✔ Remember the difference between a closed circulatory system, where the blood is always in vessels, and an open system, where the blood flows through the body cavity.

Questions

1   Fish and humans both have a closed circulatory system. What is a closed circulatory system? E

2   Why do you think insects do not have red blood cells or haemoglobin in their blood? C

3   Explain why fish need only a two-chambered heart.

4   Why do humans and other mammals need a four-chambered heart?

5   Find out more about the contribution William Harvey made to our understanding of the circulatory system. A*

A Explain why the left ventricle wall is thicker than the right ventricle wall.

B A measurement of blood pressure inside the arteries when the heart beats gives 115 mmHg. In the capillaries it is 40 mmHg, and in the large veins 2 mmHg. Explain these different pressures.

The human heart

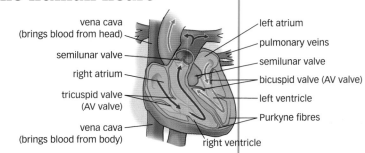

left atrium
pulmonary veins
semilunar valve
bicuspid valve (AV valve)
left ventricle
Purkyne fibres
right ventricle

vena cava (brings blood from head)
semilunar valve
right atrium
tricuspid valve (AV valve)
vena cava (brings blood from body)

▲ Section through a human heart showing the path of oxygenated and deoxygenated blood

Heart muscles contract to cause the blood to move. It contracts rhythmically to squeeze blood out of the **atria**, into the **ventricles** and then out into the arteries and around the body. The powerful heart muscle needs a continuous supply of glucose, fatty acids, and oxygen so that the muscle cells can respire aerobically and release energy for contraction. The strong contractions of the heart mean that blood leaving the heart in the arteries is at high pressure. As it passes along the circulatory system through increasingly branching arterioles to the capillaries, the blood pressure falls. In the wide tubes of the veins the blood pressure is very low; valves are needed to keep the blood flowing in one direction.

The left ventricle wall is thick muscle that produces enough pressure to push blood in the arteries all over the body. The right ventricle wall is thinner and the muscle is less powerful – it only has to send blood as far as the lungs. The lungs are delicate and too much pressure in the blood entering them could damage them.

The rate at which the heart contracts is controlled by a group of cells called the pacemakers. These produce a small electrical current that stimulates the cardiac muscle to contract.

The pulse: a measure of heart rate

As the ventricles contract and send blood into the arteries, the thick, muscular, and elastic walls of the arteries expand and recoil as a spurt of blood enters. This is the **pulse** that is transmitted all along the length of the arteries in the body. You can detect it where an artery passes over a bone or is near to your skin. Pulse rate is a measure of heart rate.

The cardiac cycle (heartbeat)

The series of events during one contraction is the cardiac cycle.

- The sinoatrial node (**SAN**) produces electrical impulses.
- These spread quickly across the two atria, which contract.
- This forces open the atrioventricular (AV) valves and pushes blood into the ventricles.
- A patch of muscle fibres called the atrioventricular node (**AVN**) conducts the impulses to special conducting muscle fibres, called Purkyne fibres, which carry the impulses to the tip of the ventricles.
- The two ventricles contract. This closes the AV valves and pushes blood out of the ventricles, through the open semilunar valves, into the arteries.
- The atria relax and fill with blood.

Then the cycle starts again. Each cycle is one heartbeat.

Changing the heart rate

When you exercise, your skeletal muscles respire more oxygen and glucose and make more carbon dioxide, which enters the blood. Part of the brain detects the extra carbon dioxide in the blood. It sends impulses to the heart's pacemaker to speed up the heart rate.

You also make more adrenaline when you exercise, and when you are frightened or excited. Adrenaline travels in your blood and affects many target tissues, including the heart's pacemaker, which speeds up the heart rate.

An increased heart rate also delivers more oxygen and glucose to the heart muscle itself, via the coronary arteries. The heart muscle needs to respire more if it is beating more times each minute.

Monitoring the heart

Doctors and cardiac technicians can measure the electrical activity in your heart. They get a trace called an **ECG** (electrocardiogram) and this tells them whether your heart is normal or not. A patient with an irregular heart rate or one that is too fast or too slow may need an artificial pacemaker fitted.

An echocardiogram uses ultrasound to make a scan and show any heart defects.

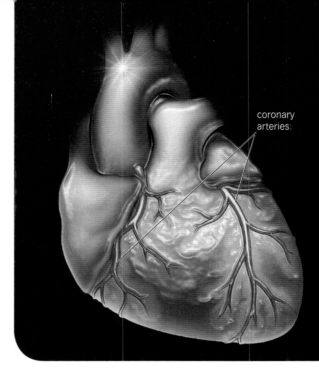

coronary arteries

▲ The coronary arteries, which carry oxygenated blood from the aorta to the heart muscle

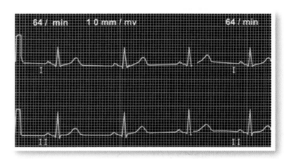

▲ A normal heartbeat shown on an ECG trace

Questions

1 Explain how heart muscle causes blood to move. ↓E

2 Explain why your heart rate needs to increase when you exercise. ↓C

3 Find out why some people need an artificial pacemaker.

4 A person exercising has a pulse rate of 120 beats per minute. How long does each cardiac cycle last? ↓A*

Learning objectives

After studying this topic, you should be able to:

- ✔ know that artificial pacemakers are used to control heartbeat
- ✔ explain the effects of different problems with the heart
- ✔ compare artificial pacemakers and valve replacements with a heart transplant
- ✔ discuss the carrying of donor cards

A Explain why some people need an artificial pacemaker.

B Explain why a patient with a hole in the heart feels tired.

There are many heart diseases and conditions, including:

Artificial pacemakers

Some people have an irregular heartbeat. They can have an artificial pacemaker. This is usually implanted just under the skin in the chest. A wire passes from it into a vein and into the right atrium.

The pacemaker has a long-life battery. It sends impulses to the heart muscle, to make it contract at the correct rhythm. A pacemaker can detect when the person is more active, and sends impulses to the heart at an increased rate.

Some people have a damaged AVN. Its impulses do not travel to the ventricles. In this case the artificial pacemaker wire goes to the ventricle and makes it contract.

Pacemakers have to be replaced about every ten years.

Hole in the heart

Some people have a 'hole in the heart'. Blood can flow directly from one side of the heart to the other. There is less oxygen in the blood, causing fatigue and breathlessness. The hole may be repaired with surgery.

Why a hole in the heart means less oxygen

Fetuses have a small hole between the left and right atria. They obtain oxygen from the placenta. Oxygenated blood enters the right side of the heart and flows through the hole to the left atrium, and then to the head and body. There is a connecting vessel between the pulmonary artery and the aorta, so most blood bypasses the lungs.

At birth, the baby needs to oxygenate its blood via the lungs rather than the placenta. The hole closes and the blood follows the normal circulation. In some babies, the hole does not close, allowing oxygenated blood to flow from the left to the right atrium. This means that a smaller amount of oxygenated blood leaves the left ventricle, and the body tissues receive less oxygen. Patients suffer fatigue and breathlessness. The right side of the heart has to work harder to cope with the increased flow of blood through it. A hole in the heart can be repaired with surgery.

▲ An artificial heart valve. The wires are used to secure the valve in place in the patient's heart. Heart-assist devices may be used after surgery to take the strain off the heart.

Damaged heart valves

As people age, their heart valves may become stiff. Valves may also be damaged, such as by bacterial infection (endocarditis). If the valves in the heart do not close properly, blood will flow backwards. This leads to heart failure, and not enough oxygenated blood can reach body tissues.

Surgeons can replace faulty heart valves with artificial valves or valves from pigs or cows. Because the heart valves have no capillaries supplying them, there is no **rejection** of these transplanted valves.

Blocked coronary arteries

As you get older, and especially if you eat too much saturated fat and smoke tobacco, fatty deposits or plaques build up in your artery walls. These can become quite large and obstruct the flow of blood. If this happens in your coronary arteries, your heart muscle does not get enough oxygenated blood. Heart muscle cells cannot respire anaerobically, and without enough oxygen they cannot release enough energy to contract efficiently. You may develop angina, or have a heart attack.

Surgeons can correct this condition with **bypass surgery**. A piece of blood vessel, usually a vein, is taken from the patient's arm or leg and transplanted to bypass the blockage (or blockages) in the coronary artery.

When people have had a heart attack, surgeons can quickly insert a stent, a tube to open up the blocked coronary arteries. If this is done soon enough, the damage to the heart from the heart attack is slight.

Heart transplants

Since the first heart transplant in 1967, many of these operations have been carried out in the UK each year.

A heart transplant is a **traumatic** operation and the recipient must take drugs to suppress the immune system and prevent rejection. There is a shortage of donor hearts. Heart valve replacement and artificial pacemakers are less traumatic with no risk of rejection, but pacemakers have to be replaced. All operations carry the risk of infection.

Donor cards

Some people carry donor cards so that doctors can take their organs when they die, without expecting bereaved relatives to make a painful decision. Because there is a shortage of donors, another system could be used. Everyone would be a potential donor unless they carried a card to opt out. Some people would opt out for religious reasons; Jehovah's Witnesses regard blood as sacred.

Key words

rejection, bypass surgery, traumatic

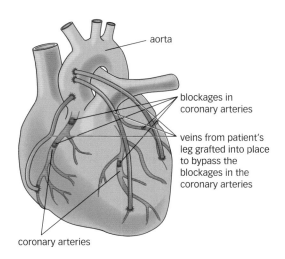

aorta

blockages in coronary arteries

veins from patient's leg grafted into place to bypass the blockages in the coronary arteries

coronary arteries

▲ How blocked coronary arteries are bypassed. The resulting ease of blood flow relieves angina and reduces the risk of a heart attack.

Questions

1   List four diseases or conditions of the heart.

2   What causes a heart attack?

3   Why are there no problems with rejection of transplanted heart valves?

4   Discuss the pros and cons of the opt-out rather than opt-in system for organ donation.

5   Discuss the relative advantages and disadvantages of heart transplant surgery compared with valve replacement or having an artificial pacemaker fitted.

E

C

A*

Key words

platelets, fibrin, agglutinins

▲ Donated blood is stored in plastic bags. A chemical to prevent clotting is added. The bags are carefully labelled and refrigerated.

Did you know...?

This is how the blood clots:
- The **platelets** in blood are exposed to air.
- This causes a series of chemical reactions.
- Eventually a soluble protein in your plasma changes to insoluble **fibrin**.
- Fibrin fibres form a clot.

Blood transfusions

- In 1818 Dr James Blundell performed the first successful transplant of human blood to a patient with a haemorrhage (bleeding).
- In 1840 a haemophiliac was treated by a blood transfusion at St George's Hospital, London. In haemophilia the blood does not clot, so sufferers who cut themselves keep on bleeding.
- In 1901 an Austrian doctor discovered human blood groups and transfusions became safer. In the next ten years, scientists found that if they added anticoagulant and refrigerated the blood, it would keep for some days.
- Blood banks were established during the First World War.
- In 1950 plastic bags replaced breakable glass bottles for storing the blood.
- People may voluntarily give blood three times a year. This keeps the blood banks full to supply hospitals. Blood is warmed before being transfused into a patient.

In a transfusion, blood groups are now carefully matched between the donor and recipient. There are four main blood groups called A, B, AB, and O. These are further subdivided into groups called Rhesus positive and negative.

Why are anticoagulants needed?

If you cut yourself, your blood should clot to heal the wound. This prevents bacteria from entering and stops blood loss.

Blood kept in a bag would clot in this way. Chemicals are added to block the chemical reactions and prevent clotting (coagulation).

We need vitamin K to help blood clot. Bacteria in our gut make vitamin K, but we can also get it from green vegetables and cranberries.

Abnormal clotting

People with haemophilia have blood that clots very slowly.

People with fatty deposits in their arteries may develop clots in the arteries. These could cause heart attacks or strokes. Smoking tobacco and drinking alcohol increase the risk of blood clots forming. Warfarin, aspirin, and heparin reduce the ability of the blood to clot and can be used to reduce the risk of strokes in some people.

Who needs a transfusion?

Some examples are:

- people who have lost a lot of blood through injury or during surgery
- haemophiliacs
- some cancer patients.

A Why is it useful for your blood to clot when you cut yourself?

B Why are blood clots in blood vessels dangerous?

Why are some blood transfusions unsuccessful?

If the donor and recipient bloods are not matched properly, agglutination or clumping happens. The blood cannot circulate and the recipient dies.

Your red blood cells have proteins called **agglutinins** (a type of antigen) on their membranes. There are different shaped agglutinins. Your blood plasma has antibodies against the agglutinins. You don't have antibodies in your plasma that can react with the antigens on your own red blood cells.

When transfusing blood, doctors have to think about the antibodies clumping the red cells together. They need to consider how the antibodies of the recipient will react to the donor's red blood cells.

Matching donors and recipients

- People of group O can donate blood to anyone as their red blood cells do not have any antigens, so the recipient's antibodies have nothing to react with.
- People of group AB can receive any type of blood as they do not have any antibodies in their plasma to react to donors' antigens.
- People of group A cannot receive group B blood because their anti B antibodies would coagulate it.
- People of group B cannot receive group A blood because their anti A antibodies would coagulate it.

People are also classified according to the rhesus factor. Your blood is rhesus positive if your plasma has a D protein, and rhesus negative if it does not. Rhesus-negative people cannot receive rhesus-positive blood as they would make antibodies against the D protein.

Blood group	Agglutinins (antigens) on surface of red blood cells	Antibodies in plasma
A	type A	anti B
B	type B	anti A
AB	type A and type B	none
O	none	anti A and anti B

Questions

1. Who might need a blood transfusion?
2. How can the risk of blood clots be reduced?
3. Describe how blood clots when you cut yourself.
4. Why do you think people of blood group O are called universal donors?
5. Why do you think people of blood group AB are called universal recipients?
6. Explain why people of blood group A cannot receive blood from donors of blood group B.

A Why did the first living organisms on Earth, early bacteria, respire anaerobically?

B How did photosynthesising bacteria alter the Earth's atmosphere?

▲ The leopard frog *Rana pipiens* lives in grasslands and woodlands throughout North America. It eats insects and sometimes small fish. It returns to water to breed.

Aerobic respiration

The first life forms on Earth, three and a half billion years ago, were ancient types of bacteria. These obtained energy from chemical reactions. Some used anaerobic respiration. There was no free oxygen in the Earth's atmosphere at that time. Then some bacteria developed the ability to photosynthesise. This released free oxygen into the atmosphere. Oxygen killed many of the anaerobic bacteria around at the time, but some survived. Some coped with oxygen, and most of the life forms that have since evolved use aerobic respiration. Some organisms can use both anaerobic and aerobic respiration, depending upon the conditions. You probably know that your muscle cells can respire anaerobically for a while.

Gaseous exchange

If an organism respires aerobically, it has to get oxygen to its cells (and then to the mitochondria in its cells). The waste carbon dioxide from aerobic respiration has to be removed from the organism as it is toxic; it would lower the pH and disrupt enzyme activity. The exchange of these two gases, into and out of the organism, is called gaseous exchange.

Single-celled organisms

Simple one-celled organisms such as aerobic bacteria and amoebae have a large surface area compared with their volume. There is enough cell surface membrane to allow sufficient oxygen to diffuse into the cell. The carbon dioxide produced can all diffuse out.

Earthworms

Earthworms have many cells, but they are long and thin. They have a large surface area compared to their volume. Oxygen diffuses through their thin, **permeable** skin and into their blood vessels. The blood carries oxygen from the skin to respiring cells. It also carries carbon dioxide from respiring cells to the skin. Earthworms, like all organisms, contain a lot of water. They do not have waterproof skin, as humans do, so they secrete mucus to stop themselves drying out. They also live in damp places.

Amphibians

Most of the gaseous exchange in a frog happens across its skin. Frogs also have simple lungs, and can obtain oxygen from the floor of their mouth.

Water loss

Because their skin is permeable to gases, frogs are susceptible to excessive water loss. To avoid drying out they need to live in damp places. Some survive in drier habitats by having a layer of slime over the skin.

Fish

Fish also have gills for gaseous exchange. Remember that fish have a single circulatory system.

- The blood flows from the heart to the gills.
- The gills have filaments which give a very large surface area.
- Each filament is well supplied with blood.
- As the fish swims, it gulps water into its mouth.
- Then with the mouth closed, it raises the floor of its mouth and forces the water out over the gills.
- Oxygen dissolved in the water diffuses into the fish's blood at the gills.
- Carbon dioxide diffuses from the blood in the gills into the water.
- The oxygenated blood then flows to the fish's body organs.

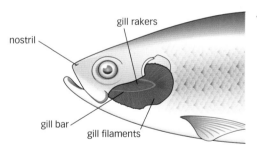

The position of the gills in a fish. The gill flap is cut away. The gill bar supports the filaments.

gill rakers
nostril
gill bar
gill filaments

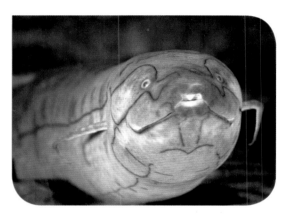

The South American lung fish. It has a pair of lungs, one on either side of its throat.

Exam tip — OCR

- Do not confuse gaseous exchange with breathing. Breathing is the ventilation movement that brings air to the gaseous exchange surface. Fish are ventilating when they open their mouths, gulp water, then close their mouths and open the gill flaps to force water over the gills. Gaseous exchange is the diffusion of oxygen and carbon dioxide into and out of the blood at the gills or lungs.
- Do not confuse either breathing or gaseous exchange with respiration. Respiration happens in the cells.

Questions

1. Explain why all living organisms that respire aerobically need to have gaseous exchange.
2. Explain why larger complex organisms need a special surface for gaseous exchange.
3. Make a table to compare gaseous exchange in: (a) an earthworm (b) an amoeba (c) a frog (d) a fish.
4. Describe how fish force water over their gills.
5. Explain why frogs are at risk of drying out.

Learning objectives

After studying this topic, you should be able to:

- ✓ identify the main parts of the human respiratory system
- ✓ explain the terms breathing, inspiration, expiration, and respiration
- ✓ describe ventilation and gaseous exchange
- ✓ explain how the alveoli are adapted for efficient gaseous exchange

Key words

respiration, breathing, ventilation, residual air, tidal volume, vital capacity, lung capacity

Did you know...?

If you could get all your alveoli and open them out and lay them flat side by side, they would cover an area about half the size of a football pitch. They tuck away neatly in your lungs inside your chest.

Exam tip **OCR**

- ✓ The human respiratory system is the system that enables you to breathe. Remember that **respiration** is what happens inside cells – the release of energy from glucose.

The main parts of the human respiratory system

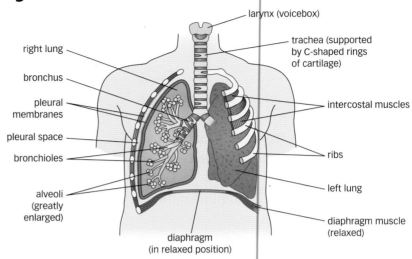

▲ This diagram shows a surface view of the left lung, and a section through the right lung showing the airways and air sacs inside. Pleural membranes cover the lung and the inside of the rib cage. The pleural space between them contains pleural fluid, which allows easy slippage of the moving lungs during breathing, and also helps prevent the lungs from collapsing.

Breathing (ventilation)

Your lungs are your gaseous exchange surface. The many millions of air sacs (alveoli) in the lungs give a large surface area for oxygen to diffuse into your blood and for carbon dioxide to leave your blood and be breathed out. **Breathing**, or **ventilation**, is how you get the air in and out of your lungs.

Inspiration (breathing in)	Expiration (breathing out)
• Your intercostal muscles contract and raise your rib cage up and out. • Your diaphragm flattens. • These two things increase the volume inside your chest and lungs. • The air pressure in your lungs is lower than outside. • So air enters the lungs from outside. It passes along the trachea, bronchi, and bronchioles to the alveoli.	• Your intercostal muscles relax and your rib cage lowers. • Your diaphragm domes upwards. • These two things reduce the volume in your chest. • The air pressure in your lungs is greater than outside. Your elastic alveoli also recoil (snap back) to normal size. • So air is pushed out from your lungs to outside. However, some air stays – this is **residual air**. If it didn't stay, your alveoli would close up.

Using a spirometer

Doctors may measure a patient's lung function, using a spirometer. The patient breathes while attached to a machine. It can measure

- **tidal volume** – the volume of air you breathe in, in one breath
- **vital capacity** – the maximum volume of air you can breathe in, plus your tidal volume, plus the maximum volume of air you can breathe out after taking a big breath in
- **lung capacity** – your vital capacity plus your residual air.

The alveoli

The alveoli form your gaseous exchange surface. They link your blood to the air. At the alveoli:

- Oxygen diffuses from the alveoli into the bloodstream.
- Carbon dioxide that has entered your blood at your body tissues diffuses from your blood into the alveoli, to be breathed out.

Like all of your organs and tissues, the alveoli and the lungs are moist. Your cells are about 70% water, as all the chemical reactions inside them take place in solution. Oxygen actually diffuses quicker when not in solution, but your lungs are moist. Fortunately, oxygen will dissolve in the very thin film of moisture and will still diffuse in solution.

The alveoli are surrounded by blood capillaries. The walls of your alveoli are just one single layer of cells. The walls of your capillaries are also just one single layer of cells. So the oxygen and carbon dioxide do not have far to diffuse. Alveoli are adapted for efficient gaseous exchange because they

- are permeable
- have a large surface area
- have thin walls
- have a good blood supply.

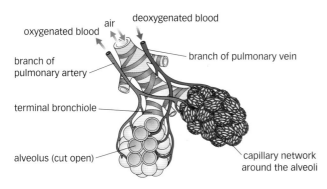

How the alveoli and capillaries in the lungs aid gaseous exchange

A Describe inspiration (how you breathe in).

B Describe expiration (how you breathe out).

Questions

1 Where does gaseous exchange happen in humans?

2 When you breathe out, the exhaled air contains much more carbon dioxide than inhaled air. Explain where the extra carbon dioxide has come from and how it got to the lungs.

3 Explain how your gaseous exchange surface is well adapted for efficient gaseous exchange.

4 Look at the diagram below. It is a spirometer trace on graph paper. For the person whose trace this is, find:
(a) their tidal volume
(b) their vital capacity.

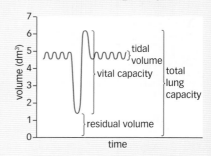

A spirometer trace for a 15-year-old boy

5 Explain why your vital capacity is not the same as your lung capacity.

Learning objectives

After studying this topic, you should be able to:

- ✓ know about diseases of the respiratory system, including pneumonia, asthma, and lung cancer, and their causes
- ✓ explain what happens during an asthma attack

Key words

macrophage, constrict

Did you know...?

People often say that cancerous cells divide very quickly. This is not true. They do not divide any quicker than normal dividing cells; they just do not 'know' when to stop dividing. This is because something, such as the tar in tobacco smoke, has caused a mutation to the genes that control cell division. Lung cancer is slow growing. It takes up to 30 years for a lung cancer tumour to become large enough to detect. Smokers may think they are fine after 20 years of smoking, but the tumour may be growing slowly and not yet causing symptoms.

A How is the respiratory system protected from infection?

B Explain why damaged cilia can make you more prone to lung infection.

How the respiratory system protects itself

You have hairs in your nose which can trap large particles of dirt in the air you breathe in. However, small particles and pathogens may get past these hairs.

There is a layer of cells lining the trachea and bronchi. Some of these cells have cilia and some secrete mucus.

- The mucus traps small particles and pathogens such as bacteria, viruses, and fungal spores.
- The cilia beat and waft the mucus up to the back of the throat.
- Once there it can be swallowed, and the stomach acid kills the trapped pathogens. Or it can be removed by coughing or blowing your nose.

You also have special white blood cells, called **macrophages**, that squeeze out of capillaries and patrol the lung tissues. They ingest foreign particles and some pathogens.

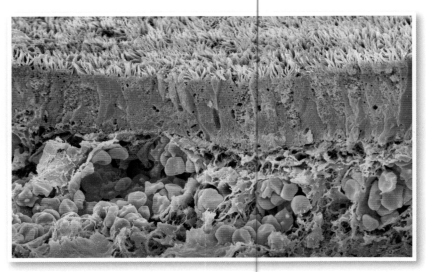

▲ Section through the lining of the trachea, seen with a scanning electron microscope (× 600). False colour has been added.

What happens if this sweeping system is not working?

The airways end in the lungs and go no further – they are a dead end. Any pathogens entering the lungs will cause infection unless they are trapped and wafted back up the airways, out of the lungs. If the cilia are not working properly, small particles and pathogens remain in the lungs and can cause disease.

Some respiratory diseases

Disease	Cause	Symptoms
Bronchitis	Virus or bacteria, can also be triggered by breathing in smoke	Cough (often bringing up a yellow-grey mucus), sore throat, wheezing, blocked nose.
Asbestosis	Asbestos fibres trapped in the alveoli. This is an occupational disease. Some people have been exposed to the fibres during their work.	Inflammation and scarring of the alveoli, leading to difficulty breathing and reduced gaseous exchange. May lead to cancer.
Cystic fibrosis	Genetic and inherited	Cells lining the airways are affected. Thick mucus is secreted. Cilia are not hydrated enough and cannot waft. Mucus with trapped pathogens builds up, and this leads to chest infections and reduces gaseous exchange. Lungs eventually become damaged.
Lung cancer	Most commonly tar in tobacco smoke	Cells lining the bronchioles keep on dividing, forming a tumour. This reduces the surface area for gaseous exchange, and causes chest pain and a prolonged cough, with blood.
Asthma	Inhaling pollen or other allergens, infection, cold air, hard exercise, or stress	Difficulty breathing, wheezing, tight chest. Can be treated with bronchodilator drugs taken via an inhaler. Lining of the airways becomes inflamed, causing a build up of fluid. The muscles in the bronchi contract. This makes the bronchi constrict (become narrower), restricting the airways.

▲ Lung cancer. Coloured scanning electron micrograph of a small cancerous tumour filling an alveolus of the lung (×400). Some of the cancer cells have separated from the main tumour. If they enter the blood, they may be carried to other tissues and set up secondary tumours.

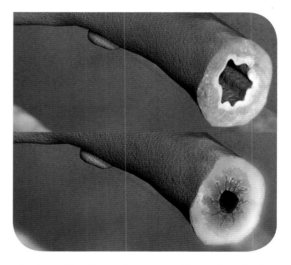

▲ A section through a normal bronchus (top) and an inflamed, **constricted** bronchus during an asthmatic attack (bottom)

Questions

1 Describe what happens during an asthma attack.

2 Describe how lung cancer may develop.

3 Explain how some people developed asbestosis after working for a long time where they were exposed to asbestos fibres.

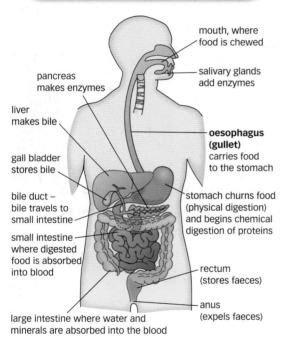

mouth, where food is chewed

salivary glands add enzymes

pancreas makes enzymes

liver makes bile

oesophagus (gullet) carries food to the stomach

gall bladder stores bile

bile duct – bile travels to small intestine

stomach churns food (physical digestion) and begins chemical digestion of proteins

small intestine where digested food is absorbed into blood

rectum (stores faeces)

anus (expels faeces)

large intestine where water and minerals are absorbed into the blood

▲ The human digestive system and its functions

What happens to the food you eat?

While food is in your gut, it is still really outside your body. The large molecules in the food have to be broken down (digested) into smaller molecules so that they can pass across your gut wall and into your blood or lymph. Then your circulatory system takes the digested food to your cells and tissues. Here, you use the food for energy or growth and repair.

Physical digestion

Chewing food in your **mouth** and squeezing food in your **stomach** are both forms of physical digestion. The resulting smaller pieces of food can move more easily through the rest of the digestive system.

Chemical digestion

Carbohydrates, fats, and proteins are digested by specific enzymes in certain parts of the digestive system.

Food	Type of enzyme	Part of gut where enzyme works	Products of digestion
carbohydrates	**carbohydrases**	mouth and small intestine	starch, converted to maltose and then to glucose, a simple sugar
fats (lipids)	**lipases**	small intestine	fatty acids and glycerol
proteins	**proteases**	stomach and small intestine	amino acids

Enzymes have a specific optimum pH

You have hydrochloric acid in your stomach, giving it a very low pH of between 1 and 2. This is primarily to kill any pathogens in your food. The protease enzyme in your stomach is well adapted to this low pH and will not work at higher pH values. However, other enzymes in your mouth and small intestine work best at higher pH values of between 7 and 8.

Bile

To help you digest fats in the small intestine, your liver makes bile. Bile is stored in your gall bladder and released into the small intestine. Bile emulsifies the fats (breaks the fats into smaller droplets). This gives the lipase enzymes more surface area to work on.

Exam tip · OCR

✓ Always try to use technical terms. Talk about food being digested, rather than being broken down.

A Describe the functions of each of the following:
(a) oesophagus (b) stomach (c) small intestine
(d) large intestine.

B Explain the difference between physical and chemical digestion.

Absorption of digested food in the small intestine

The products of digestion diffuse across the wall of the **small intestine** into the blood plasma or lymph.

Adaptations of the small intestine

The small intestine is well adapted to absorb digested food efficiently:

- It is very long.
- It has a large surface area because its lining is folded and has finger-like projections called villi.
- The cells covering each villus have microvilli, which increase the surface area even more.
- The lining is thin.
- There is a good blood supply.

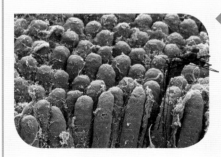

◀ Coloured scanning electron micrograph of villi in the small intestine (× 100)

The large intestine

The **large intestine** absorbs water and some minerals into the blood. The semi-solid waste (faeces) that is left in the large intestine is then passed out of the anus. This is called egestion.

Questions

1 What is the function of the large intestine?

2 Where in your digestive system are each of the following chemically digested? (a) carbohydrates (b) fats (c) proteins

3 Digested food enters your blood in your small intestine and leaves your blood at body tissues. Why does it leave your blood at your body tissues?

4 What is the function of bile in digestion?

5 The pH in your stomach is around 1.2 and in your small intestine it is about 7.8. Proteins are digested in both places. Do you think the same protease enzyme works in both places? Explain your answer.

6 Explain how the small intestine is well adapted to efficiently absorb digested food.

Key words

urea

A   Explain the difference between egestion and excretion.

B   Name four organs of excretion.

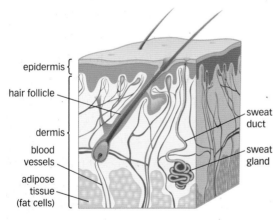

A section of human skin

epidermis
hair follicle
dermis
blood vessels
adipose tissue (fat cells)
sweat duct
sweat gland

Did you know...?

The skin is your largest organ. It weighs about 4–5 kg.

Waste disposal

During digestion, the semi-solid waste (faeces) that is left leaves your body via your anus. This is egestion, not excretion – this waste was not made in your body.

Some chemical reactions in your cells make toxic waste products. Respiration produces water and carbon dioxide. Your body has to remove toxins, otherwise you would be poisoned. Your body also has to regulate the amount of salts and water in it. It is important that the concentration of water molecules in your blood plasma is kept constant. Too much water, and blood cells would swell and burst. Too little water, or too much salt, and they would shrivel and not function. Your nerves would not work properly if there were too many or too few salts in your body.

The main organs of excretion

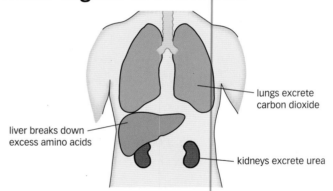

lungs excrete carbon dioxide

liver breaks down excess amino acids

kidneys excrete urea

▲ The main organs of excretion and their functions

The skin

Your skin makes sweat to cool you. The water in the sweat uses your body heat to evaporate. Sweating also gets rid of excess water and salts.

The lungs

Your respiring cells make carbon dioxide. It is carried in the blood to the lungs and then diffuses into the alveoli to be breathed out. So your lungs excrete carbon dioxide that was made in your cells. The carbon dioxide would otherwise poison you because it would lower your blood pH. Your enzymes would not work properly and you would die. As carbon dioxide levels in your blood increase they are detected by the brain. The brain then increases your breathing rate to remove the carbon dioxide more quickly.

The liver

Your liver breaks down old red blood cells. The chemicals from them go into the bile and pass out with the faeces. Your liver also breaks down hormones and medicines or other drugs, such as alcohol.

If you have eaten more protein than your body needs, the liver breaks down excess amino acids into ammonia. Ammonia has a high pH and is very soluble, so if it got into your blood it would be very harmful. Enzymes would not be able to function. In your liver cells the ammonia reacts with carbon dioxide (another waste product) to make **urea**. Urea is toxic, but not as toxic as ammonia. Your blood carries the urea to your kidneys, which remove it.

The kidneys

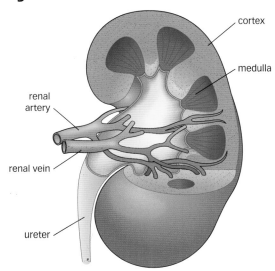

▲ The structure of the kidney. Blood flows in through the renal artery, is filtered and leaves the kidney in the renal vein. The waste urine, containing water, salts, and urea, passes down the ureter to the bladder.

Each of your kidneys has about one million filtering units. Blood enters your kidney in the renal artery. It is filtered under high pressure and lots of substances are filtered out:
• glucose   • salts   • water   • urea.

Then the useful substances:
• all the glucose   • some salts   • some water
are reabsorbed into the blood. The remaining liquid, called urine, passes down the ureter to the bladder. It is stored in the bladder and passed out when convenient.

As well as removing urea, your kidney also regulates the amount of salts and water in your body.

Exam tip   OCR

✔ Remember that it is the water in sweat that evaporates, not the sweat itself. The evaporation changes water from a liquid to a gas, and that takes heat energy from your skin, blood, and body. This is how sweating cools you.

Questions

1 For each organ you named in Question B, state its main excretory product.

2 Explain why carbon dioxide has to be removed from the body.

3 How do you think the amount of urea in your urine would change if you started eating a high protein diet? Explain your answer.

4 How do you think the water content of your urine would change if you drank a lot of tea and lemon squash? Explain your answer.

5 How do you think the water content of your urine would change on a hot day if you ran around and did not drink any extra water? Explain your answer.

6 How do you think your urine would change after you ate a very salty meal?

Learning objectives

After studying this topic, you should be able to:

- ✔ explain how the structure of the kidney tubule enables it to filter blood and produce urine
- ✔ explain how the amount of water in the blood is regulated
- ✔ explain the principle of the dialysis machine

Key words

glomerulus, selective reabsorption, afferent arteriole, efferent arteriole, pituitary gland

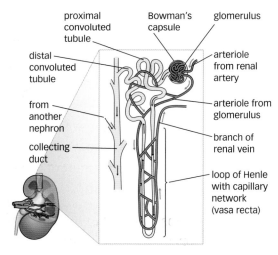

▲ The position of nephrons in the kidney, and the structure of a nephron

A Why is it important that salts and water in the blood are carefully regulated?

The nephron

You have learnt about the gross structure of a kidney. There are about a million filtering units, called nephrons, in each kidney. Each nephron consists of

- a knot of capillaries, called a **glomerulus**, inside a capsule, where high pressure filtration occurs
- a region for **selective reabsorption**, where useful substances eg glucose pass into the blood
- a region for salt and water regulation.

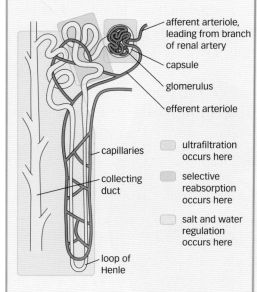

◀ Detailed structure of a nephron showing the regions for high pressure filtration, selective reabsorption, and salt and water regulation. The tubule is surrounded by capillaries so that substances can easily pass back into the blood.

High pressure filtration

Blood enters your kidney, in the renal artery, under high pressure. Many arterioles branch off from the renal artery and one arteriole goes to each glomerulus. Blood goes from the **afferent arteriole** into the glomerulus. It then leaves the glomerulus in another arteriole, called the **efferent arteriole**.

The efferent arteriole has a narrower diameter than the afferent arteriole. This produces a bottleneck effect. The blood cannot leave the glomerulus as fast as it is entering, so it is under high pressure, and the capillaries of the glomerulus are very leaky. The result is high pressure filtration. Substances with small molecules – water, salts, urea, glucose, amino acids, vitamins, and spent hormones – are filtered out of the blood. They pass along the tubules of the nephron dissolved in liquid that was squeezed out from the glomerulus.

From the first part of the nephron, all the useful substances – glucose, amino acids, vitamins, some salts, and some water – are reabsorbed by selective reabsorption. The loop of Henle, the rest of the tubule, and the collecting duct regulate the amount of salt and water in the body.

- If your blood is very watery, less water is reabsorbed from the kidney tubules and a lot of dilute urine is produced.
- If your blood is not very watery, more water is reabsorbed from the kidney tubules and a smaller volume of concentrated urine is produced.

Antidiuretic hormone (ADH)

The hormone ADH is released from a gland in the brain, your **pituitary gland**, directly into the blood. Your blood carries it to its target organs, the kidneys. This hormone makes the walls of the collecting duct more permeable to water, so more water can be reabsorbed into the blood.

A negative feedback mechanism is involved. As your blood passes through your brain, your hypothalamus detects how watery it is.

- If your blood is watery, less ADH is released. Less water is reabsorbed in the kidneys and more water is lost in urine. This adjusts the water content of your blood.
- If your blood is not very watery, more ADH is released. More water is reabsorbed in the kidneys and less water is lost in urine.

Renal dialysis

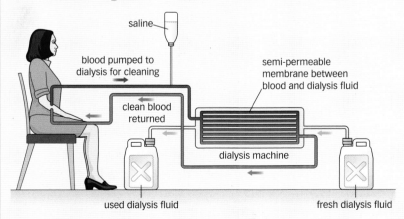

Sometimes people's kidneys stop working properly. When this happens their blood can be filtered by a dialysis machine.

Exam tip

✔ How can you remember when more ADH is released? Diuresis means *making urine*. Anti- means *against*. Antidiuretic hormone reduces the volume of urine. More ADH is released if your blood/body needs to conserve water – if you have been sweating and/or not drinking much. Less ADH is released if your blood is watery – if you have been drinking a lot.

✔ How can you remember which is the afferent and which is the efferent arteriole? *Affere* is Latin and means to carry *towards*; *effere* is Latin and means to carry *away from*.

Questions

1 What substances are reabsorbed into the blood during selective reabsorption?

2 Explain how high pressure filtration occurs in the glomerulus.

3 Describe how ADH release is controlled using negative feedback.

↓
A*

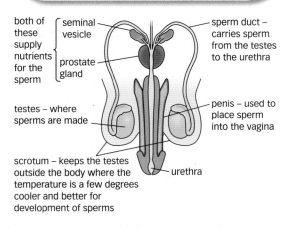

both of these supply nutrients for the sperm { seminal vesicle

prostate gland

sperm duct – carries sperm from the testes to the urethra

testes – where sperms are made

penis – used to place sperm into the vagina

scrotum – keeps the testes outside the body where the temperature is a few degrees cooler and better for development of sperms

urethra

🔺 The male reproductive system and its functions

Did you know...?

At puberty males produce small amounts of oestrogen and progesterone and females produce small amounts of the male sex hormone, testosterone. In females testosterone causes pubic hair and hair under the arms to grow.

Growth and development

At birth we can tell what sex the child is because of the external **genitals** – the primary sexual characteristics. At puberty, children's bodies begin to change into those of sexually mature adults. This stage of a person's life is called adolescence, and lasts several years. The first thing that happens is that the ovaries in females, and testes in males, develop and begin to produce the **sex hormones**.

The female sex hormones oestrogen and progesterone are made in the ovaries. They are involved in controlling the menstrual cycle.

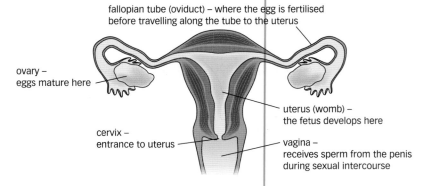

fallopian tube (oviduct) – where the egg is fertilised before travelling along the tube to the uterus

ovary – eggs mature here

uterus (womb) – the fetus develops here

cervix – entrance to uterus

vagina – receives sperm from the penis during sexual intercourse

🔺 The female reproductive system and its functions

Secondary sexual characteristics

At puberty, your sex hormones cause your secondary sexual characteristics to develop.

Male secondary sexual characteristics	Female secondary sexual characteristics
• The voice breaks (deepens). • Hair grows on the face and body. • The body becomes more muscular. • Genitals develop. • The testes start making sperm.	• The breasts develop. • Pubic hair and hair under the arms grows. • The hips widen. • Periods start (menstruation) and eggs mature.

A Name the female and male sex hormones.

B List four secondary sexual characteristics for males and four for females.

The menstrual cycle

At puberty, females begin to have a menstrual period each month. They have a monthly menstrual cycle.

Several hormones help coordinate the menstrual cycle.
- The pituitary gland in the brain releases a hormone called FSH.
- FSH causes an egg in one of the ovaries to mature.
- It also stimulates the ovaries to make the hormone oestrogen.
- Oestrogen stimulates the pituitary gland to release another hormone, LH.
- LH triggers the release of the egg (**ovulation**) from the ovary.
- Oestrogen also inhibits further production of FSH and it repairs the uterus lining (the endometrium, which is the innermost layer of the uterus wall).
- Progesterone maintains the uterus lining and inhibits LH.

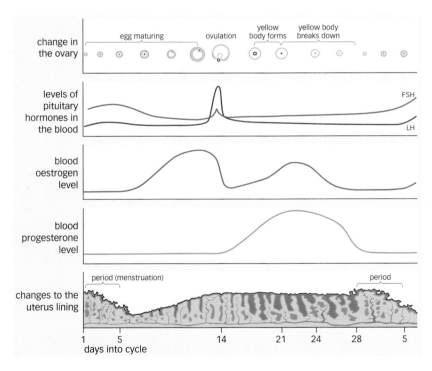

Events in the menstrual cycle

Conception happens if a sperm meets the egg and fertilises it. If the egg is not fertilised, at the end of the cycle the uterus lining passes out of the body. This is the period. If the egg is fertilised then the uterus lining stays so that the fetus can develop.

Key words

genitals, sex hormones, ovulation, conception

Exam tip OCR

✔ It may seem complicated, but you need to learn the menstrual cycle and the names and functions of all the hormones involved.

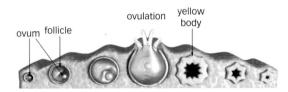

▲ Changes in the ovary during the menstrual cycle. The egg develops in a follicle. It then bursts out of the follicle. The empty follicle develops into a yellow body which makes progesterone; this stops menstruation.

Questions

1 Where is FSH made in the body?
2 What does FSH do?
3 What is the function of progesterone?
4 What is the role of oestrogen in the menstrual cycle?
5 During which part of the menstrual cycle is a woman most likely to conceive?
6 When during the menstrual cycle is the level of LH highest?

Learning objectives

After studying this topic, you should be able to:

- ✓ explain how female hormones can be used to reduce fertility
- ✓ explain how FSH can be used to treat infertility
- ✓ describe other treatments for infertility and discuss the arguments for and against fertility treatments
- ✓ discuss ethical issues raised by fetal screening

▲ Contraceptive pills in a blister pack. Each pack contains enough pills for one month. They are usually taken for 21 days of each month and then not taken for 7 days, so the woman has a period.

Key words

contraception, IVF, amniocentesis, miscarriage

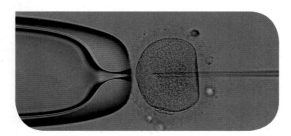

▲ A human sperm being injected into a human egg

Controlling fertility with female hormones

Humans can control fertility by using female sex hormones. These hormones can be used to reduce fertility or to promote fertility.

Reducing fertility

During pregnancy, both oestrogen and progesterone levels are high and they inhibit FSH and LH production from the pituitary gland. This prevents the development and release of any more eggs.

Scientists realised that if women took oestrogen and progesterone in a daily pill, the high levels in the body would mimic pregnancy and prevent ovulation. Without ovulation you cannot become pregnant. Preventing pregnancy is called **contraception**.

The first contraceptive (birth-control) pills contained high amounts of oestrogen. They prevented ovulation but many women suffered from side-effects. Contraceptive pills now contain a much lower dose of oestrogen and some progesterone, or just progesterone. These give fewer side-effects.

Increasing fertility

Some couples are infertile and therefore cannot conceive. Possible causes of infertility are:

- blocked fallopian tubes or sperm ducts
- eggs do not develop or are not released from ovaries
- the testes do not produce enough sperms.

Fertility treatment may help.

A procedure called in vitro fertilisation (**IVF**) may be used to treat women who cannot become pregnant naturally. *In vitro* means 'in glass'. In IVF:

- The woman is injected with FSH, which stimulates her ovaries to produce eggs.
- The eggs are then collected from the woman and mixed with the man's sperm in a glass dish.
- To make the procedure more likely to work, healthy sperms are selected and one is injected into each egg.
- The fertilised eggs begin to develop into embryos.
- When they are tiny balls of cells, two are chosen and inserted into the woman's uterus.

Other treatments for infertility

Treatment	Description and reason for treatment
Artificial insemination	If the male's sperm count is low, sperm can be donated from another male and inserted into the woman's vagina. Also used for single women or lesbian couples who wish to become pregnant.
Egg donation	A woman may donate some of her eggs to another woman who cannot make eggs. Women undergoing IVF often donate 'spare eggs'.
Surrogacy	If a woman has had her uterus removed, another woman (the surrogate mother) may have the first woman's embryo (the result of IVF) implanted in her uterus. After the birth the surrogate mother gives the baby back to its biological mother.
Ovary transplants	So far only a few ovary transplants have been carried out, with the donor being the identical twin of the recipient. This could restore the fertility of women who undergo early menopause and are no longer fertile, or who have had radiation treatment for cancer. A woman could have her ovaries removed before being treated for cancer, have them frozen and have them transplanted back after the treatment.

Being childless can cause distress and sadness to people who want a family, and fertility treatments allow some people to have a child who could not do so otherwise. However, these treatments are very expensive and there is no guarantee they will work. All medical procedures carry some risk.

Checking fetal development

Ultrasound scans are used to check fetal development. However, some abnormalities cannot be seen on a scan. Down's syndrome is caused by the presence of an extra chromosome. To check for Down's syndrome, doctors can insert a needle into the uterus and take some amniotic fluid containing fetal cells. This procedure is called **amniocentesis**. The cells are grown in a lab so that they divide. Their chromosomes can be observed under a microscope and counted.

If the fetus has an extra chromosome, the couple have to decide whether to terminate the pregnancy. Some people think that screening out disabilities means that disabled people are undervalued in society. There is a 1% (1 in 100) chance that amniocentesis could cause a **miscarriage** and could abort a healthy fetus.

A What does IVF stand for?

B Explain how FSH can be used to increase fertility in women who cannot conceive (become pregnant).

Questions

1 Name two female hormones produced in the ovaries.

2 Discuss the advantages and disadvantages of: (a) IVF (b) egg donation (c) surrogacy (d) ovary transplants.

3 Some fertility drugs contain a chemical that inhibits oestrogen. How do you think this might increase fertility?

4 Some families have a history of a particular genetic disorder. In these cases, fertilisation can be in vitro and the embryos can be tested for genetic defects. Only healthy embryos will be implanted. Do you think this is a good idea? Give reasons for your answer.

Monitoring growth and development

Before you were born, doctors and midwives used ultrasound scans to monitor your development in the uterus. They monitored your rate of growth and increase in head size as well as your heart rate. This told them if you were growing and developing at a normal rate.

At birth and during the first six months, the midwife measures a baby's

- head circumference
- body length
- mass

and plots them on average growth charts. The baby's growth is compared with the range of average values. This regular monitoring can alert the midwife if you have any growth problems.

If a baby is growing too slowly, its pituitary gland may not be producing enough growth hormone. Growth hormone stimulates general growth, especially that of long bones and muscles. A deficiency can be treated with injections of human growth hormone.

Stages of human growth

We do not grow at a constant rate. The graph on the left shows the stages of human growth.

Learning objectives

After studying this topic, you should be able to:

- ✔ understand why a baby's length and mass are monitored
- ✔ recall the factors that determine a person's final height
- ✔ recall the main stages of growth and identify them on a human growth curve
- ✔ discuss the implications of increased life expectancy

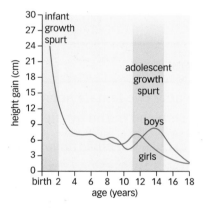

▲ The growth rate, as height gain per year, from birth to 18 years

Charts like the one above are based on an average of the population. Not everyone's growth will follow this pattern.

Exam tip **OCR**

- ✔ When using a growth rate graph, remember it shows the rate of growth (the increase in height per year), not the actual height.

infancy	– First two years of life
	– Highest rate of growth, gaining around 15–24 cm in a year
childhood	– From 2–11 years of age, until puberty starts
	– Growth occurs at a slower rate than during infancy
adolescence	– From 11–15 years of age, when puberty begins
	– Growth spurt for girls aged 10–12 and boys aged 12–15 years
maturity	– Males may continue to grow until the age of 18–20 years
	– Most females reach their full adult height by 16 years of age
old age	– Above 60–65 years
	– Physical abilities start to deteriorate

> **A** Name and describe the main stages of the human growth curve.

Your final height is determined by

- your genes – many genes determine your height potential
- your diet – you need good quality protein for growth and enough food for your energy needs
- the amount of exercise you do – exercise stimulates growth of bones and muscles
- your hormones – growth hormone, thyroxine, and insulin
- health and disease – if you are often ill or do not get enough sleep you may not grow properly.

Life expectancy

In the developed world, **life expectancy** has increased. We expect to live to between 75 and 80 years. This does not mean everyone will live this long. Many die earlier and some later. **Old age** is officially above 60–65 years but many older people carry on working and living full and active lives.

Life expectancy has increased in developed countries because we have

- less industrial disease such as asbestosis, and fewer accidents in the workplace
- healthier diets, with few cases of vitamin or mineral deficiencies
- better housing
- improved lifestyle so people can have a positive outlook on life
- vaccinations to prevent many infectious diseases
- better treatments for cancer and heart disease.

However, there may be problems with increased life expectancy:

- a large ageing population – there are more people aged over 65 than under 16 in the UK
- many of these will need medical treatment or care
- this could affect the job prospects for younger people as more older people need to keep working for economic reasons and/or because they want to
- the state pension system will need to be redesigned as it cannot afford to pay pensions for 30 or more years to people; the retirement age will also be raised.

▲ Increased life expectancy has led to a large ageing population

Questions

1. What factors determine your final height?

2. Use the graph of growth rate on the previous page to answer the following questions. What is the average height gain per year: (a) aged 1 year (b) aged 2 years (c) aged 6 years (d) for boys aged 14 years?

3. Why do you think more people are living longer in the UK today, compared with 50–100 years ago? What possible problems may arise as a result?

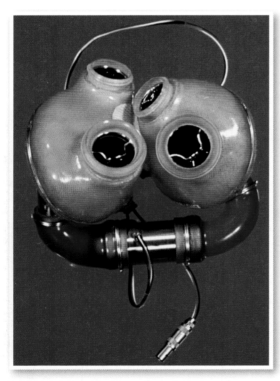

The Jarvik-7 artificial heart was developed by Dr Robert Jarvik and a biomedical engineer, Dr Lyman. It is made from polyurethane and titanium. The inside is smooth and seamless so it does not cause blood clots that would lead to strokes. Many people have had this type of artificial heart while waiting for a heart transplant. However, the wires protrude through the skin.

Mechanical replacements

Many mechanical replacements for body parts are used outside the body, for example

- heart–lung machines, used during open heart surgery to divert blood from the heart
- kidney dialysis machines, used to filter the blood of people with renal (kidney) failure, removing urea, excess salts, and water
- mechanical ventilators, used to aid breathing in patients whose rib cage muscles are paralysed.

▲ A renal dialysis machine in action

Other mechanical devices can be implanted into the body. These include:

- heart pacemakers
- artificial hearts
- artificial knee and hip joints
- eye lenses.

When medical engineers are designing these implants they need to consider certain factors, such as:

- size – this is why there is no artificial kidney that can be implanted; dialysis machines are very large
- battery life (if powered) – pacemaker batteries last 7–10 years
- body reactions – inert materials that do not react with body fluids are used to construct implants; artificial hearts are made of titanium and plastic
- strength – titanium is used for artificial joints.

> **A** Describe two mechanical organ replacements that can be used (a) outside, and (b) inside the body. Explain why they are used.

Organ transplants

Many body parts can be replaced by transplanting donated organs.

Blood transfusions	Successfully carried out for over 100 years, using blood from live **donors** that is stored in blood banks. Blood types must be matched.
Cornea transplants	Also known as corneal grafts. A cornea removed from a recently dead donor is transplanted into the recipient's eye. No risk of rejection as the cornea has no blood vessels.
Heart transplants	First carried out in 1967 in South Africa. Donors are usually recently dead, but may be living – if someone has a heart–lung transplant to replace diseased lungs, the recipient's healthy heart can be donated to someone else.
Lung transplants	Lungs from a recently dead donor may be transplanted into a recipient suffering from cystic fibrosis, for example. Usually a heart–lung transplant is carried out.
Kidney transplants	Donor may be dead or living, as we can survive with only one kidney. A close relative may donate a kidney to a recipient.
Bone marrow transplants	Used to treat leukaemia. Living donors are tissue-typed and recorded on a register so that they can be matched to a recipient. They then give bone marrow.

All donors need to be a good tissue match and the right age and size for the recipients. Living donors have to be healthy and willing to donate. There is currently a shortage of organ donors.

Rejection

With most transplants there is a risk that the recipient's immune system will reject the transplant. **Tissue matching**, matching the donor and recipient's tissue type, and **immunosuppressant drugs** both reduce the risk of rejection. However, these drugs increase the risk of infections.

Exam tip OCR

- ✔ When discussing ethical issues, be objective and give some pros and some cons.

Questions

1. Explain why tissue types for donor and recipients have to be matched for most organ/tissue transplants. C

2. Explain how a living heart donor may be used.

3. Why is there no problem of rejection with cornea grafts?

4. What problems are associated with taking immunosuppressant drugs? A*

5. Discuss the ethical issues concerning organ/tissue transplants.

Module summary

Revision checklist

- Some animals have no hard skeleton. Some have an external skeleton and some have an internal skeleton.
- Joints and muscles allow you to move. Muscles work in antagonistic pairs.
- Multicellular animals have a circulatory system to transport material to and from cells.
- Mammals have a double circulatory system consisting of heart and blood vessels (the cardiovascular system) and lymph.
- The cardiac cycle describes the events of each heartbeat.
- Artificial pacemakers, valve replacements, surgery, and heart transplants may treat disorders of the heart.
- Blood can be transfused. Blood groups have to be compatible.
- Organisms have special surfaces for gaseous exchange, such as skin, gills, and lungs, to obtain oxygen.
- Breathing moves air into and out of the lungs. Alveoli give a large surface area for gaseous exchange. Respiratory diseases include pneumonia, asthma, lung cancer, cystic fibrosis, and asbestosis.
- Food is digested to smaller molecules to be absorbed into the blood. Chewing is physical digestion; enzymes cause chemical digestion.
- Excretion is the removal of toxic waste made in the body. The skin excretes sweat; lungs excrete carbon dioxide; the kidney excretes urea, excess water, and excess salts. Urea is made in the liver from excess amino acids.
- Each kidney contains many filtering units called nephrons. Antidiuretic hormone controls how much water is reabsorbed. Renal dialysis can treat people with kidney failure.
- Secondary sexual characteristics and male and female reproductive organs develop at puberty. Hormones play an important part in growing up.
- Many treatments are available to treat infertility. Female hormones can also be used in contraceptives. Fetal development can be checked using ultrasound scans and amniocentesis.
- Humans pass through many stages of development: infancy, childhood, adolescence, and adulthood. Rate of growth depends on genes, diet, hormones, and health status.
- Some parts of the body can be replaced with mechanical devices or with organ or tissue transplants.

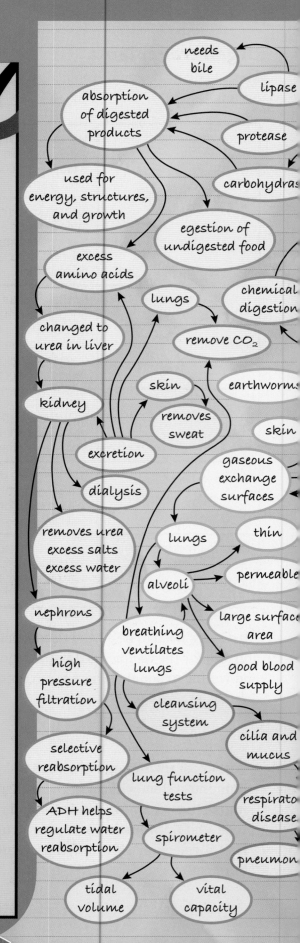

NOW USE THE B5 GRADE CHECKER ON PAGE 240

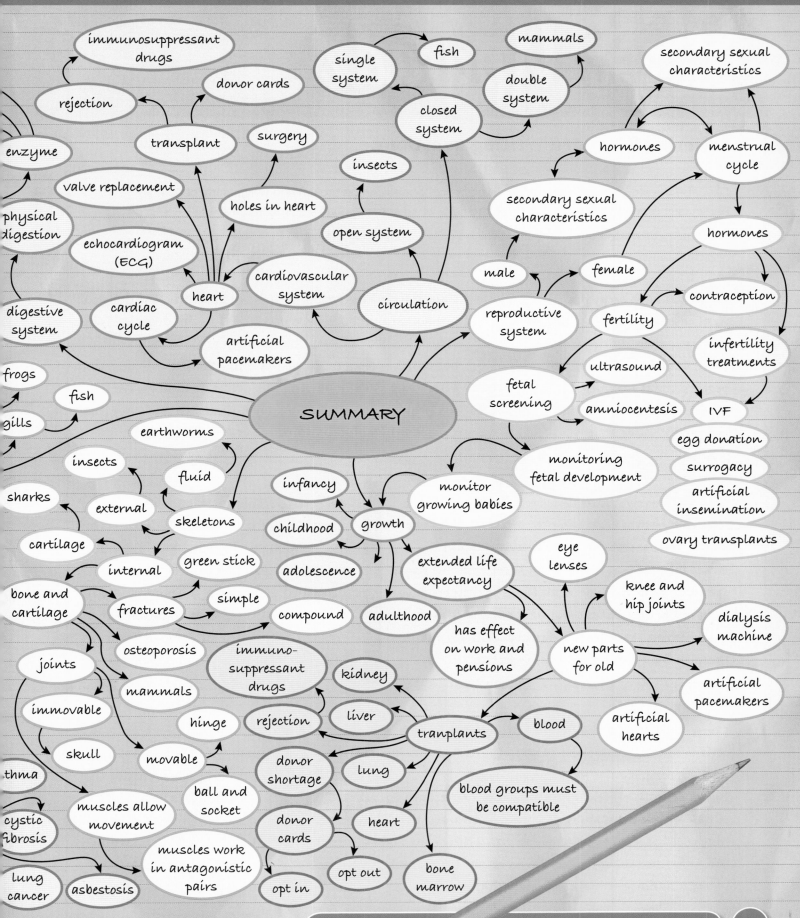

immunosuppressant drugs

rejection

donor cards

surgery

mammals

fish

single system

double system

closed system

secondary sexual characteristics

enzyme

transplant

valve replacement

holes in heart

insects

hormones

menstrual cycle

physical digestion

echocardiogram (ECG)

open system

secondary sexual characteristics

hormones

digestive system

heart

cardiovascular system

circulation

male

female

contraception

cardiac cycle

artificial pacemakers

reproductive system

fertility

infertility treatments

frogs

SUMMARY

fetal screening

ultrasound

amniocentesis

IVF

fish

gills

earthworms

fluid

infancy

monitor growing babies

monitoring fetal development

egg donation

surrogacy

insects

skeletons

childhood

growth

sharks

external

cartilage

internal

green stick

adolescence

extended life expectancy

eye lenses

artificial insemination

ovary transplants

bone and cartilage

fractures

simple

compound

adulthood

has effect on work and pensions

new parts for old

knee and hip joints

dialysis machine

osteoporosis

joints

mammals

immuno-suppressant drugs

kidney

artificial pacemakers

immovable

hinge

rejection

liver

transplants

blood

artificial hearts

skull

movable

tranplants

donor shortage

lung

muscles allow movement

ball and socket

donor cards

heart

blood groups must be compatible

cystic fibrosis

muscles work in antagonistic pairs

opt in

opt out

bone marrow

lung cancer

asbestosis

thma

Answering Extended Writing questions

Describe the structure of a long bone. Explain how bones can be broken and why elderly people are particularly prone to fractures. What are the risks when someone has a suspected fracture?

The quality of written communication will be assessed in your answer to this question.

Bones are hard because you need calcium for them. That's why you should drink lots of milk but I don't like it. Old people's bones break easily. You have to get the bone set in plaster.

↓ E

Examiner: This response has not answered the question. It has stated that bones are hard, but has not described their structure. The answer does not explain why older people's bones may break more easily; it just repeats the question. The risks associated with a suspected fracture have not been given. The reference to plaster, although true, is not relevant. The spelling, punctuation, and grammar are good.

There is marrow inside bones where red blood cells are made. At the ends there is cartilage. This is so joints work smoothly. Bone is living tissue. Bones break if you knock them sharply. Some people, specially old people have weak bones so they break more often. their bones don't have enough calcium. If you break your arm and the bone sticks out through the skin, it could get infected.

↓ C

Examiner: This answer shows some knowledge of bone structure. There is an explanation of why older people suffer more fractures, and a risk from a fracture is described. However, if the bone is sticking out through the skin as the candidate describes, this is a definite fracture and not a suspected one. There are a few grammatical errors.

Long bones have a shaft and inside is marrow where blood cells are made. At each end there is cartilage which is smooth and slippery. It helps joints work.
Bones contain protein and calcium and they are strong. But if you knock them sharply or fall awkwardly they can break. Many old people have osteoporosis and their bones break easily. You shouldn't move someone who might have a broken bone as it could damage it more, especially the spine.

↓ A*

Examiner: A clear answer using lots of technical terms properly. Each part of the question has been answered correctly. The answer is easy to follow and the spelling, punctuation, and grammar are good.

Exam-style questions

1 Here is a list of body organs:
muscle   heart   kidney   skin   bone

A01 **a** Which organ contains hair follicles?

A01 **b** Which organ receives blood from the coronary artery?

A01 **c** Which two organs may be joined together by a tendon?

A01 **d** Which organs carry out excretion?

2 Some women find it difficult to become pregnant. They may use IVF, which involves taking eggs from the woman just before ovulation.

A01 **a** What does IVF stand for?

A01 **b** Which organ in a woman's body makes eggs?

A01 **c** What normally happens in a woman's body at ovulation?

A01 **d** During IVF, what is added to an egg to fertilise it?

3 **a** Which gas is excreted by the lungs?

A01 **b** What happens in the lungs to cause
A02 an asthma attack?

4 In 1901, Dr Landsteiner discovered blood groups. He said there were three. Scientists now know that there are four blood groups.

A01 **a** Name the four blood groups.

A02 **b** Which group is safe for anyone?

A01 **c** Some people have an inherited condition that means their blood does not clot properly. What is the name of this condition?

A01 **d** Explain the difference between a single and a double circulatory system.

5 The graph gives information on organ transplants between 1996 and 2005.

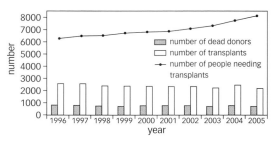

A03 **a** Describe the general trends over the 9 year period shown by the graph.

A02 **b** Describe the 'opt out' organ donation system that could be adopted to boost organ donation.

6 Bypass surgery can treat blocked coronary arteries using a piece of vein from a patient's arm or leg.

A02 **a** Explain why blocked coronary arteries have to be bypassed.

A01 **b** A blocked coronary artery can also be treated with a stent. Explain what a stent is.

Extended Writing

7 Describe how single-celled organisms,
A01 earthworms, frogs, fish, and humans carry out gaseous exchange.

8 Describe the causes and symptoms of
A01 lung cancer and asthma. How can an asthma attack be treated?

9 Explain how the small intestine is well
A01 adapted for digestion of food and absorption of the products of digestion.

A01 Recall the science

A02 Apply your knowledge

A03 Evaluate and analyse the evidence

B6

Beyond the microscope

Why study this module?

As soon as biologists had the microscope as a basic laboratory instrument, a whole new micro world opened up for us. As microscopes have become more precise, so has our understanding of a new branch of biology called microbiology. From this has come the new scientific field of biotechnology.

In this module you will study the amazing world of the microbe, learning about types of microbes – bacteria, viruses, and fungi. These microbes can be either harmful or helpful. Harmful microbes can cause disease. You will study the ways in which diseases can be transmitted, and their treatment with antibiotics. At the same time, you will consider the early work of some of the pioneers of microbiology. The uses of microbes in the brewing and biofuel industries will also be explored.

You will enter the microscopic worlds of soil and water, investigating some of the impacts of human pollution. Some of the more high-tech uses of microbes will be reviewed, such as the use of microbial enzymes in the food, medical, and detergent industries. Finally, you will examine the use of bacteria or their enzymes in the biotechnological techniques of genetic engineering and DNA fingerprinting.

You should remember

1 The structure of microbial cells.
2 Harmful and helpful microbes.
3 How enzymes work.
4 The action of genes.

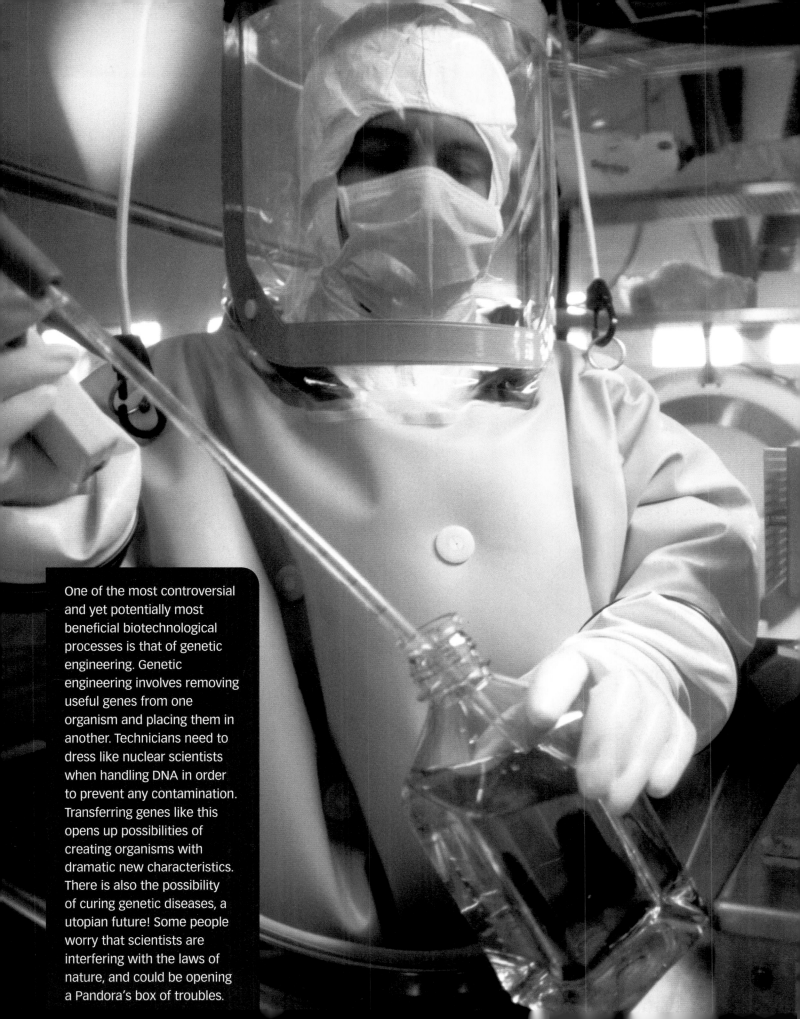

One of the most controversial and yet potentially most beneficial biotechnological processes is that of genetic engineering. Genetic engineering involves removing useful genes from one organism and placing them in another. Technicians need to dress like nuclear scientists when handling DNA in order to prevent any contamination. Transferring genes like this opens up possibilities of creating organisms with dramatic new characteristics. There is also the possibility of curing genetic diseases, a utopian future! Some people worry that scientists are interfering with the laws of nature, and could be opening a Pandora's box of troubles.

1: The biology of bacteria

 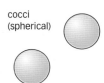

cocci (spherical)

▲ Cocci bacteria (*Staphylococcus aureus*) which cause acne spots (×7000)

 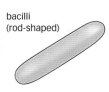

bacilli (rod-shaped)

▲ Bacillus bacteria (*Escherichia coli*) which can cause food poisoning (×3000)

 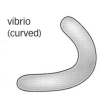

vibrio (curved)

▲ Vibrio bacteria (*Vibrio cholerae*) which cause the disease cholera (×3500)

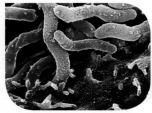 

spirilli (spiral)

▲ Spiral bacteria (*Helicobacter pylori*); which cause stomach ulcers (×12 000)

Life under the microscope

There is a wide range of organisms that can only be seen using microscopes. Some of these microscopic organisms, or microbes, are helpful to humans; others are harmful. There are three main groups – bacteria, fungi, and viruses.

Bacteria

The microbes that make up the **bacteria** kingdom are single-celled organisms. They are extremely small – a typical bacterium is only a few **microns**, or a few thousandths of a millimetre, long. Bacteria are very important to us. There are many different bacteria, and we can tell them apart and classify them by their shape (see left).

Bacterial cells

At first sight bacterial cells look quite simple. However, they carry out all the functions of other cells.

Bacterial cells can only just be seen using a light microscope. To see fine detail, biologists use high powered microscopes called electron microscopes. These microscopes magnify thousands of times more than a light microscope.

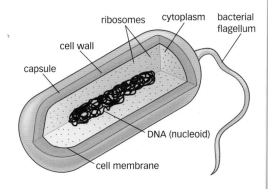

◀ A typical bacterial cell

The electron microscope reveals the following features of bacterial cells:

- cell membrane, controlling the movement of molecules into and out of the cell
- cytoplasm, a jelly-like substance where most of the cell's reactions occur
- cell wall, having the same function as in a plant cell of maintaining the shape of the cell and preventing it from bursting, but made of a different chemical instead of cellulose
- loop of DNA, controlling the cell and its replication. Bacterial cells do not have a nucleus.

- capsule, a slimy protective capsule around the outside of the cell wall in some bacteria. It is this capsule that protects bacteria against antibiotics
- flagellum, whip-like flagella for movement in some bacteria.

Reproduction in bacteria

Bacteria can reproduce very fast. Most of the time they reproduce by dividing into two, and they can do this as quickly as once every two hours. This type of division is called binary fission.

An unfortunate consequence of this is that harmful bacteria, such as those that spoil food, can reproduce fast. So food such as milk left out in a warm room will go off very quickly. If you then eat this food, the bacteria may reproduce very quickly in your body. The rate of reproduction may be too fast for your immune system to handle, making you ill.

Bacterial habitats

Bacteria have such a wide range of adaptations that they are found living in almost all environments on Earth. They can live from the depths of the ocean up to the highest mountain peaks. They span cold arctic wastes to volcanic areas and hot springs.

Bacteria survive by obtaining energy from a wide range of sources – some from the Sun by photosynthesis, but others from dead bodies, and from chemical reactions in their cells.

Growing bacteria in the lab

To study bacteria in the lab, they are grown on a jelly called agar in a plate-like dish called a Petri dish. The plates are incubated to keep them warm, and the bacteria grow very fast.

Whenever you grow bacteria you need to take care not to contaminate the plates with other bacteria, and not to allow the bacteria to infect yourself. To do this you need to keep instruments and surfaces free of microbes, or **sterile**. Working in this way is called aseptic or sterile technique.

When bacteria are grown commercially to make a product, they are grown in huge numbers. This is done in a large tank called a fermenter. Again, sterile technique is important.

A Why do biologists need powerful electron microscopes to study bacterial cells?

B Which part of a bacterium performs the function of a nucleus?

Exam tip OCR

✔ When making a list of the parts of a bacterial cell, focus on the parts that are not found in a plant or animal cell.

Did you know...?

There are bacteria that can survive very high temperatures. They have been found living in environments at temperatures above 80 °C.

Questions

1 Describe the common shapes of bacteria.

2 What is the function of the flagellum?

3 How do bacteria reproduce?

4 Explain why sterile technique is important.

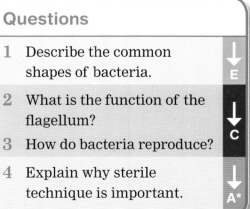

Learning objectives

After studying this topic, you should be able to:

- ✔ know the structure of fungi and viruses
- ✔ explain how yeasts and viruses multiply

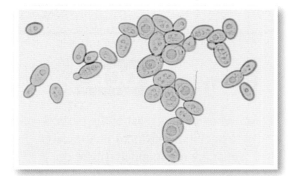

▲ Baker's yeast seen under a powerful light microscope (× 1000)

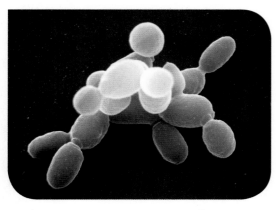

▲ A group of yeast cells all budding from one another

Yeast growth rate

For every 10 °C rise in temperature, the growth rate of yeast doubles. This is only true up to an optimum temperature, above which the yeast's enzymes begin to be damaged.

Fantastic fungi

Fungi are another important kingdom of organisms. They include mushrooms, moulds, and importantly yeasts. Yeasts are commercially useful to us in the making of bread and beers.

Yeasts are single celled, but larger than a bacterial cell. They can be clearly seen under a light microscope, but the internal detail can be seen better using an electron microscope.

The features of a fungal cell

Fungal cells have many parts in common with other cells. The fungal cell has a membrane, cytoplasm, and nucleus which function as they do in plant cells. The cell wall is similar to a plant or bacterial cell. It has the same function, but is made of a different chemical called chitin.

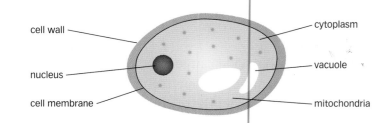

cell wall — cytoplasm
nucleus — vacuole
cell membrane — mitochondria

▲ A typical fungal cell

Reproduction in yeast

Yeast cells reproduce mainly asexually by a process called budding. The nucleus divides first, then a bulge forms on the side of the parent cell, which will develop into a new cell. Often the cells remain joined.

Budding can be a fast process. Like binary fission in bacteria, it allows the population of cells to increase rapidly. The optimum growth rate is controlled by

- availability of food
- temperature
- pH
- amount of waste products.

A Name three types of fungi.

B State one way in which a fungal cell and a bacterial cell are: (a) similar (b) different.

C Explain what budding is in yeast.

Viruses

One fascinating group of organisms is the **viruses**. Viruses are much smaller than bacteria or fungi. They are so small they were not seen until the electron microscope was invented. They are about one-hundredth the size of a bacterium.

Viruses do not have a cell structure, and they do not carry out many of the processes of living things. For these reasons, some biologists don't consider viruses to be living things.

The features of a virus

Viruses are made of a protein coat inside which is the genetic material. They cannot live independently – they can only live inside the cells of another organism, called the **host**. Each virus can only invade specific host cells; for example, animal viruses cannot invade plant cells. However, plant, animal, and bacterial cells all have viruses that can invade them. Once inside a host's cell, the virus takes over the cell.

Reproduction in viruses

The virus takes over the host cell in order to reproduce itself. This reproduction occurs in four main steps.

1 The virus attaches to a specific host cell.

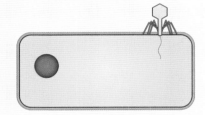

2 The genetic material from the virus is injected into the host cell.

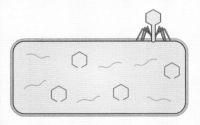

3 The viral genes cause the host cell to make new viruses.

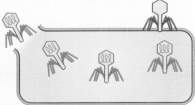

4 The host cell splits open, releasing the new virus.

▲ The four main stages in viral reproduction

Key words

fungi, viruses, host

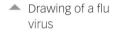
coat

genetic material

▲ Drawing of a flu virus

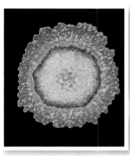

▲ A flu virus as revealed by an electron microscope (× 300 000)

Exam tip OCR

✓ If you are asked to compare the reproduction of a fungus and a virus, list the processes and show how they are different.

Questions

1 Arrange the following cells in size order, smallest first: bacteria, virus, yeast.

2 Why were viruses not seen until relatively recently?

3 Explain why some biologists think that viruses are not living things.

4 Explain why a virus needs a host to reproduce.

E

C

A*

3: Transmission of disease

Key words

pathogen, contamination, transmission

▲ A cut in the skin forms a potential site for the entry of microbes

Keeping the microbes out

Some microbes, called **pathogens**, cause disease. The body has a number of ways of preventing microbes getting in and causing disease. These features are sometimes referred to as our first line of defence.

Feature	How it prevents entry of microbes	How microbes may overcome the barrier
Skin	Acts as a physical barrier to prevent microbes entering. Washing reduces numbers of microbes on skin. Blood clots at a cut to form a scab and seal the skin.	Cuts in the skin allow microbes in. Insect bites penetrate the skin. Infected needles carry microbes through the skin.
Digestive system (through mouth)	Acid in the stomach kills bacteria.	Eating undercooked food or drinking infected water containing large numbers of microbes.
Respiratory system (through nose)	Cells lining the airways produce a sticky mucus which traps microorganisms. Fine hair-like cilia move the mucus with trapped microbes up to the throat for swallowing.	Some airborne microbes such as cold viruses can get past the cilia. Smoking stops the cilia working.
Reproductive system	Acidic urine kills many microbes.	Some microbes are resistant to acid. Microbes are passed from one person to another by sexual contact.

A List three ways that microbes can enter the body through the skin.

B Describe two ways in which the entry of microbes is prevented in the lungs.

C Why does eating food which is starting to go off make you ill?

Breaking and entering

In order to survive, microbes need to find and enter a host. There are a number of ways that they can get past the host's defences. Here are just a few.

- **Contaminated** food: many bacteria such as *Salmonella* and *E. coli* are common on unwashed vegetables and meat. If the food is not washed or cooked correctly, the bacteria will grow and reproduce. They will then be ingested along with the food. High levels of the bacteria will lead to food poisoning. These bacteria can even spread from uncooked food to cooked food, if people are not careful about food hygiene.
- Contaminated water: cholera is a disease caused by drinking water contaminated with sewage. This water contains the bacterium *Vibrio cholerae*, which causes the disease.
- Contact: many microbes are spread or **transmitted** by direct contact with an infected person. The microbe can also be transferred by touching a surface that an infected person has touched. One common example of this is athlete's foot, which is caused by a fungus called *Trichophyton*.
- Airborne transmission: viruses like the influenza virus are spread in small water droplets in the air. When someone sneezes, the droplets are fired out into the air for someone else to breathe in.

Natural disasters can spread disease

Natural disasters such as volcanic eruptions and earthquakes can disrupt the systems that prevent the spread of diseases. Cholera and food poisoning may spread easily because

- sewage pipes may be broken, causing sewage to leak out
- water supply systems may be damaged, cutting off the supply of clean fresh water
- electricity may be cut off, so food cannot be refrigerated
- many people may lose their homes and live crowded together in camps, where disease can spread
- the health service may become over-stretched, and lacking in supplies.

> **D** Explain why it is important to wash your hands after sneezing.

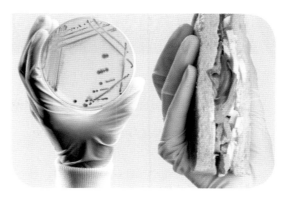

▲ Samples from food can be cultured on an agar plate to test for *E. coli* in the food

◀ Athlete's foot is a common fungal disease spread by direct contact

▲ An open well can easily become polluted, leading to cholera

▲ Sneezing fills the air with cold or flu viruses

Questions

1 Explain how the boy in the picture on the previous page can prevent his knee from becoming infected. ↓ E

2 Explain why colds and flu may easily be transmitted on a crowded bus. ↓ C

3 What do you think would be the main priorities to prevent disease after a major disaster? ↓ A*

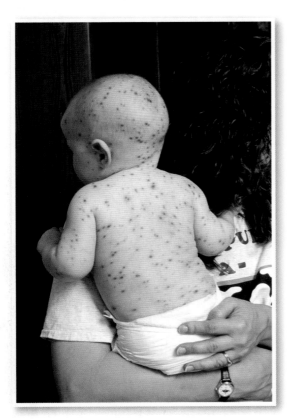

▲ This baby is suffering from chickenpox, a viral disease

Diseases and their microbes

Disease is a state in which the body is not healthy. There are many different diseases, with different causes and different symptoms. Some microbes can cause disease, and these disease-causing microbes are called a pathogen. If the pathogen spreads rapidly from one person to another, the disease is described as infectious. There are pathogens in all the groups of microbes – bacteria, viruses, and fungi.

Bacterial diseases

The table shows some examples of diseases caused by bacterial pathogens. The **symptoms** of a disease are the effects that a patient feels.

Disease	Pathogen and means of transmission
Cholera	Caused by a *Vibrio* bacterium transmitted in contaminated drinking water. The symptoms of the disease are severe diarrhoea and vomiting which lead to dehydration. Cholera is often fatal and develops particularly quickly in children.
Food poisoning	Bacteria are ingested in contaminated food. The symptoms include stomach pains, diarrhoea, and vomiting. It can be so severe that it can be fatal in children and elderly people.

Viral diseases

Here are some examples of viral diseases.

Disease	Pathogen and means of transmission
Influenza	The influenza virus is usually breathed in. Flu is one of the most common diseases. The symptoms include headaches, a running nose, coughs, and sneezes. The disease can occasionally be fatal in weak and elderly people.
Chickenpox	This disease spreads by direct contact, or by breathing in viruses transmitted by an infected person coughing. Symptoms include a rash on the skin that becomes very itchy. Headaches and fevers are also common. Chickenpox is not usually fatal.

Fungal diseases

Fungal diseases include:

Disease	Pathogen and means of transmission
Athlete's foot	The fungus infects the skin between the toes because it is often moist here. The symptoms include cracked flaking skin. It can be painful and in severe cases may bleed.

How an infectious disease develops

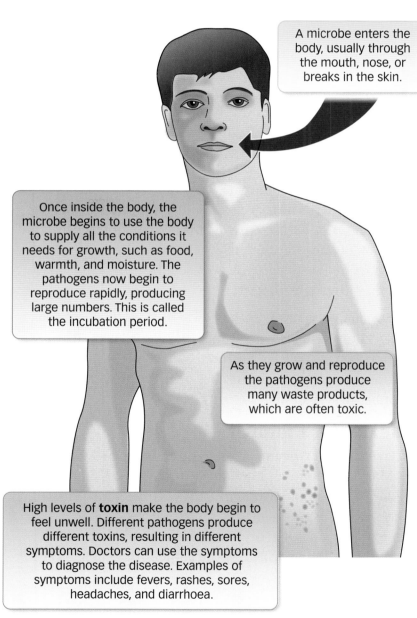

A microbe enters the body, usually through the mouth, nose, or breaks in the skin.

Once inside the body, the microbe begins to use the body to supply all the conditions it needs for growth, such as food, warmth, and moisture. The pathogens now begin to reproduce rapidly, producing large numbers. This is called the incubation period.

As they grow and reproduce the pathogens produce many waste products, which are often toxic.

High levels of **toxin** make the body begin to feel unwell. Different pathogens produce different toxins, resulting in different symptoms. Doctors can use the symptoms to diagnose the disease. Examples of symptoms include fevers, rashes, sores, headaches, and diarrhoea.

▲ Once inside your body, a pathogen reproduces and causes the symptoms of disease

A What is a pathogen?

B What are the symptoms of cholera?

C What makes cholera a particularly serious disease?

Questions

1 How do we get food poisoning?

2 Why is heart disease not termed an infectious disease?

3 Describe how a pathogen produces its symptoms.

4 Explain why you do not feel ill as soon as a microbe enters your body.

5 Explain how a doctor might use a person's symptoms to diagnose a disease.

E
C
A*

▲ Louis Pasteur   ▲ Joseph Lister

◄ Sir Alexander Fleming

It's a mystery

Until the 1800s, people did not know about microbes. They thought that food decayed because moulds would spontaneously generate on food. Diseases were explained as the effects of evil spirits, or caused by bad smells. There are three great microbiologists who revolutionised our understanding of infectious diseases.

Louis Pasteur

A French scientist called Louis Pasteur (1822–95) proved that decay was caused by microorganisms in the air. He went on to explain that microbes entering the body would cause disease. He proposed the idea that if we could stop microbes entering the body, we could prevent illness. These ideas are known as the germ theory.

Joseph Lister

Armed with the knowledge that microbes entering the body caused illness, Joseph Lister (1827–1912) developed the idea of **antiseptics**. These are solutions that kill microbes. Lister was a surgeon, and he sprayed his instruments with a solution of carbolic acid. This killed microbes on the instruments, which greatly reduced the number of postoperative infections.

Today, many types of antiseptic are used. They are much safer than the acids used by Lister. We use them to kill bacteria on all types of surfaces and on our skin. This contains the spread of microbes, and greatly reduces the number of infections.

Alexander Fleming

More recently, Alexander Fleming (1881–1955) worked in St Mary's Hospital in London. He discovered that a mould called penicillin produced a chemical that would kill bacteria. The fungus grew on one of his agar plates of bacteria. It caused an area where the bacteria could not grow, as they were killed by the penicillin.

During the Second World War scientists were able to make sufficient penicillin to give to a patient, and the patient recovered from the illness. Penicillin was the drug that killed bacteria – the first **antibiotic**.

A Who proposed that microbes caused disease?

B Explain how Lister made surgical procedures safer.

C Explain why the discovery of penicillin was so important.

Resistance to antibiotics

Antibiotics were regarded as wonder drugs. However, they cannot cure all infectious diseases:

- Antibiotics do not kill viruses. This is because viruses do not feed, and do not have a cell structure to damage. These are the two main ways that antibiotics work on bacteria.
- Some bacteria can develop **resistance** to an antibiotic, and the drug no longer works on them.

How bacteria develop resistance

The development of antibiotic resistance by bacteria is one of the best examples of evolution by natural selection.

- A mutation occurs in some bacteria, which gives them resistance to the antibiotic.
- Treatment by the antibiotic kills the bacteria in the population that do not have this mutation, so are not resistant.
- The bacteria with the resistance survive.
- The surviving bacteria reproduce, passing the resistance gene on.
- Eventually, the whole population becomes resistant.

Modern doctors are very aware of the problems of antibiotic resistance. They have changed their use of antibiotics over the last 20 years. There are two main practices that they now follow:

1. Doctors only prescribe antibiotics when really necessary. They do not use them for viral conditions or minor illnesses. This reduces the chance of antibiotic-resistant bacteria becoming the most common strain.
2. Patients are encouraged to complete the course of any antibiotics that they are given. This way all the microbes should be killed before resistance can fully develop.

Questions

1 Before Pasteur, what did people think caused infectious diseases? ↓ E

2 Explain why it was important that Lister was aware of the work of other scientists like Pasteur, before he made his discoveries.

3 Why do you think the original penicillin discovered by Fleming is virtually useless today? ↓ C

4 Explain why modern biologists need to carry out large numbers of clinical trials on any new antibiotic, before it can be used by doctors. ↓ A*

▲ These dairy products are made using processes that depend on bacteria

A Name three useful products made by bacteria.

B Explain why cheese and yoghurt are important in the diet.

Microbes in industry

Microbes are not all bad. Both bacteria and fungi can be used by humans to carry out useful tasks, such as to make a useful product on both a domestic and a commercial scale.

Products from bacteria

Bacteria have been used in a variety of ways for centuries. However, with our greater understanding of bacteria modern biologists have been able to make more efficient use of them. Today bacteria are used in the manufacture of:

- Yoghurt: this popular dairy product made for over 5000 years. It is made by adding the bacterium *Lactobacillus* to milk. Yoghurt is a very nutritious food which is rich in protein, calcium, and vitamins.
- Cheese: another common dairy product made for about 5000–8000 years. Cheese is made by causing milk to curdle, or separate into a solid curd and liquid whey. Curdling can be achieved using a mix of enzymes and bacteria such as *Lactobacillus*. The solid part of the milk is then turned into cheese. Like yoghurt, cheese is rich in protein, calcium, and vitamins.
- Vinegar: used for at least 5000 years, it was even recorded in Egyptian times. It is produced by the acidifying of wine, cider, or beer to produce wine, cider, and malt vinegars. The production of vinegar uses bacteria such as *Acetobacter*.

▲ Vinegars are made by the action of *Acetobacter* on wine, cider, or beer

- Silage: a common winter fodder for cattle, which has been in use since the 1880s. Green cut vegetation is piled up in a large heap and covered in plastic, or placed in a silo. The vegetation is broken down by **fermentation**, or anaerobic respiration. The process will occur naturally, but it is speeded up by adding another *Lactobacillus* species.
- Composting: a natural process used for at least 2000 years. Since the 1920s it has become important in organic farming. The dead remains of plants and animals are digested by bacteria and fungi to form nutrient-rich soils. Often the remains are simply piled up at the end of the harvest and allowed to rot down until the next planting season.

▲ Silage bales in Wales

> **C** How is silage important to farmers?

A closer look at yoghurt-making

The yoghurt industry is worth millions of pounds a year. Making yoghurt involves adding bacteria to milk. Like all processes involving microbes, it is important that all equipment is sterile – clean and free from microbes – throughout the process.

▲ Quality control sampling in a yoghurt-making factory

▲ Colours and flavours are added to make the final product

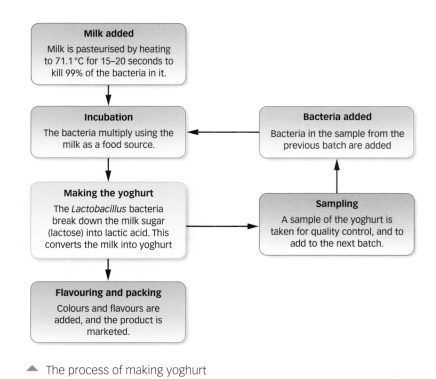

Milk added
Milk is pasteurised by heating to 71.1 °C for 15–20 seconds to kill 99% of the bacteria in it.

Incubation
The bacteria multiply using the milk as a food source.

Bacteria added
Bacteria in the sample from the previous batch are added

Making the yoghurt
The *Lactobacillus* bacteria break down the milk sugar (lactose) into lactic acid. This converts the milk into yoghurt

Sampling
A sample of the yoghurt is taken for quality control, and to add to the next batch.

Flavouring and packing
Colours and flavours are added, and the product is marketed.

▲ The process of making yoghurt

Exam tip — OCR

✔ Remember the process of yoghurt-making as a sequence of steps.

Questions

1 Why are fruit and sugar added to many yoghurts?

2 Explain why sterile technique is important when producing yoghurt.

3 Explain why a sample from a previous batch is added at the start of the yoghurt-making process.

Learning objectives

After studying this topic, you should be able to:

- ✔ know that yeast is used in the brewing process
- ✔ understand the process of brewing to produce a range of alcoholic drinks
- ✔ understand how alcoholic drinks can be made stronger

Useful fungi

As well as bacteria, fungi are also used to make useful products commercially. Yeast is probably the most widely used fungus. Among other products, fungi are used to make alcoholic drinks and bread.

Brewing

Brewing is the production of alcoholic drinks by the process of fermentation. Yeast makes the alcohol by fermenting sugars found in plants, usually in the fruit or grain (seed).

- Wine is made from grapes.
- Beer and lager are made from malted barley.
- Cider is made from apples.

Step	Process	Explanation
1.	Malting	This happens in beer- and lager-making. The barley seeds start to germinate (grow), which converts the starch stored in the seeds into sugar.
2.	Extracting the sugar	The plant material is either crushed or soaked in water to get the sugar out.
3.	Flavouring	Wines get their flavour from the fruit juice used, while beers are flavoured with hops, the female flowers of the hop plant, *Humulus lupulus*.
4.	Adding yeast	The container is sealed to prevent air and other microbes entering. The yeast can respire aerobically for a very short time, until any oxygen in the container is used up. This allows the yeast to reproduce. The liquid is kept warm.
5.	Fermentation	The culture quickly becomes anaerobic and the yeast starts to produce alcohol. If there is too much oxygen in the container, anaerobic respiration does not occur and vinegar is produced. This process happens in large stainless steel vats called fermenters. The mixture is kept at a constant temperature of 25–30°C, which gives the best rate of respiration to produce alcohol. This temperature also gives a better flavour.
6.	Extracting the wine and beer	After fermentation is over, the liquid is separated from the yeast cells. Usually the yeast is allowed to sink to the bottom to separate it out of the liquid. The liquid may need clarifying by a filtration process.
7.	Pasteurising and packaging/bottling	The product is heated and quickly cooled to kill any remaining microbes. This gives the product a longer shelf life when stored in bottles.

The fermentation reaction

This is the anaerobic respiration reaction (without oxygen) that occurs in the yeast cells:

glucose (sugar) → ethanol (alcohol) + carbon dioxide

Symbol equation for the fermentation reaction

Here is the symbol equation for anaerobic respiration in yeast: $C_6H_{12}O_6 \rightarrow 2C_2H_5OH + 2CO_2$

Making it stronger

There is a limit to the concentration of alcohol that can be produced by the brewing process. Alcohol is toxic and eventually kills the yeast in the fermenter when it reaches a certain concentration. Some yeasts can tolerate more alcohol than others. This results in drinks with different alcohol contents:

* Beers and lagers usually contain 3–5% alcohol.
* Wines usually contain 11–12% alcohol.

Spirits such as vodka and whiskey contain high levels of alcohol. To make spirits, the first step is fermenting plant material, similar to the production of beers and wines.

* Rum is made from sugar cane.
* Whiskey is made from malted barley.
* Vodka is made from potatoes.

Spirits typically contain 40% alcohol. To increase the concentration of alcohol from the fermentation process, the liquid is **distilled**. To do this the liquid is placed in a large container, or still, and heated. The alcohol boils at a temperature of about 80°C, which is lower than the boiling point of water. The alcohol rises up the column as a vapour, leaving the water behind. The vaporised alcohol passes along a collecting arm, and cools. This product contains a lot more alcohol than the fermentation liquid.

◀ Stills at a whiskey distillery. Alcohol is distilled off the fermentation liquid to produce a spirit with a higher alcohol content. Distillation can only be carried out in premises licensed for the production of alcohol.

Key words

brewing, distillation

Did you know...?

Food processing factories produce waste water containing sugars. Yeast can be used to ferment the sugars and clean the waste water.

Exam tip   OCR

✔ The fermentation process is a sequence of steps. Remember the differences between brewing and making yoghurt.

A Which microbe is involved in the making of alcohol?

B Name the two products of alcoholic fermentation.

C Why are hops added to beer?

Questions

1 Name two alcoholic drinks produced by fermentation.   ↓ E

2 Why do spirits keep longer than beers and wines?   ↓ C

3 Explain why fermentation alone does not produce spirits.

4 Explain why the temperature must be carefully regulated:
   (a) in the brewing process
   (b) in the distilling process.   ↓ A*

Learning objectives

After studying this topic, you should be able to:

- ✔ know that biological materials can be used as a fuel source
- ✔ give examples of biofuels
- ✔ understand the production, uses, and composition of biogas
- ✔ know that fuel can be made from alcohol

Key words

biofuel

A What is the source of energy for making biofuels?

B Name three types of biofuel.

Balancing the books

To burn fuels while maintaining no overall increase in greenhouse gases is a difficult balancing act. When we burn biofuels we have grown, the carbon dioxide taken in during photosynthesis is then released during the combustion.

However, land is needed to grow these crops. In some areas forests are cleared for the cash crop and this leads to a loss of plants to absorb carbon dioxide, and an increase in carbon dioxide released by decaying wood. It also causes a loss of habitat.

Greener fuels

The burning of fossil fuels harms the environment as it produces waste gases including carbon dioxide, which leads to global warming. A variety of fuels from biological materials can be used as an alternative. These are called **biofuels**. They are better for the environment because the carbon dioxide produced when they burn is balanced by the carbon dioxide they use in photosynthesis while they are growing.

What are biofuels?

As in fossil fuels, the energy in biofuels originates from sunlight used in photosynthesis. Photosynthesis produces the biomass in plants, and this biomass can be used directly or indirectly as biofuel. Wood can be burnt directly to release energy. Fast-growing trees can be used to fire power stations.

Common biofuels include wood, biogas, and alcohol.

Advantages of using biofuels	Disadvantages of using biofuels
Reduce fossil fuel consumption by providing an alternative fuel.	Cause habitat loss because large areas of land are needed to grow the plants.
No overall increase in levels of greenhouse gases, as the plants take in carbon dioxide to grow, and release it when burnt.	Habitat loss can lead to extinction of species.
Burning biogas and alcohol produces no particulates (smoke).	Data shows that some biofuels transfer less energy than other fuel types.

~~Biogas~~ Borgias

Biogas is made by the fermentation of carbohydrates in plant material and sewage by bacteria. This fermentation occurs naturally, for example in marshes, septic tanks, and even inside animals' guts. Biogas is also produced at some landfill sites, where the gas can be burnt. Sometimes the biogas can explode, making the landfill site unusable for many years.

Biogas is a mixture of gases that will burn in oxygen, forming a useful fuel:

- methane (50–75%)
- carbon dioxide (25–50%)
- hydrogen, nitrogen, and hydrogen sulfide (less than 10%).

Small-scale biogas production

In remote areas of Nepal and India biogas is made for families and used for cooking. The fermentation happens in a large tank sunk into the ground, which keeps the temperature constant. The family place organic material like dead plants and animal waste in the tank. The bacteria digest this waste, releasing the gas.

Biogas production on a larger scale

The gas is generated commercially in large anaerobic tanks. Wet plant waste or animal manure is constantly added, and the gas produced is removed. Gas production is fastest at a temperature of 32–35 °C, because the fermenting bacteria grow best at this temperature. The remaining solids need to be removed from the tanks and can be used as a fertiliser in some cases.

Biogas has a number of uses:
- as vehicle fuel
- to generate electricity
- for heating systems.

Bioethanol

Alcohol is produced from plant material by yeasts in brewing. On a larger scale this alcohol can be used as a fuel. Mixed with petrol it produces gasohol, which is a common fuel for cars. This is a particularly economic fuel in countries that produce large amounts of plant waste, such as Brazil. Brazil has no oil reserves and plenty of sugar cane waste to make the alcohol.

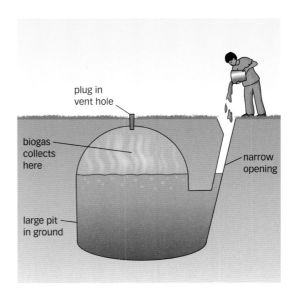

▲ Section through a biogas digester

Problems with biogas

There are a few technical issues with the production of biogas. First, since many different waste materials are used, a large range of bacteria are needed to digest the waste.

Biogas is a cleaner fuel than petrol or diesel, as fewer particulates are released. However, burning biogas releases 4.5–8.5 kWh/m³ of energy compared with natural gas, which releases 9.8 kWh/m³. This is because biogas contains less methane than natural gas.

A final difficulty is that if the biogas becomes mixed with air, so that there is more oxygen and the methane content drops to 5–20%, the mixture becomes explosive. This is not a problem when the gas is contained and not allowed to mix with the air.

Questions

1 Explain why biogas from landfill sites is particularly dangerous.

2 Give two reasons why gasohol is used in Brazil.

3 Why must a biogas digester be kept airtight?

4 Explain why using biofuels should not contribute to any net increase in greenhouse gases, in contrast to using fossil fuels.

Learning objectives

After studying this topic, you should be able to:

- ✔ know that the land surface is covered in rock or soil
- ✔ know the composition of soil
- ✔ describe organisms that live in the soil
- ✔ understand the importance of the earthworm

Key words

humus

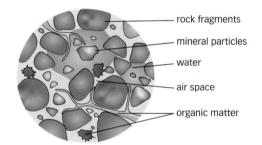

▲ The constituents of soil

rock fragments
mineral particles
water
air space
organic matter

Soil constituent	How to test a soil sample for it
moisture	Weigh, bake, and reweigh sample
humus	Weigh, burn, and reweigh sample
air	Weigh the sample and measure its volume

A Name three types of soil.

B Which type of soil retains water best?

Solid ground

The land surface is covered in either bare rock or soil. Rock is weathered to form the soil.

What is soil?

Soil contains a number of different components:

- Fragments of rock (minerals) – these are produced when rock is weathered. The size varies, and this determines the type of soil.
- Air spaces – gaps between the particles.
- Water – this fills some of the spaces between particles.
- Dead material – fragments of dead plants, animals, or organic waste.
- Living organisms – there is a huge variety of life in and on the soil. Plants rely on the soil for minerals, water, and to anchor them.

Soils have different structures depending on the size of their particles.

Soil type	Particle size	Air spaces	Permeability to water
clay small clay particles tiny air spaces	small (less than 0.002 mm)	few and small	low – water is retained in soil; soil can flood
loam clay and sand particles many air spaces of different sizes	mixture of small and large	many and variable in size	medium – water retention is good
sand large sand particles many large air spaces	large (0.05–2 mm)	many and large	poor – little water retained in soil

Soil as a habitat

Most organisms in the soil need water and also oxygen for respiration. The amounts of water and oxygen in a soil depend on the soil particle size.

If the particles are small (clay soil) there will be few air spaces, and they will often be full of water, reducing oxygen levels.
- If the particles are big (sandy soil) there will be plenty of oxygen in the air spaces, but the water will drain away.

An ideal soil (loam) has a mixture of particle sizes, providing both air spaces and water retention. Gardeners improve their soil by digging to allow in air and to increase drainage.

Dead material decomposes in the soil to produce **humus**. This releases minerals into the soil which are needed by plants for growth. Humus adds a fibrous quality to soil – it tends to hold soil particles apart, improving aeration. It also helps retain water in the soil.

Soil pH also affects what can live there. Some plants such as heathers grow well in acidic soil. Many plants prefer relatively neutral soils. Alkaline soils are rare in the UK. Many farmers add lime to neutralise acidic soils so that they can grow more crops.

What lives in soil?

There is a whole community of organisms living in soil, linked together to form a food web.

Worms pull dead leaves down into the soil, burying them. This organic material is then slowly decayed by bacteria and fungi, improving the nutrient content of the soil.

Earthworm burrows create gaps which aerate the soil. As the worms move through the burrows they push air through them. The cavities also allow water to drain more freely, reducing the chance of flooding.

The earthworm mixes the soil by eating soil and passing out waste elsewhere in the soil.

Earthworms release calcium carbonate into their gut to help the digestion of leaves. This then passes out in their waste, and has the added bonus of helping to neutralise acidic soils.

▲ Earthworms as soil improvers

Questions

1 List the main components of soil.

2 Using the food web, explain why soils with little detritus contain few organisms.

3 Detritivores eat detritus. Name three detritivores in the soil food web.

4 If a gardener used an insecticide that killed ground beetles, what might happen to the earthworm population?

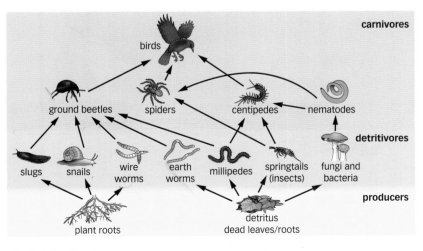

carnivores

birds

ground beetles   spiders   centipedes   nematodes

detritivores

slugs   snails   wire worms   earth worms   millipedes   springtails (insects)   fungi and bacteria

producers

plant roots   detritus dead leaves/roots

▲ Soil food web

Learning objectives

After studying this topic, you should be able to:

- ✔ list some advantages and disadvantages of living in water
- ✔ know that phytoplankton are the producers in ocean food webs
- ✔ explain seasonal fluctuations in plankton numbers

Key words

plankton

Water regulation

In fresh water, too much water can enter the body by osmosis. This is not a problem for plants, as cell walls stop cells expanding and prevent excess water getting in. In animals, excess water must be removed from the body. Freshwater fish urinate frequently, removing the excess. Microscopic organisms such as amoebae have a cell structure called the contractile vacuole, into which the excess water goes. The vacuole then moves to the cell surface, fuses with it, and releases the water.

Sea water is salty, and this affects osmosis. Many invertebrates have bodies at the same salt concentration as the sea and so have no problem, but some larger fish do not. They actively get rid of the salt in the water they drink.

Living in water

There is a huge diversity of life in water, including microorganisms.

The wonders of water

There are several advantages of living in water:

- Buoyancy – water is more dense than air, so it gives more support to the organisms that live in it. The largest animal, the blue whale, can measure up to 30 m in length and weigh up to 170 tonnes. These animals could not support their weight on land.
- Removal of waste – animal waste is washed away and does not build up, as it is greatly diluted in the water and broken down.
- Steady temperature – surface waters vary in temperature, but not as much as the air does. Water requires a lot of energy to heat it up. The waters at the poles are at about 0 °C, while temperatures near the Equator can be up to 30 °C. Deeper water has a very stable temperature, about 4 °C. Aquatic organisms do not have to cope with extremes or rapid changes in temperature.
- Ready water supply – living in fresh water means that there is no risk of dehydration.

The woes of water

There are also disadvantages of aquatic habitats:

- Movement – water is more dense than air, making it harder to move through, so aquatic animals use more energy.
- Water balance – water is everywhere; the problem is balancing the amount of water in the body.

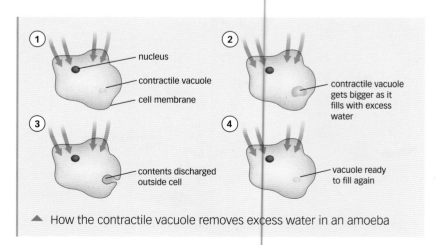

▲ How the contractile vacuole removes excess water in an amoeba

Aquatic food webs

There are microscopic organisms living in water called **plankton**. There are two types:

- Phytoplankton are photosynthetic microorganisms – they are producers.
- Zooplankton are animal-like microorganisms – they are consumers.

Plankton float in the open waters, moving in currents. The numbers of the phytoplankton vary during the year. Three factors control their numbers:

Factor	Seasonal effect	Effect of depth
Light	As day length increases, the numbers of phytoplankton increase.	Light only penetrates surface waters, so phytoplankton are limited to the surface waters.
Temperature	As surface water temperatures rise in spring, the numbers of phytoplankton increase.	At depth the temperature is a constant 4°C, too cold for phytoplankton to grow.
Minerals	Minerals rise to the surface during the winter, so there is a ready supply for phytoplankton in the spring.	Mineral concentrations increase at depth, but phytoplankton are limited there by light and temperature.

Seasonal changes in phytoplankton numbers will influence the numbers of zooplankton.

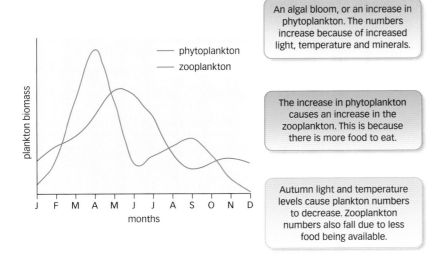

An algal bloom, or an increase in phytoplankton. The numbers increase because of increased light, temperature and minerals.

The increase in phytoplankton causes an increase in the zooplankton. This is because there is more food to eat.

Autumn light and temperature levels cause plankton numbers to decrease. Zooplankton numbers also fall due to less food being available.

▲ Seasonal cycles in plankton populations in the North Atlantic

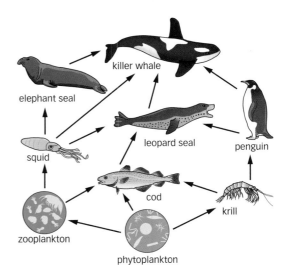

▲ A marine food web

Aquatic grazing

Grazing food webs, based on photosynthetic producers, are common in the surface layers of the oceans.

In deep water food webs do not start with phytoplankton as there is no light. Food chains at these depths rely on dead food falling from above, called marine snow. These are detrital food chains.

Other food chains start with bacteria – producers that get their energy from chemical reactions in a process called chemosynthesis.

Questions

1 Explain why phytoplankton do not grow in the deep oceans. ↓ E

2 Why is the phytoplankton population at its peak in April? ↓ C

3 Explain why the phytoplankton population is low in June, when growing conditions are good. ↓ A*

Learning objectives

After studying this topic, you should be able to:

- know that organisms are affected by pollution
- understand the steps in the process of eutrophication
- appreciate that pollutants can build up in some species

Key words

eutrophication, indicator species

▲ Scientists cleaning a pelican caught in the 2010 oil spill in the Gulf of Mexico. It was estimated that hundreds of thousands of gallons were spilling into the water each day.

Exam tip   OCR

- Learn the steps in the sequence of eutrophication. It may appear as a long-answer question.

What a waste!

Unfortunately, humans generate a lot of waste. Many of these wastes pollute water, affecting the number and type of organisms (including microscopic ones) that live there.

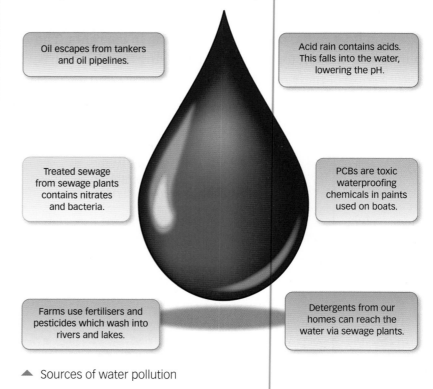

Oil escapes from tankers and oil pipelines.

Acid rain contains acids. This falls into the water, lowering the pH.

Treated sewage from sewage plants contains nitrates and bacteria.

PCBs are toxic waterproofing chemicals in paints used on boats.

Farms use fertilisers and pesticides which wash into rivers and lakes.

Detergents from our homes can reach the water via sewage plants.

▲ Sources of water pollution

A Name two pollutants of water.

B Explain how fertilisers sprayed on crops get into water.

C In 2010 there was a rupture in an oil pipeline off the coast of New Orleans, which released vast quantities of oil into the sea. What is the effect of oil on wildlife?

Eutrophication: a case study

One major pollutant of water is nitrates. Nitrates enter the water in untreated sewage or directly from fertilisers. When this happens the process of **eutrophication** occurs.

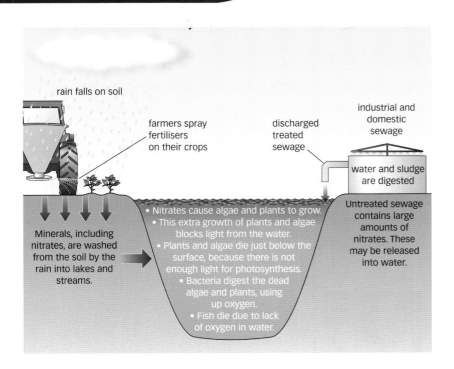

rain falls on soil

farmers spray fertilisers on their crops

discharged treated sewage

industrial and domestic sewage

water and sludge are digested

Minerals, including nitrates, are washed from the soil by the rain into lakes and streams.

- Nitrates cause algae and plants to grow.
- This extra growth of plants and algae blocks light from the water.
- Plants and algae die just below the surface, because there is not enough light for photosynthesis.
- Bacteria digest the dead algae and plants, using up oxygen.
- Fish die due to lack of oxygen in water.

Untreated sewage contains large amounts of nitrates. These may be released into water.

▲ River pollution causing severe algal bloom

Indicators of pollution

Biologists can get an idea of the level of water pollution by looking for the presence of **indicator species**. For example:

- pH changes in water can be indicated by a reduced number of amphibians in polluted streams and bogs.
- Reduced oxygen levels are indicated by rat-tailed maggots.

Poisoned whales

Certain chemicals do not break down in the environment quickly. Examples include commonly used industrial chemicals called PCBs, and the pesticide DDT. You may remember that chemicals like these can build up in food chains. They will eventually reach toxic levels in the top carnivores.

Both of these chemicals can build up in the bodies of whales over many years. The result is that some whales, such as killer whales, are among the most contaminated animals on Earth. PCBs are known to suppress the immune systems of these animals. This may contribute to the decrease in their numbers. Before the 1960s, whaling was common practice in many communities. Humans ate the whale meat. The whale meat was so contaminated that the levels of PCBs had a harmful effect on the people who ate it.

Questions

1 What is the effect of pollution on the numbers of aquatic organisms?

2 Draw a flow diagram to describe eutrophication.

3 Explain how indicator species might suggest reduced oxygen levels in water.

4 Environmentally friendly detergents do not contain as many nitrates and phosphates as mainstream detergents. Explain how this will reduce eutrophication.

5 Explain how PCBs build up in whale meat.

E

C

A*

Learning objectives

After studying this topic, you should be able to:

- ✔ understand how enzymes are used in the food industry to make food sweeter
- ✔ know that enzymes are used in biological washing powders

Key words

enzyme technology, biological washing powders

A Give one reason why enzymes are used in a variety of industries.

B Name two industries that use enzymes, and suggest why they are used.

C Why are different enzymes used in different industries?

Exam tip   **OCR**

- ✔ Remember that, like all catalysts, enzymes speed up a reaction but don't get used up.

Making microbes work for us

Enzymes are catalysts, and in biotechnology scientists often use enzymes to speed up chemical reactions. This use of enzymes in industry is called **enzyme technology**. Bacteria are easy to grow in large quantities, so they are used to produce these enzymes on a large scale.

Industrial uses of enzymes

Industry	Enzyme	Use
dairy (eg cheese making)	protease (eg rennet)	Causes solids (curds) to separate from the liquid (whey) in milk.
food processing	proteases	Digest proteins in foods such as soy and citrus products, to remove bitter tastes.
fruit juice	cellulases	Break down cell walls in the fruit, releasing juice.
	amylases	Reduce cloudiness and increase sweetness by breaking down starch.
medical	glucose oxidase	Present in kits used by people with diabetes to test for glucose in urine or blood.
biological washing powder	proteases, lipases, and amylases	Remove organic stains such as food and grass stains from laundry.

Sweet enough?

The food industry makes great use of enzymes. As a nation we have a very sweet tooth. Processed foods and soft drinks contain a lot of sugar to sweeten the product. The sugar extracted from plants like sugar cane is called sucrose. This is not as sweet to the taste as other sugars like fructose unless it is broken down by enzymes.

An enzyme called invertase (sucrase) digests sucrose into glucose and fructose. The food industry now has a much sweeter product. They can use fructose to sweeten food. This way less sugar is needed to produce a sweet product. This is common practice in producing low calorie foods and drinks.

Cleaning power

Biological washing powders contain soap powder, enzymes, and minerals. Why are the enzymes added?

- Enzymes digest stains.
- Enzymes digest fibres in the dirt, releasing bobbles.
- They allow stain removal to occur at a lower temperature, which saves energy and money.

These washing powders contain several different enzymes, each of which does a different job. The enzymes break down the stains into small soluble products that wash off the fabric. Unfortunately, the enzymes in biological washing powders don't work at high temperatures or extreme pH levels.

Disadvantages of biological washing powders

Biological washing powders allow us to use less energy and to machine wash delicate fabrics, because they do not need high temperatures. However, there are a few limitations to using enzymes in this way:

- The enzymes may be destroyed at high temperatures so do not work for a hot wash.
- The enzymes are pH sensitive, so they may not work so well in areas of the country with particularly acidic or alkaline water.
- They may cause allergies.

▲ Slimming products

Amylases digest carbohydrate stains such as starch from foods like pasta and flour.

Lipases digest fats and fatty stains like grease.

Proteases digest protein stains such as blood.

▲ Biological washing powders contain a combination of enzymes

D Suggest why people might want to reduce their sugar intake.

E Explain why less fructose than sucrose is needed to sweeten food.

Questions

1 Why are enzymes used in cheese making?

2 Explain why biological washing powders are better at removing stains than non-biological powders.

3 Why is it not efficient to use biological washing powders in a hot wash?

Learning objectives

After studying this topic, you should be able to:

✓ know that enzyme technology is used in medicine

✓ understand immobilised enzymes and their advantages

✓ be aware of the use of immobilised enzymes in coping with lactose intolerance

Key words

immobilised

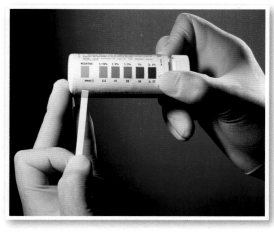

▲ Reagent sticks are used to test for glucose in urine. They contain a range of enzymes.

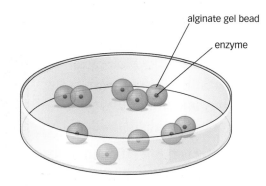

alginate gel bead

enzyme

▲ Alginate beads can be used to immobilise enzymes

Doctor, doctor!

The medical industry makes great use of enzymes. Two examples are:

* Testing for sugar – people with diabetes need to keep a watchful eye on the glucose levels in their urine or blood. The normal blood glucose level is from 4–8 mmol/l. Diabetics often experience higher levels. They monitor their blood glucose level to prevent it rising for too long, as persistent high levels can damage blood vessels in organs like the eyes. If their blood glucose level falls too low, they could become unconscious. Testing could be done using the food test called Benedict's test for glucose. This is not very practical in our modern lives. Now we use reagent sticks to test for glucose. These sticks make use of enzymes.

* Lactose intolerance – some people don't make the enzyme lactase, and so they cannot digest the sugar lactose in their gut. Bacteria in their digestive system digest it instead, leading to diarrhoea and wind. Enzymes are now used to produce lactose-free foods.

Immobilised enzymes

Enzymes are delicate molecules. They are highly temperature sensitive. This can make them difficult for scientists to use and store. Scientists have developed a method to help make enzymes more stable and easier to use.

The enzymes are **immobilised**, which means they are attached to a more inert substance. There are two common ways of doing this. The enzyme can be added to a fibre mesh, as on reagent sticks. Another method is to produce gel beads containing the enzymes. To do this:

* The enzymes are mixed with a solution of sodium alginate.
* The mixture is dropped into a calcium chloride solution.
* This causes small beads of alginate gel to form.
* Embedded in the gel are the enzymes.

The advantages of the use of immobilised enzymes are:

* The beads are easier to use than free enzymes.
* The beads support the structure of the enzyme, making it less sensitive to temperature and pH.

- The enzyme can be removed from a reaction mixture by filtering out the beads, so the solution is not contaminated with enzymes.
- The beads can be placed in a column, and the reactants poured in at the top. The products can be drawn off at the bottom of the column.

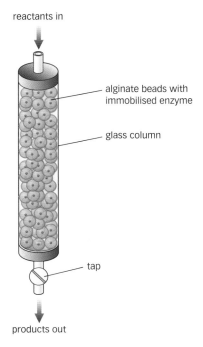

Immobilised enzymes can be used in a column to make a continuous flow of products

Lactose intolerance

Lactose is a sugar found in milk. As mammals, we are all fed on milk as babies. However, a surprisingly large number of people show some signs of lactose intolerance. This means that they are unable to digest the lactose in their diet. If they eat or drink too much lactose, it can make them unwell.

Beads can be made containing immobilised lactase enzymes. These beads are then mixed with high-lactose foods such as milk. The enzyme digests the lactose into glucose and galactose:

$$\text{lactose} \xrightarrow{\text{lactase}} \text{glucose} + \text{galactose}$$

Both glucose and galactose are easily absorbed in the gut.

A State two medical uses of enzymes.
B Explain why reagent sticks are easier to use to test for glucose than the Benedict's test.
C Explain why it is easier to remove immobilised enzymes from a reaction.

Did you know...?

Nearly all cats are lactose intolerant, so the traditional idea of giving cats a saucer of milk is actually bad for them. Special cat milk is now available, which has had the lactose removed using immobilised enzymes.

◀ Normal milk is bad for cats

Questions

1 What are the two ways in which scientists can immobilise enzymes?

2 Describe how lactose-free milk could be produced using a column.

3 Explain why using immobilised enzymes in bead columns is more economic than using free enzymes.

4 Explain why it is important for the alginate beads to be porous.

A Name two products produced by genetic engineering.

Productive bacteria

Biotechnology is a growing industry. It develops ways of using microorganisms for industrial processes.

One such process is called **genetic engineering**. It is possible to introduce a gene from one organism (the donor) into bacteria (the host), so that the bacteria will make useful protein products for us. Two well established examples of products made in this way are

• insulin: used by people with diabetes to control their blood sugar

• human growth hormone: used to treat people with reduced growth.

The process of genetic engineering involves these basic steps:

1. Identifying the gene that codes for the protein to be produced.
2. Removing it from the donor, e.g. a human cell.
3. Introducing it into a host, the bacterium.
4. Growing the bacteria on a large scale to make the product.

Engineering bacteria
Producing transgenic bacteria

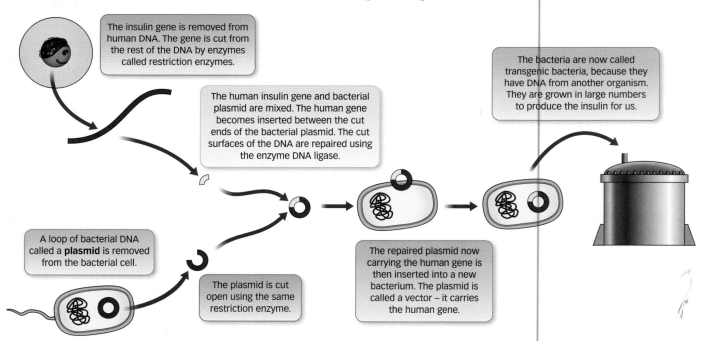

The insulin gene is removed from human DNA. The gene is cut from the rest of the DNA by enzymes called restriction enzymes.

The human insulin gene and bacterial plasmid are mixed. The human gene becomes inserted between the cut ends of the bacterial plasmid. The cut surfaces of the DNA are repaired using the enzyme DNA ligase.

The bacteria are now called transgenic bacteria, because they have DNA from another organism. They are grown in large numbers to produce the insulin for us.

A loop of bacterial DNA called a **plasmid** is removed from the bacterial cell.

The plasmid is cut open using the same restriction enzyme.

The repaired plasmid now carrying the human gene is then inserted into a new bacterium. The plasmid is called a vector – it carries the human gene.

Genetic engineering is used to produce human insulin in large quantities. Before this process was developed people with diabetes injected insulin from cows or pigs.

Cloning the bacteria

Once the plasmid has been taken up by the bacteria, these **transgenic** bacteria need to multiply to produce a large culture of bacteria, all capable of making insulin. The bacteria are placed in a large container called a fermenter. Here ideal conditions can be provided for their rapid growth and reproduction. The bacteria divide asexually, producing genetically identical copies of themselves. This is called cloning. The resulting large culture of bacteria will make large amounts of the insulin protein. This is harvested and packaged.

Checking for the gene

Genetic engineering can be tricky. Biotechnologists can't see the actual genes, and sometimes the bacteria will not take up the plasmid with the gene. These bacteria will not make the protein, so there is no point in culturing them. Biotechnologists test the bacteria to see if the gene is there. This testing uses a process called an assaying technique.

The assaying is usually done by growing the bacteria on agar with a coloured dye. The plasmid that carries the human gene also has a second gene included in it. This gene codes for an enzyme that causes a colour change in a dye, turning it blue. One of two possible events will happen on the agar:

- If the human insulin gene is in the plasmid, it damages the gene that makes the colour-change enzyme. So no colour-change enzyme is produced, and the agar around the bacteria will stay colourless.
- If the human insulin gene is not present, the colour-change gene will be intact, and will make the enzyme. The result will be that the agar will go blue.

The colourless colonies of bacteria are selected and cloned.

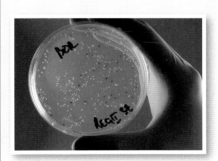

◀ An assaying technique to check whether the insulin gene has been taken up by bacteria. The blue colonies do not have the desired gene; the white colonies have taken up the gene and will be cultured.

Key words

biotechnology, genetic engineering, plasmid, transgenic

B What is a restriction enzyme?

C How does the DNA repair?

▲ Fermenter units containing bacteria that have been genetically engineered to produce proteins

Questions

1 What type of organism is the host for the insulin gene? **E**

2 Why are genetically modified organisms called transgenic organisms?

3 Explain why biotechnology companies need to clone genetically modified bacteria. **C**

4 Suggest how food, oxygen levels, and temperature could be managed inside a fermenter.

5 Why is it important to carry out an assay of the bacteria resulting from the genetic engineering process? **A***

15: Genetically modified organisms

Learning objectives

After studying this topic, you should be able to:

- ✔ know that organisms other than bacteria can be genetically modified
- ✔ explain the process of genetic modification
- ✔ appreciate the importance of enzymes in the process

Key words

restriction enzymes, sticky end, DNA ligase

Improving on nature

Biotechnologists do not only put genes into bacteria. They can also transfer genes into other organisms, including plants and animals. These are then called genetically modified (GM) organisms. By adding new genes, their genetic code is altered. But why do this?

The idea is to take a gene coding for a useful characteristic from one organism and make it work in another (host), organism. The host will then show the useful characteristic.

Examples of characteristics transferred by GM technology include:

- pesticide resistance in plants
- frost resistance in fruit
- increased shelf life in fruit
- increased milk yield in cattle.

Creating a GM organism

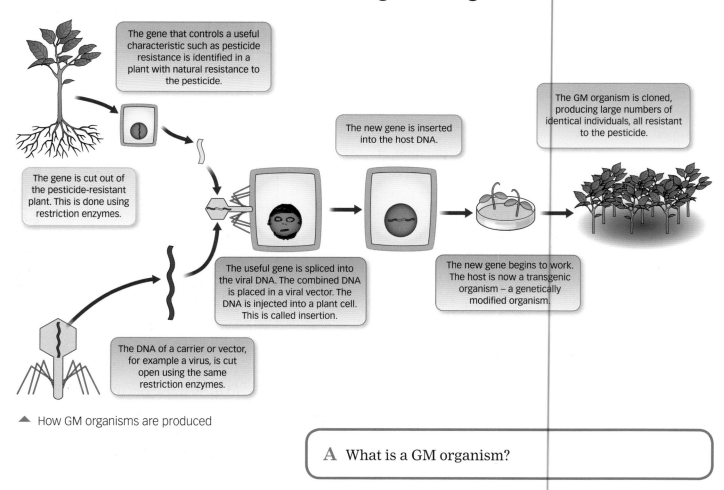

The gene that controls a useful characteristic such as pesticide resistance is identified in a plant with natural resistance to the pesticide.

The gene is cut out of the pesticide-resistant plant. This is done using restriction enzymes.

The DNA of a carrier or vector, for example a virus, is cut open using the same restriction enzymes.

The useful gene is spliced into the viral DNA. The combined DNA is placed in a viral vector. The DNA is injected into a plant cell. This is called insertion.

The new gene is inserted into the host DNA.

The new gene begins to work. The host is now a transgenic organism – a genetically modified organism.

The GM organism is cloned, producing large numbers of identical individuals, all resistant to the pesticide.

▲ How GM organisms are produced

A What is a GM organism?

High-tech enzymes

It may seem surprising that biologists are able to put genes from one organism into another and they still work. The reason for this is that DNA and the genetic code is the same for all life. It is universal, and all cells can 'read' or 'understand' the same code. The trick is to use high-tech enzymes to ensure that the DNA for the genes is put into place correctly.

Restriction enzymes make very precise cuts through the DNA. Remember that DNA is made of two parallel strands, with bases between them. Restriction enzymes do not cut straight across the strands – most of them make a staggered cut, leaving a few unpaired bases exposed on the ends of the strands. The cut surfaces are called '**sticky ends**'.

The useful thing about sticky ends is that they will stick back together a little like Velcro. The new gene to be added is also cut by the same restriction enzyme, creating the same types of sticky ends. The new gene will therefore fit into the vector's cut DNA, and the sticky ends will come together. The enzyme **DNA ligase** repairs the paired DNA strands.

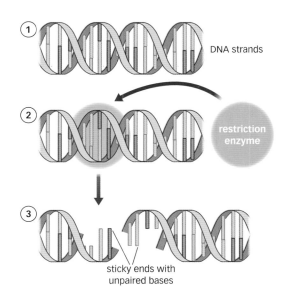

DNA strands

restriction enzyme

sticky ends with unpaired bases

▲ Restriction enzymes cut DNA strands, leaving sticky ends

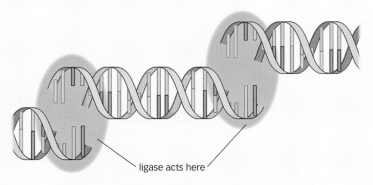

ligase acts here

▲ DNA ligase repairs DNA, incorporating the new gene

> B Name a common vector used to carry DNA into a plant cell.

Exam tip **OCR**

✔ Remember the different functions of restriction enzymes and DNA ligase in the process of genetic engineering.

Questions

1 Name some characteristics that might be transferred by GM technology. ↓ E

2 What two things are enzymes used for during the process of genetic engineering? ↓ C

3 Explain in detail how restriction enzymes cut DNA to create a sticky end.

4 Why are sticky ends useful during the process of genetic engineering? ↓ A*

5 What does DNA ligase do?

Learning objectives

After studying this topic, you should be able to:

✔ know that everyone has a unique DNA sequence

✔ describe the process of DNA fingerprinting

◀ We each have unique fingerprints

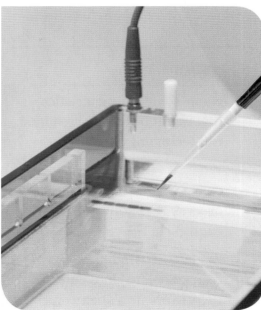

▲ Electrophoresis apparatus. The DNA fragments are placed in wells in a gel. The gel sits in a trough with a solution. An electric current passes through the solution. This causes the DNA fragments to move different amounts depending on their size.

Identifying suspects

Every individual has their own unique fingerprint. In the same way, we all have a unique sequence of DNA in all our cells. A **DNA fingerprint** is an image of certain parts of a person's DNA. It can be used to identify them. Forensic scientists use DNA samples collected at the scene of a crime to make a DNA fingerprint and identify the criminal.

> **A** What is the difference between a fingerprint and a DNA fingerprint?
>
> **B** Identical twins are clones. Would their DNA fingerprints be different? Explain why.

Making a DNA fingerprint

Forensic scientists prepare a DNA fingerprint using this process:

1. A sample of human tissue is collected from the scene of a crime, such as blood, skin, hair, or semen.
2. The DNA is extracted from the cells.
3. The DNA is cut into fragments using restriction enzymes.
4. Since each person has different DNA, the restriction enzymes cut in different places, producing fragments of different lengths.

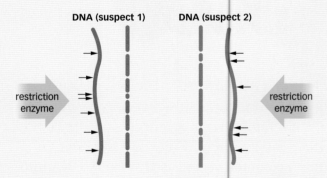

▲ A restriction enzyme recognises a particular sequence of bases

5. The fragments are separated using a kind of chromatography called electrophoresis. They are separated according to their size – smaller fragments travel further.

6. A series of colourless bands is produced on the gel.

7. To make the bands visible, a radioactive probe is added which sticks to the DNA. This can then be detected on film. The result is a film with a series of black and white bands. This is called an autoradiograph.

8. The forensic scientist compares the positions of the bands to identify the suspect.

9. The position of the bands should match if the suspect and the sample from the scene of the crime have the same DNA.

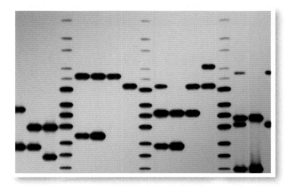

▲ An autoradiograph of DNA fragments. The radioactive probe bound to the different sized DNA fragments shows up on the film.

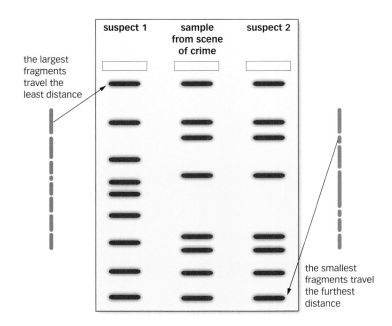

▲ The DNA fingerprint from the scene of the crime sample is compared with the DNA fingerprints of suspects

Exam tip OCR

✓ To interpret DNA fingerprints, look for similar band patterns between two samples.

Storing data

It is possible to store DNA fingerprints on computer records. This is useful for the police, as they can build up a large database of DNA fingerprints. It makes it easy to compare forensic evidence with the records of many potential suspects.

However, many people are concerned about storing this genetic information. They argue that storing the DNA fingerprints of innocent people is an invasion of privacy. They feel that their records should not be kept if they have not done anything wrong.

Questions

1 Why can a DNA fingerprint be used to identify a person? ↓ E

2 Discuss the ethical issues about storing DNA fingerprint records. ↓ C

3 Explain why a radioactive gene probe is used in the process of DNA fingerprinting. ↓ A*

Module summary

Revision checklist

- Bacteria live in many different habitats. They reproduce by binary fission and can be grown in labs or fermenters.
- Fungi include yeast and mushrooms. Yeast reproduces by budding.
- Viruses do not have a cell structure. They have a protein coat around some genetic material. They are not truly living and have to use another organism's cell to make copies of themselves.
- Some microorganisms cause diseases. Skin, stomach acid, acid urine and the respiratory system help prevent infection.
- After natural disasters infections spread easily by means of dirty water and sewage.
- Bacteria cause cholera and food poisoning; viruses cause flu and chickenpox; fungi cause athlete's foot.
- Louis Pasteur, Joseph Lister, and Alexander Fleming developed ways of dealing with microbes.
- Bacteria are used to make yoghurt, cheese, vinegar, silage, and compost.
- Yeast is used to make wine and beer. Wine and beer can be distilled to make spirits (brandy and whisky).
- Plant material can be used for fuel (biofuels, wood, and biogas).
- Soil is made from particles of rock, water, humus, and air. Plants grow in soil. Earthworms live in soil.
- Many organisms live in water, which provides buoyancy and a stable temperature. Freshwater organisms need mechanisms to remove excess water.
- Plankton microorganisms form the basis of many food webs. On the ocean floor, bacteria form the basis of food webs.
- Human waste such as oil spills, fertilisers, sewage, and pesticides may pollute water and affect other organisms.
- Enzymes obtained from microorganisms are used to make processed foods, washing powders, cheese, and slimming products.
- Immobilised enzymes are used in some medical products.
- Genetically modified bacteria make useful medicinal products such as insulin.
- Plants and animals can be genetically modified.
- Forensic scientists can produce DNA fingerprints.

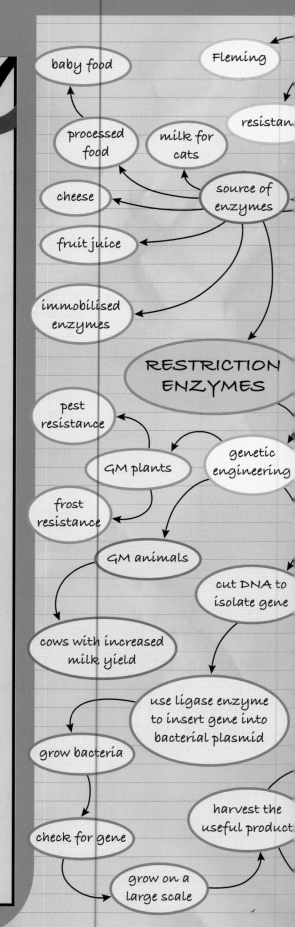

NOW USE THE B6 GRADE CHECKER ON PAGE 242

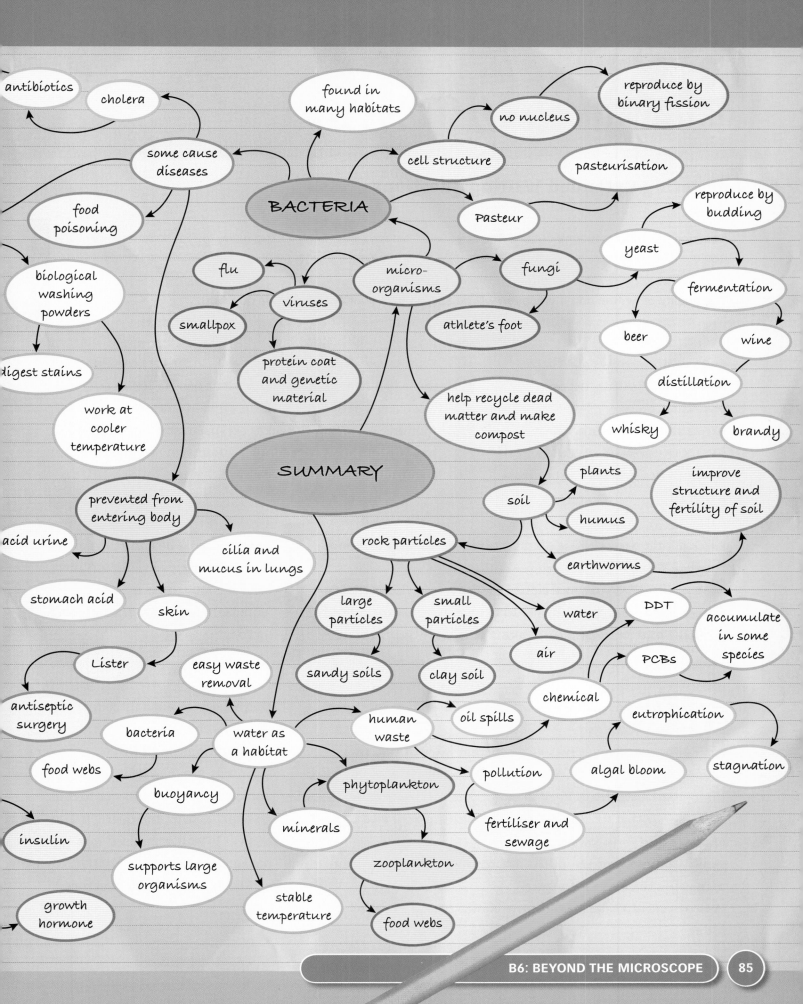

antibiotics

cholera

found in many habitats

no nucleus

reproduce by binary fission

some cause diseases

cell structure

pasteurisation

BACTERIA

Pasteur

reproduce by budding

food poisoning

yeast

biological washing powders

flu

micro-organisms

fungi

fermentation

beer

wine

smallpox

viruses

athlete's foot

digest stains

protein coat and genetic material

distillation

work at cooler temperature

help recycle dead matter and make compost

whisky

brandy

SUMMARY

plants

improve structure and fertility of soil

soil

humus

prevented from entering body

rock particles

earthworms

acid urine

cilia and mucus in lungs

large particles

small particles

water

DDT

accumulate in some species

stomach acid

skin

air

PCBs

Lister

easy waste removal

sandy soils

clay soil

chemical

eutrophication

antiseptic surgery

bacteria

water as a habitat

human waste

oil spills

stagnation

food webs

buoyancy

phytoplankton

pollution

algal bloom

insulin

minerals

fertiliser and sewage

supports large organisms

zooplankton

growth hormone

stable temperature

food webs

Answering Extended Writing questions

Describe the important contributions that scientists Pasteur, Lister, and Fleming made to the modern treatments of diseases. How can doctors and patients reduce the incidence of bacteria becoming resistant to antibiotics?

The quality of written communication will be assessed in your answer to this question.

QUESTION

I was away when we did Pasteur and Lister. Fleming invented penicillin.

People shouldnt take antibiotics unless they really need them or they will become resistant to them.

↓ E

Examiner: Being away is no excuse for this candidate, as there is information in the student book! Fleming discovered penicillin, he didn't invent it. However, Fleming is linked to the correct discovery. The second part of this answer is confused. Bacteria become resistant to antibiotics, not people.

Pasteur said germs cause disease. Lister developed antiseptic surgery. Fleming discovered penicillin.

Doctors shouldnt give antibiotics for colds and flu as these are caused by viruses. Doctors should tell patients to take all their medicine and patients should take it all even if they feel better.

↓ C

Examiner: The contribution of each scientist is briefly outlined. The second part is answered concisely. Very few grammatical errors.

People used to think diseases were caused by evil spirits or a punishment from god.

Pasteur studied silkworms and saw that microorganisms caused diseases. Doctors didn't believe him at first.

Lister used antiseptics during surgery to kill bacteria on skin. Before that hardly anyone survived surgery and lots of people died form infected wounds.

Fleming discovered penicillin. Bacteria wouldn't grow in a dish where there was a fungus.

Patients should take all their antibiotics even if they feel better.

↓ A*

Examiner: A good introduction here sets the scene. The contributions of all three scientists are outlined clearly and correctly. The answer to the last part is brief but correct. The answer is well organised into paragraphs and there are no spelling or grammatical errors.

Exam-style questions

1

a **i** *(A01)* Enzymes are used in the food industry to make sugars sweeter. Name one other use of enzymes in the food industry.

ii *(A02)* Enzymes are present in diabetic reagent sticks. Why do people with diabetes use reagent sticks?

iii *(A01)* Enzymes can be immobilised by making them into beads. Which chemical is used to make the beads?

alginate   lipase   pesticide   PCB

b *(A01)* Yeast can be used to make wine. What process do the yeast cells carry out?

i photosynthesis

ii digestion

iii fermentation.

2

a *Salmonella* bacteria can cause food poisoning.

i *(A01)* Describe how these bacteria enter the body.

ii *(A01)* Food poisoning can be treated with antibiotics. What are antibiotics?

iii *(A02)* Some bacteria are resistant to antibiotics. Describe how bacteria become resistant to antibiotics.

b *(A01)* Explain why viruses are described as not really living.

c *(A01)* List three ways in which the body tries to prevent infection by bacteria or viruses.

↓ E

↓ C

3 A student investigated the effect of temperature on yeast activity. The table shows her results.

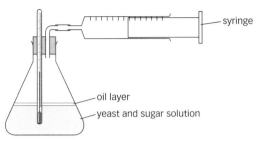

syringe

oil layer
yeast and sugar solution

temperature, °C	10	20	30	40	50	60
time to make 5 cm³ carbon dioxide, minutes	24	38	5	2	15	56

a *(A02)* Which result is anomalous?

b *(A02)* Why was the layer of oil placed over the yeast and sugar solution?

c *(A02)* How did she make the investigation valid (fair)?

↓ A*

Extended Writing

4 *(A01)* Describe what soil is made of. Why are earthworms important in the soil?

↓ E

5 *(A01)(A03)* Describe the composition of biogas and how it is made. State two advantages and two disadvantages of using biofuels.

↓ C

6 *(A01)(A03)* Describe how DNA fingerprinting is carried out. Why are some people concerned about a national database to store people's DNA?

↓ A*

A01   Recall the science
A02   Apply your knowledge
A03   Evaluate and analyse the evidence

C5

Quantitative analysis

Why study this module?

Most of the substances around you are likely to have been manufactured. Scientists and engineers must know how much of each raw material they need, and how much waste is likely to be made. There are many different ways to measure and calculate quantities in chemistry. Such quantitative analysis is useful to consumers like you, too.

In this module, you will investigate how to determine the formula of a compound. You will learn about ways to measure the concentration of acids and other solutions. Sulfuric acid is such an important industrial chemical that economists have often linked a country's economic success to its production of the acid. You will discover how it is made and how the reaction conditions are chosen to produce it economically. You will also find out why sulfuric acid is a strong acid but ethanoic acid is a weak acid.

Precipitation reactions are used in laboratory tests for metal ions and other ions. You will find out more about them and how they can produce useful insoluble salts.

You should remember

1 How to measure the volume of gas produced in a reaction.

2 How to calculate the masses of the different substances involved in a reaction.

3 Food often contains many different ingredients, including additives.

4 Ammonia is made from nitrogen and hydrogen in a reversible reaction.

5 Acids and alkalis have different properties, and they can take part in neutralisation reactions.

6 Water can be tested using chemical reactions.

This amazing sight is not on an alien planet. Instead, it is a 1.5 m geyser formed by accident at Fly Ranch in Nevada, USA. A geothermal energy company drilled a test well in 1964 and reached a source of hot water. The water was not hot enough for their purposes, so they sealed the well. The seal did not hold, allowing hot water to reach the surface. Calcium carbonate and other minerals dissolved in the water precipitate out as it cools, forming these spectacular solid deposits.

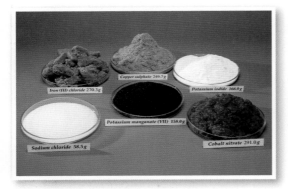

▲ The amount of each of these different substances is one mole

Amount of substance

What do 18 g of water molecules have in common with 44 g of carbon dioxide molecules? The answer is that they both contain the same number of atoms and molecules. They each contain one mole of molecules, and they each contain three moles of atoms.

The **mole** is the unit for amount of substance. One mole of anything contains the same number of particles. There would be the same number of £1 coins in a mole of £1 coins as there would be carbon atoms in a mole of carbon atoms. That number is huge, around 6×10^{23}, or 6 followed by 23 zeros. In everyday life it would make no sense to use the mole, but it does for tiny particles like atoms and molecules.

Mole calculations

No one could sit down to count out 1 mole of something. Even if they could count at the rate of one million objects per second, it would take longer than the age of the universe to complete the task. Fortunately, the mass of 1 mole of a substance is linked to its **relative formula mass**, M_r. To do this, you add together the **relative atomic masses**, A_r, for all the atoms in the formula for the substance.

Defining relative atomic mass

Chemists have chosen the carbon-12 atom, ^{12}C, as their standard atom. Its relative atomic mass is 12 exactly. The relative atomic mass of an element is the average mass of an atom of that element, compared with the mass of 1/12th of an atom of carbon-12. Chemists make it 1/12th the mass so that the mathematics is easier.

The mass of 1 mole of a substance is its relative formula mass in grams. This is called its **molar mass**. Its units are g/mol. The word 'mole' is abbreviated to 'mol' in units.

For example, the relative formula mass of water is 18. This means that 1 mole of water has a mass of 18 g – its molar mass is 18 g/mol. The relative formula mass of carbon dioxide is 44, so its molar mass is 44 g/mol. One mole of water contains the same number of molecules as one mole of carbon dioxide.

More mole calculations

This equation links moles, mass, and molar mass:

number of moles = mass ÷ molar mass

It can be used to work out the number of moles of an element from the mass of that element, or the number of moles of a compound from the mass of that compound. For example, suppose you had 36 g of water. Its molar mass is 18 g/mol, so you would have 36 ÷ 18 = 2 mol of water.

If you know the number of moles of a compound, you can also work out the masses of each of the different elements present. For example, suppose you had 1 mol of carbon dioxide molecules. You would have 1 mol of carbon atoms and 2 mol of oxygen molecules (because the formula is CO_2). This would give you $1 \times 12 = 12$ g of carbon atoms, and $2 \times 16 = 32$ g of oxygen atoms. Notice that if you add 12 g and 32 g together, you get 44 g. This is the mass of 1 mol of carbon dioxide molecules.

Worked example 1

What is the molar mass of magnesium hydroxide, $Mg(OH)_2$?

A_r of Mg = 24, A_r of O = 16, and A_r of H = 1.

M_r of magnesium hydroxide,
$Mg(OH)_2 = 24 + 2 \times (16 + 1)$
$= 24 + 34 = 58$.

So its molar mass = 58 g/mol.

Worked example 2

What is the molar mass of water, H_2O?

A_r of H = 1 and A_r of O = 16.

M_r of water, $H_2O = (2 \times 1) + 16$
$= 2 + 16 = 18$.

So its molar mass = 18 g/mol.

Questions

Use these A_r values to help you to answer the questions: H = 1, C = 12, O = 16, Na = 23, Ca = 40

1   What is the unit for amount of substance?

2   What is molar mass, and what are its units?

3   The formula for sodium hydroxide is NaOH.

   (a) Calculate its relative formula mass.

   (b) Calculate its molar mass.

4   Calculate the molar mass of

   (a) calcium hydroxide, $Ca(OH)_2$

   (b) calcium hydrogencarbonate, $Ca(HCO_3)_2$.

5   Define the relative atomic mass of an element.

6   Calculate the following:

   (a) The number of moles of carbon atoms in 6 g of carbon.

   (b) The number of moles of compound in 20 g of sodium hydroxide, NaOH.

7   What is the mass of atoms of each element in 36 g of water, H_2O?

A   How many moles of magnesium atoms are there in 12 g of magnesium?

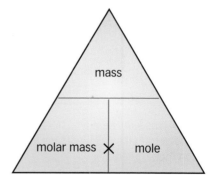

▲ This 'magic triangle' may help you with mole calculations

2: Reacting masses

▲ Industrial lime kilns heat limestone (calcium carbonate) to make calcium oxide, which is used to make cement

A What mass of carbon dioxide is made from 50 g of calcium carbonate?

B What mass of calcium carbonate is needed to make 11 g of carbon dioxide?

Conservation of mass

Mass is conserved during a chemical reaction. The total mass of reactants before the reaction is the same as the total mass of products formed during the reaction. This is because no atoms are created or destroyed during the reaction. They are only rearranged to form new substances. This is why in a balanced symbol equation the number and type of atom on each side of the equation must be the same. The idea of **conservation of mass** can be used to work out the mass of a substance released to the surroundings in a chemical reaction, or to work out the mass of a substance gained from the surroundings.

Losing mass

In a **thermal decomposition** reaction, a single substance breaks down or decomposes to form two or more other substances. For example, calcium carbonate breaks down when heated, forming calcium oxide and carbon dioxide:

$$\text{calcium carbonate} \rightarrow \text{calcium oxide} + \text{carbon dioxide}$$
$$CaCO_3 \rightarrow CaO + CO_2$$

Carbon dioxide is a gas, so it escapes into the air during the reaction. If 100 g of calcium carbonate is decomposed, 56 g of calcium oxide is left behind. The difference in mass is the mass of carbon dioxide released, in this case (100 − 56) = 44 g:

$$CaCO_3 \rightarrow CaO + CO_2$$
$$100\text{ g} \rightarrow 56\text{ g} + 44\text{ g}$$

The masses are directly proportional to each other. So, for example, 200 g of calcium carbonate would make 112 g of calcium oxide and 88 g of carbon dioxide.

These calculations can be very useful. Suppose you wanted to make 33 g of carbon dioxide. What mass of calcium carbonate would you need? Here is how you would work it out:

$$\text{mass of calcium carbonate needed} = \frac{100}{44} \times 33 = 75\text{ g}$$

Gaining mass

In some reactions, a substance is gained during the reaction. For example, oxygen is gained from the air when magnesium is heated strongly:

$$\text{magnesium} + \text{oxygen} \rightarrow \text{magnesium oxide}$$
$$2Mg + O_2 \rightarrow 2MgO$$

If 48 g of magnesium is heated, 80 g of magnesium oxide forms. The difference in mass is the mass of oxygen gained, in this case (80 − 48) = 32 g:

$$2Mg + O_2 \rightarrow 2MgO$$
$$48\,g + 32\,g \rightarrow 80\,g$$

> **C** What mass of oxygen is gained by 12 g of magnesium when it forms magnesium oxide?

Again, the masses are directly proportional to each other. So, for example, 24 g of magnesium would absorb 16 g of oxygen, forming 40 g of magnesium oxide.

Suppose you wanted to absorb 4 g of oxygen. What mass of magnesium would you need?

$$\text{mass of magnesium needed} = \frac{48}{32} \times 4 = 6\,g$$

> **D** What mass of magnesium is needed to absorb 20 g of oxygen? Show your working out.

Mole calculations

It is possible to carry out reacting mass calculations using moles, the balanced equation, and the relative formula masses (or relative atomic masses, if appropriate).

Worked example

Hydrogen reacts with oxygen to form water vapour:

$2H_2 + O_2 \rightarrow 2H_2O$

What mass of water can be made from 6 g of hydrogen gas?

A_r of H = 1 and A_r of O = 16

M_r of H_2 = (2 × 1) = 2

amount of H_2 = 6 ÷ 2 = 3 mol

Looking at the equation, 2 mol of H_2 would make 2 mol of H_2O, so 3 mol of H_2 would make 3 mol of H_2O.

M_r of H_2O = (2 × 1) + 16 = 18, so its molar mass is 18 g/mol.

mass = number of moles × molar mass

= 3 × 18 = 54 g

Questions

1 What does conservation of mass mean?

2 3.1 g of copper carbonate decomposes to form carbon dioxide and 2.0 g of copper oxide. What mass of carbon dioxide is formed?

3 2.4 g of carbon is burned in air, forming 8.8 g of carbon dioxide. What mass of oxygen is gained?

4 When 20.0 g of zinc is heated, 24.9 g of zinc oxide forms.

(a) What mass of oxygen is gained?

(b) What mass of oxygen would be gained by 50.0 g of zinc?

5 Nitrogen reacts with hydrogen to form ammonia:

$$N_2 + 3H_2 \rightarrow 2NH_3$$

A_r of H = 1, A_r of N = 14

(a) Work out the molar masses of nitrogen, hydrogen, and ammonia.

(b) How many moles are there in 2.8 g of nitrogen gas?

(c) How many moles of ammonia would this form?

(d) Work out the mass of ammonia formed.

Learning objectives

After studying this topic, you should be able to:

- ✔ work out the mass of an element in a known mass of a compound
- ✔ calculate the percentage by mass of an element in a compound using experimental data
- ✔ calculate the percentage by mass of an element in a compound from its formula

▲ The front of the Wales Millennium Centre in Cardiff is made from steel coated with copper oxide

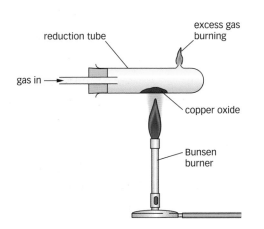

▲ Copper oxide can be reduced to copper using hydrogen or methane

Half and half?

The formula for copper oxide is CuO. You may think that, because the formula contains one Cu and one O, 50% of the mass of copper oxide would be due to copper and 50% to oxygen. If so, you would be wrong. This is because the atoms of different elements usually have different masses, and this needs to be taken into account. The way this is done involves the relative atomic mass of the elements in the substance, and its relative formula mass. It can also involve carrying out experiments.

Masses from experimental data

Copper oxide can be reduced to copper using hydrogen:

$$\text{copper oxide} + \text{hydrogen} \rightarrow \text{copper} + \text{water}$$
$$CuO + H_2 \rightarrow Cu + H_2O$$

The copper oxide must be hot for this to work, and the excess hydrogen has to be burnt off to make the experiment safe. The mass of the empty reduction tube is measured. After adding some copper oxide, the mass of the reduction tube with its contents is measured before the reaction and again after the reaction.

Here are some example results.

		mass (g)
A	empty reduction tube	31.9
B	reduction tube + copper oxide	34.9
C	reduction tube + copper	34.3

The mass of copper oxide can be calculated using these results:

- mass of copper oxide (B – A) = 34.9 – 31.9 = 3.0 g

The masses of copper and oxygen in the original copper oxide can also be calculated:

- mass of copper (C – A) = 34.3 – 31.9 = 2.4 g
- mass of oxygen (B – C) = 34.9 – 34.3 = 0.6 g

Notice that the mass of copper, plus the mass of oxygen, equals the mass of copper oxide used.

Percentage masses from experimental data

The masses from the copper oxide experiment can be used to calculate the percentage mass of each element in copper oxide. For example, for copper:

$$\text{percentage of copper} = \frac{\text{mass of copper}}{\text{mass of copper oxide}} \times 100$$

$$= \frac{2.4}{3.0} \times 100 = 80\%$$

A Use the method shown to calculate the percentage of oxygen in copper oxide.

B Explain why the percentages of copper and oxygen in copper oxide must equal 100%.

Percentage masses from formulae and atomic masses

The formula of a compound, and the relative atomic masses of the elements it contains, can be used to calculate percentage masses. These are the steps needed:

1. Calculate the relative formula mass of the compound using the relative atomic masses.
2. Multiply the relative atomic mass of the element in the question by the number of its atoms in the compound.
3. Work out the percentage using the numbers from Steps 1 and 2.

Worked example

Ammonium nitrate, NH_4NO_3, is used as an artificial fertiliser. Calculate the percentage by mass of nitrogen in ammonium nitrate. A_r of N = 14, A_r of H = 1, and A_r of O = 16.

1. M_r of NH_4NO_3 = 14 + (4 × 1) + 14 + (3 × 16) = 80
2. mass of N = 2 × 14 = 28 (notice that N appears twice in the formula)
3. percentage of N = $\frac{28}{80}$ × 100 = 35%

✔ Make sure you understand how experimental data are used to find the masses of the different elements in a compound, and how these masses are used to find the percentage of each element in the compound.

Questions

1 2.0 g of magnesium oxide, MgO, contains 1.2 g of magnesium. What mass of oxygen does it contain?

2 7.5 g of glucose, $C_6H_{12}O_6$, contains 0.5 g of hydrogen and 4.0 g of oxygen. What mass of carbon does it contain?

3 Use the answers to Questions 1 and 2 to calculate the following:

(a) The percentage by mass of oxygen in magnesium oxide.

(b) The percentage by mass of hydrogen in glucose.

(c) The percentage by mass of carbon in glucose.

Use these A_r values to help you to answer Questions 4 and 5:
H = 1, O = 16, Na = 23, S = 32, Cu = 63.5

4 Calculate the percentage by mass of sodium in sodium hydroxide, NaOH.

5 Calculate the percentage by mass of oxygen in copper sulfate, $CuSO_4$.

4: Empirical formulae

Butane is used as bottled gas for camping stoves

Different formulae

You usually see a substance described by its **molecular formula**. This shows the number and type of each atom in a molecule. For example, the molecular formula of butane is C_4H_{10}. It shows that each butane molecule contains four carbon atoms and ten hydrogen atoms. Sometimes it is useful to describe a substance by its displayed formula. A **displayed formula** shows the atoms in a molecule and the bonds between them. The **empirical formula** of a compound is yet another type of formula. It is often the first formula to be worked out for a newly discovered compound.

The displayed formula of butane shows its atoms and the bonds between them

> **A** What does the molecular formula for ethane, C_2H_6, tell you about an ethane molecule?

Empirical formula

An empirical formula shows the simplest whole number ratio of each type of atom in a compound. For example, the molecular formula of butane is C_4H_{10}. You can divide both numbers by two to get a simpler formula: C_2H_5. This is the empirical formula for butane. The 2 and 5 in the formula are whole numbers, and you cannot make the formula any simpler while keeping whole numbers. For example, if you divide the formula again by 2 you get $CH_{2.5}$, and 2.5 is not a whole number.

> **B** What is the empirical formula for ethane, C_2H_6?

The empirical formula can be worked out by looking for a number that is common to all the numbers in the chemical formula. For example, C_3H_6 can be divided by 3 to get the empirical formula CH_2.

Empirical formulae from experimental data

The empirical formula of a compound can be calculated from experimental data. For example, magnesium is oxidised to magnesium oxide when it is heated in air. The reaction is usually carried out in a crucible. Here are some example results.

		mass (g)
A	empty crucible	23.70
B	crucible + magnesium	24.42
C	crucible + magnesium oxide	24.90

From these results, the mass of magnesium is (24.42 − 23.70) = 0.72 g and the mass of oxygen is (24.90 − 24.42) = 0.48 g. The empirical formula can be worked out using these steps.

1. Write each element's symbol	Mg	O
2. Write each mass in g	0.72	0.48
3. Write each A_r	24	16
4. Find the number of moles	$0.72 \div 24 = 0.03$	$0.48 \div 16 = 0.03$
5. Divide by the smallest number	$0.03 \div 0.03 = 1$	$0.03 \div 0.03 = 1$
6. Check for whole numbers, write the formula	MgO	

You can also find the empirical formula if you know the percentage composition by mass of the compound (see the previous spread). Use the same method as shown above, but write the percentages as grams in Step 2. For example, assume you have 100 g of the compound, so 75% would be written as 75 g and 25% as 25 g.

▲ Magnesium is oxidised to magnesium oxide when it is heated in a crucible

Exam tip **OCR**

✓ Take care at the last step not to round up or down too much. For example, $A_{0.75}X$ is not AX. Instead, multiply by four to get A_3X_4.

Questions

1 What is an empirical formula?

2 Which of these formulae is an empirical formula, and why? C_5H_{12}, $C_6H_{12}O_6$, Pb_2O_4.

3 Write the empirical formulae for the other two substances in Question 2.

4 Work out the empirical formula for ethanoic acid, CH_3COOH.

Use these A_r values to help you answer Questions 5 and 6:

$H = 1$, $C = 12$, $O = 16$, $S = 32$

5 An oxide of sulfur contains 50% sulfur and 50% oxygen by mass. Work out its empirical formula.

6 A 2.3 g sample of compound X contains 1.2 g carbon, 0.3 g hydrogen, and 0.8 g oxygen. Work out its empirical formula.

◀ It is important that the concentration of an intravenous saline drip is correct

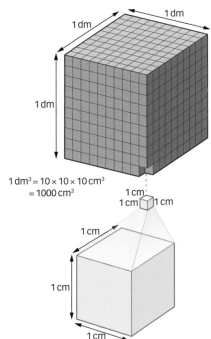

$1\,dm^3 = 10 \times 10 \times 10\,cm^3$
$= 1000\,cm^3$

▲ A cubic decimetre (blue) contains one thousand cubic centimetres (yellow)

Concentration

Patients recovering in hospital may be given an intravenous drip. This is a sterile solution delivered slowly into a vein. There are different drips, but the most common is a normal saline drip. This contains sodium chloride at the same **concentration** as blood. It is important to match the concentration because there could be problems if the drip were too dilute or too concentrated. The concentration of sodium chloride in a normal saline drip is 9 g/dm³ or 0.154 mol/dm³. How are these concentrations worked out?

Solutes and solutions

A **solution** consists of a **solvent**, which is usually water or another liquid, and a **solute**. The solute is the substance that dissolves in the solvent. A dilute solution contains relatively few solute particles. The more solute particles that are dissolved in the solvent, the more concentrated the solution becomes. A very concentrated solution will contain relatively large numbers of solute particles.

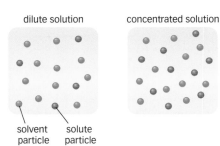

dilute solution   concentrated solution

solvent particle   solute particle

◀ The more concentrated a solution is, the more crowded it is with solute particles

Volumes

To work out the concentration of a solution, you need to know the volume of the solution, and the mass or amount of solute dissolved. This is why the concentration of sodium chloride in a normal saline drip is measured in g/dm³ or mol/dm³. It tells you that each cubic decimetre of solution contains 9 g of sodium chloride, which is 0.154 mol of sodium chloride.

The unit of volume used, the cubic decimetre or dm³, is the same volume as 1000 cm³. Volumes can be measured in either unit, dm³ or cm³, so it is important to be able to convert from one to the other.

A How many cubic centimetres are there in a cubic decimetre?

Here are the two conversions you need:
- to go from cm^3 to dm^3, divide by 1000
- to go from dm^3 to cm^3, multiply by 1000.

For example, 25 cm^3 is 25 ÷ 1000 = 0.025 dm^3. Going the other way, 0.4 dm^3 is 0.4 × 1000 = 400 cm^3.

Calculating concentrations

The concentration in mol/dm^3 is calculated by dividing the amount of solute by the volume of solution:

$$\text{concentration in mol/dm}^3 = \frac{\text{amount of solute in mol}}{\text{volume of solution in dm}^3}$$

Worked example

What is the concentration of 500 cm^3 of a solution containing 4.5 g of sodium chloride?

amount of sodium chloride = mass ÷ molar mass = 4.5 ÷ 58.5

= 0.077 mol

volume of solution = 500 ÷ 1000 = 0.5 dm^3

concentration of solution = 0.077 ÷ 0.5 = 0.154 mol/dm^3

Did you know...?

The litre is the special name for cubic decimetre. The litre used to be defined as the volume of 1 kg of pure water at 4 °C. This meant that the litre was 1.000028 dm^3 until 1964, when it was redefined as 1 dm^3.

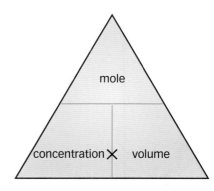

▲ This 'magic triangle' may help you with concentration calculations

Questions

1 Give two units for concentration of solution.

2 Are the solvent particles least crowded in a dilute solution or a concentrated solution?

3 Convert the following volumes into dm^3.
   (a) 2000 cm^3 (b) 500 cm^3 (c) 120 cm^3

4 Convert the following volumes into cm^3.
   (a) 1.5 dm^3 (b) 0.1 dm^3 (c) 0.05 dm^3

5 Calculate the concentration of 250 cm^3 solution containing 0.1 mol of solute.

6 Calculate the number of moles of solute in 2 dm^3 of a 0.5 mol/dm^3 solution.

7 Calculate the volume of a 2 mol/dm^3 solution that contains 0.5 mol of solute.

↓ E

↓ C

↓ A*

Exam tip | **OCR**

✔ Make sure you can rearrange the equation so you can find the amount of solute given the volume of solution and its concentration, and the volume of solution given its concentration and the amount of solute.

Key words

concentration, solution, solvent, solute

Learning objectives

After studying this topic, you should be able to:

- ✔ explain the need to dilute certain mixtures
- ✔ calculate the volumes needed for diluting solutions
- ✔ interpret information on food packaging about GDA
- ✔ carry out calculations based on GDA for sodium

Key words

guideline daily amount (GDA)

A Explain why orange squash labels say 'dilute to taste'.

Exam tip   OCR

- ✔ Another way to work out the amount of water to add is to multiply the starting volume by the number of times the solution will be diluted, then subtract the starting volume.

▲ This scientist is carrying out accurate dilutions on various substances for analysis

The need for dilution

You may dilute substances in your everyday life. For example, orange squash and fruit cordial are usually sold in a concentrated form. The labels tell you to 'dilute to taste', which means you should add enough water so that the taste is not too strong for you. Baby milk powder must be mixed with just the right volume of water to make it the right concentration, otherwise the baby could be harmed. Liquid medicines may be diluted to avoid giving an overdose.

Scientists need to dilute substances accurately so that they can carry out tests on them. If the concentration is too low or too high, their machines may give an inaccurate reading, or may not even detect the substance.

Diluting solutions

A solution is diluted simply by adding water to it, then mixing. However, some calculations are needed if an accurate new concentration is needed. For example, suppose you had 20 cm^3 of a 1.0 mol/dm^3 solution and wanted to dilute it to a 0.1 mol/dm^3 solution. What would you do?

The volume of water to add can be calculated using this equation:

$$\text{volume of water to add} = \left(\frac{\text{starting concentration}}{\text{target concentration}} - 1\right) \times \text{starting volume}$$

In this example, you would need to add 180 cm^3 of water:

$$\text{volume of water to add} = \left(\frac{1.0}{0.1} - 1\right) \times 20$$
$$= (10 - 1) \times 20$$
$$= 9 \times 20 = 180 \text{ cm}^3$$

Guideline daily amounts

Your body needs various nutrients in the right amounts to be healthy. For example, you may become overweight if you eat too much fatty or sugary food. On the other hand, you may become underweight if you do not eat enough. Nutritionists are scientists who study nutrients in food, how they are used by the body, and the relationships between diet, health, and disease. They have worked out a **guideline daily amount**, or **GDA**, for the amount of energy and various nutrients we need each day. The table on the right shows some GDAs.

	Energy (calories)	Sugars (g)	Total fat (g)	Saturated fat (g)	Salt (g)
Children (5–10 years)	1800	85	70	20	4
Women	2000	90	70	20	6
Men	2500	120	95	30	6

Food manufacturers often include information about GDAs on their food labels. These show the amount of energy, sugar, fat, saturated fat, and salt provided by the food. They may also show the percentage of the GDAs provided by the food. This is to help people choose food for a healthy diet. The GDA shown for an adult is usually the GDA for a woman. For example, a portion of food containing 5 g of saturated fat will provide 25% of an adult's GDA for saturated fat:

$$\text{percentage of GDA} = \frac{5}{20} \times 100 = 25\%$$

▲ This label on a packet of biscuits shows the percentage of various GDAs provided by two biscuits

Salt and sodium in food

Common salt is sodium chloride, NaCl. The sodium ions it contains are needed for transmitting nerve signals and muscular contraction. All foods contain salt in varying amounts, and most processed foods contain added salt. However, too much salt can cause health problems including high blood pressure, leading to an increased risk of heart disease. The GDA for an adult is 6 g, which is about a teaspoon. Some food labels show the salt content of the food, some show its sodium content, and some show both.

The percentage by mass of sodium in sodium chloride is 39.3%. So 1 g of salt is the same as $1 \times 39.3 \div 100 = 0.393$ g of sodium. However, sodium ions can come from other sources in food, so this conversion may be inaccurate. For example, monosodium glutamate, commonly used to enhance the flavour of food, contains sodium ions.

Questions

1 Explain why medicines may need to be diluted.

2 Look at the food label. Which substance was present in the smallest amount, and which in the largest amount?

3 A scientist wanted to dilute 10 cm³ of a 0.5 mol/dm³ solution to 0.1 mol/dm³. How much water must be added?

4 The label on a packet of naan bread shows that each portion contains 1.8 g of salt. What percentage of an adult's GDA is this?

5 Food naturally contains sodium chloride, NaCl.

(a) Show that the percentage by mass of sodium in sodium chloride is about 39%. A_r of Na = 23 and A_r of Cl = 35.5

(b) If the adult GDA for salt is 6 g, what is the adult GDA for sodium?

(c) Explain why this conversion may be inaccurate.

Learning objectives

After studying this topic, you should be able to:

- ✔ describe and explain the changes that happen when an acid reacts with an alkali
- ✔ interpret simple pH curves
- ✔ sketch a pH titration curve

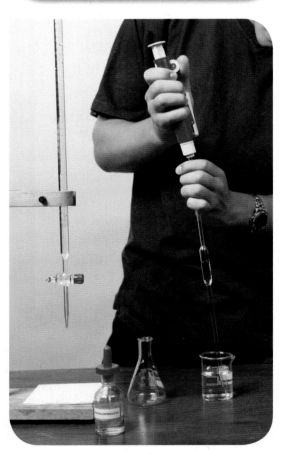

▲ This is the apparatus needed to add acids to alkalis accurately. The conical flask will go underneath the burette.

A What is neutralisation?

B Why is it more usual to add an acid to an alkali, than to add an alkali to an acid?

Neutralisation reactions

Neutralisation reactions happen when an acid reacts with an alkali:

$$acid \;+\; alkali \;\rightarrow\; salt \;+\; water$$

Acids form solutions with a **pH** less than 7, and **alkalis** form solutions with a pH more than 7.

A **neutral** solution has a pH of 7. The pH decreases when an acid is added to an alkali, and it increases when an alkali is added to an acid.

Changes in pH can be followed using universal indicator and a pH colour chart. They can also be followed using a pH meter. This is a device that can measure and display the pH of a solution. Some designs consist of a pH electrode connected to a datalogger, while others are all-in-one devices.

Investigating changes in pH

It is important that small volumes of acid or alkali can be added so that an accurate pH curve can be recorded. The **burette** is a long glass tube with a tap at the bottom. Graduations up the side show the volume of liquid delivered. Strong alkalis such as sodium hydroxide solution can damage glass. This means that, although a burette can be filled with an alkali, it is usual to fill one with an acid.

The alkali is measured using a **pipette**, filled safely using a **pipette filler**. The alkali is transferred to a conical flask. This is more convenient than a beaker. Its narrow neck and sloping sides means that the acid and alkali can be mixed without them sloshing over the sides.

With the pH electrode in the conical flask, the tap on the burette is opened to add acid slowly to the alkali. When investigating changes in pH, it is usual to add twice as much acid as the volume of alkali used. A graph of pH on the vertical axis against volume of acid added on the horizontal axis is called a **pH curve**.

pH curves

The diagrams show typical pH curves involving a strong acid such as hydrochloric acid, and a strong alkali such as sodium hydroxide solution. In each case, the conical flask contained 25 cm³ and the burette delivered a total of 50 cm³.

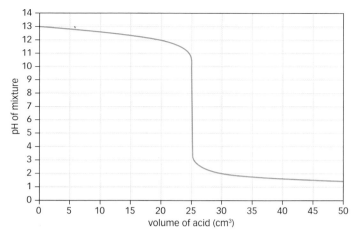

▲ A pH curve for adding an acid to an alkali

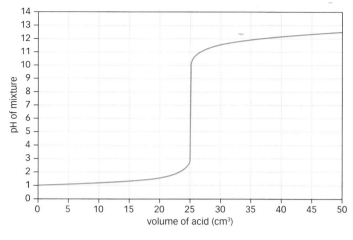

▲ A pH curve for adding an alkali to an acid

C In general, where does the sudden change of pH happen?

D What was the pH when 20 cm³ of acid was added to 25 cm³ of alkali?

Key words

neutralisation reaction, acid, pH, alkali, neutral, burette, pipette, pipette filler, pH curve, end point

Notice in both pH curves that the pH changes only gradually at first and at the end. The **end point** of the reaction is when the acid and alkali exactly neutralise each other. There is a sudden change in pH at the end point. These pH curves can be used to determine the volume of acid or alkali at the end point, and the pH when different amounts of acid or alkali are added.

Questions

1 What happens to the pH when an acid is added to an alkali?

2 Name the two pieces of glassware used to measure liquids when determining a pH curve.

3 Use the pH curve for adding acid to alkali to answer these questions.
   (a) What was the pH of the alkali at the start?
   (b) What was the pH of the mixture after 30 cm³ of acid had been added?
   (c) What volume of acid was needed to exactly neutralise the alkali?

4 Use the pH curve for adding alkali to acid to answer these questions.
   (a) What was the pH of the mixture when 10 cm³ of alkali had been added?
   (b) What volume of alkali was needed to reach a pH of 11.5?
   (c) What was the total volume of the mixture at the end point?

↓ E
↓ C
↓ A*

▲ Litmus, a single indicator, is blue above pH 8.3 and red below pH 4.5

◀ Phenolphthalein, a single indicator, is pink above pH 10.0 and colourless below pH 8.2

Indicators

The changes in pH in an experiment to find a pH curve can be followed using a pH meter, or using a suitable **indicator**. An indicator has different colours, depending on its pH. Phenolphthalein and litmus are **single indicators**. Each one contains a single substance, which gives a sudden change in colour at the end point:

- Phenolphthalein is pink in alkaline solutions and colourless in acidic solutions.
- Litmus is blue in alkaline solutions and red in acidic solutions.

Universal indicator is a **mixed indicator**. It contains several different indicators. Each one changes colour over a different range of pH values. This is why universal indicator gives a continuous colour change. It lets you find the approximate pH of a solution, but it is not suitable if you want to know the precise end point in a titration.

▲ Universal indicator has a range of colours, from red in acids to purple in alkalis. Green means neutral.

> **A** What is the difference between a single indicator and a mixed indicator?

Titrations

Titration is a method to find the concentration of an acid or alkali using a neutralisation reaction. It is carried out in the same way as finding a pH curve. However, a single indicator such as phenolphthalein is used, instead of a pH meter or a mixed indicator such as universal indicator. Phenolphthalein gives a sudden colour change between pink and colourless at the end point.

A known volume of alkali, usually 25 cm³, is added to a conical flask using a pipette and pipette filler. A few drops of phenolphthalein are added to produce a pink tinge. Acid is added slowly from a burette until the pink colour just disappears. The difference between the start and end readings on the burette gives the **titre**. This is the volume of acid needed to exactly neutralise the alkali.

The titre is used to work out the concentration of either the acid or the alkali, provided the concentration of the other one is known. It is important that the titre is accurate, otherwise the calculated concentration will be wrong. A titration is repeated until several consistent titres are obtained. Any **anomalous** titres (ones that are too high or too low compared to the others) are ignored, and the mean titre is calculated. The table shows how titration results may be recorded.

Key words

indicator, single indicator, mixed indicator, titration, titre, anomalous

B What is the titre in a titration?

	Run 1	Run 2	Run 3	Run 4
End reading (cm³)	21.2	41.0	21.2	41.2
Start reading (cm³)	0.0	21.2	1.0	21.2
Titre (cm³)	21.2	19.8	20.2	

Titration calculations

Imagine that a titration is carried out involving 0.1 mol/dm³ hydrochloric acid and 25.0 cm³ of an unknown concentration of sodium hydroxide:

$$HCl + NaOH \rightarrow NaCl + H_2O$$

If the mean titre of acid is 24.0 cm³, what is the concentration of the sodium hydroxide?

Convert all volumes to dm³: the titre of HCl is 24.0 ÷ 1000 = 0.024 dm³ and the volume of NaOH is 25.0 ÷ 1000 = 0.025 dm³.

- amount of HCl = concentration × volume = 0.1 × 0.024 = 0.0024 mol

Looking at the balanced equation, you can see that 1 mol of HCl will react with 1 mol of NaOH. So 0.0024 mol of HCl will react with 0.0024 mol of NaOH.

- concentration of NaOH = amount ÷ volume = 0.0024 ÷ 0.025 = 0.096 mol/dm³

Questions

1 Describe the colours of universal indicator, litmus, and phenolphthalein in acids and alkalis. → E

2 Calculate the titre in Run 4 of the table on the left.

3 Explain why several consistent readings are needed in titrations.

4 Explain why a single indicator, rather than a mixed indicator, is used in titrations. → C

5 The results in the table on the left are from a titration in which 0.2 mol/dm³ hydrochloric acid was added to 25.0 cm³ of a sodium hydroxide solution. Calculate the concentration of the alkali. → A*

▲ Results from crash tests help make cars safer

Did you know...?

Sensors in an air bag make the decision to trigger the chemical reaction within 15 to 30 milliseconds of the start of a crash. It takes about 20 to 30 milliseconds for the bag to fill with hot nitrogen. Overall, the air bag is fully inflated within about 60 milliseconds of the crash starting.

A Why is upward displacement over water not so suitable for measuring the volume of carbon dioxide produced in a reaction?

Making gases

A car air bag inflates in a fraction of second because it rapidly fills with hot nitrogen gas. Solid sodium azide decomposes when an electric current is passed through it, triggered by crash sensors in the air bag:

$$\text{sodium azide} \rightarrow \text{sodium} + \text{nitrogen}$$
$$\text{NaN}_3 \rightarrow \text{Na} + 1\tfrac{1}{2}\text{N}_2$$

Many other chemical reactions release gases as one or more of their products. The course of these reactions can be followed by measuring the volume or mass of the gases produced.

Measuring volumes

A **gas syringe** is a gas-tight glass syringe used for measuring the volumes of gases. It usually measures volumes up to 100 cm³. Gas syringes can be used to measure the volume of any gas, including carbon dioxide, hydrogen, and oxygen. The syringe is connected to the reaction container by tubing. As the reaction occurs, gas fills the gas syringe and pushes the plunger out. Graduations on the side show the volume of gas contained in the gas syringe.

◀ This gas syringe is being used to measure the volume of carbon dioxide produced when calcium carbonate reacts with hydrochloric acid

Gases can also be collected over water in an upturned measuring cylinder. This is filled with water, then turned upside down in a trough of water. Air pressure keeps the water inside the cylinder. A delivery tube is led from the reaction container and into the mouth of the measuring cylinder. As the reaction occurs, gas fills the measuring cylinder and pushes the water out. Graduations on the side show the volume of gas contained. The same method, called **upward displacement**, also works using an upturned burette. However, upward displacement is only accurate if the gas is not very soluble in water. It does not so work well for soluble gases such as carbon dioxide.

Measuring masses

Gases do have mass, even though this is much less than for the same volume of a solid or liquid. For example, 100 cm³ of carbon dioxide has a mass of 0.18 g at 25 °C and normal pressure. This means that the release of gas during a reaction can be followed using a balance. The balance has to have a suitable resolution, such as ±0.01 g, to be able to make precise readings. The reaction container, with its contents, is placed on the balance. As the reaction takes place, the gas escapes and the total mass of the container and its contents goes down. The difference in mass is due to the gas that has escaped.

This method is not suitable for all gases. The molar mass of carbon dioxide is 44 g/mol, but the molar mass of hydrogen is just 2 g/mol. This means that 100 cm³ of hydrogen at 25 °C and normal pressure only has a mass of 0.008 g. This is too little to be measured by the sort of balances normally found in a school laboratory.

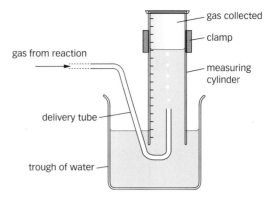

▲ Measuring the volume of a gas in an upturned measuring cylinder or burette works well for gases such as hydrogen and oxygen

◀ This balance is being used to measure the loss of carbon dioxide when calcium carbonate reacts with hydrochloric acid. The cotton wool stops any liquid escaping.

Questions

1. Give two ways in which the volume of a gas produced in a reaction can be measured.

2. Describe how the mass of a gas produced in a reaction can be measured.

↓E

3. Zinc carbonate decomposes when heated, producing zinc oxide and carbon dioxide. Describe two suitable ways to measure the gas produced.

4. Magnesium reacts with hydrochloric acid, producing magnesium chloride and hydrogen. Describe two suitable ways to measure the gas produced.

↓C

5. Hydrogen peroxide rapidly decomposes in the presence of a suitable catalyst, producing water and oxygen. The molar mass of oxygen is 32 g/mol. Suggest why the production of oxygen could be followed using a gas syringe, upward displacement over water, or by measuring the mass lost during a reaction.

↓A*

Key words

gas syringe, upward displacement

▲ Magnesium ribbon reacts vigorously with hydrochloric acid

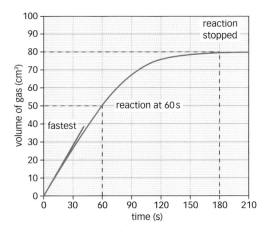

▲ The volume of hydrogen produced as magnesium reacts with hydrochloric acid

Following reactions

Magnesium reacts with hydrochloric acid, forming magnesium chloride and hydrogen:

magnesium + hydrochloric acid → magnesium chloride + hydrogen

$$Mg + 2HCl → MgCl_2 + H_2$$

The reaction can be followed by measuring the volume of hydrogen produced at regular intervals. This can be done using a gas syringe or by upward displacement over water into an upturned measuring cylinder or burette. The graph below shows the results from one such experiment.

The graph has several important features. Notice that the line starts off steeply and eventually becomes horizontal. Its gradient decreases as the reaction continues. This shows that the rate of reaction decreases as the reaction carries on. It is fastest at the start, when the gradient is greatest. The reaction has stopped when the line becomes horizontal. The reaction has stopped by 180 s, as no more hydrogen is produced after that. The total volume of hydrogen produced in the reaction was 80 cm³.

It is possible to work out how much gas was produced at a particular time. For example, by 60 s after the start of the reaction the volume of gas produced was 50 cm³.

> **A** How long did it take to produce 60 cm³ of hydrogen?

Limiting reactants

A reaction will stop when one of the reactants is all used up. You cannot tell from the graph whether the magnesium ribbon was all used up at the end, or the hydrochloric acid was all used up. If you could see that all the magnesium ribbon was used up at the end, the magnesium would be the **limiting reactant**. The hydrochloric acid would have been in **excess** – there would have been more than enough of it to react with all the magnesium. The graph on the next page shows what happens when different amounts of magnesium are used.

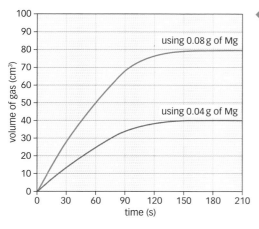

◀ The volume of hydrogen produced when two different masses of magnesium are used

Notice that the more magnesium used, the steeper the gradient. This shows that the rate of reaction was greater. In addition, more hydrogen was made. The amount of product is directly proportional to the amount of reactant: 40 cm³ of hydrogen was made when 0.04 g of magnesium was used, but double this was made when 0.08 g of magnesium was used. If the hydrochloric acid had been the limiting reactant, the same volume of hydrogen would have been produced in both reactions, and some magnesium would have been left in excess.

> **B** What volume of hydrogen should be made if the experiment is repeated with 0.06 g of magnesium?

Calculation involving gases

The amount of product formed depends upon the amount of the limiting reactant used in the reaction. The more reactant particles there are, the more of these particles react to make product particles. Remember that the mole shows the amount of a substance.

One mole of any gas occupies the same volume at room temperature and pressure, **rtp**. This **molar volume** is 24 dm³. So 1 mol of hydrogen occupies 24 dm³ at rtp, and so does 1 mol of carbon dioxide. The number of moles of gas can be calculated using this equation:

$$\text{amount of gas} = \text{volume of gas at rtp} \div \text{molar volume at rtp}$$

For example, 1.2 dm³ of carbon dioxide at rtp contains $1.2 \div 24 = 0.05$ mol.

Questions

1 How can you tell, from a graph of volume of gas against time, that a reaction has stopped?

2 Use the graph showing the volume of hydrogen produced by 0.04 g of magnesium to help you answer these questions.

   (a) What volume of gas was produced by 60 s?

   (b) How long did it take to produce 20 cm³ of hydrogen?

↓ E

3 Use the graph showing the volume of hydrogen produced by 0.04 g of magnesium to help you answer these questions.

   (a) What volume of gas was produced by 95 s?

   (b) How long did it take to produce 18 cm³ of hydrogen?

↓ C

4 What is a limiting reactant?

5 Calculate the amount, in moles, of each of the following gases at rtp:

   (a) 48 dm³ of oxygen

   (b) 6 dm³ of carbon dioxide

   (c) 120 cm³ of hydrogen

↓ A*

Learning objectives

After studying this topic, you should be able to:

- ✔ describe that some reversible reactions reach equilibrium
- ✔ describe how a change in conditions may change the position of equilibrium
- ✔ explain why a reversible reaction may reach equilibrium
- ✔ explain how a change in conditions may change the position of equilibrium

▲ A see-saw can move in two directions and, correctly balanced, reaches equilibrium

Exam tip   OCR

- ✔ Not all the substances in an equilibrium mixture have to be at the same concentration.

B What can you say about the rate of the forward reaction and the rate of the backward reaction at equilibrium?

Reversible reactions

In many reactions, the reaction can go in one direction only. In a **reversible reaction**, there is a forward reaction and a backward reaction. Instead of the usual arrow in the chemical equations, the symbol $\rightleftharpoons$ is used in reversible reactions. For example, the reaction between nitrogen and hydrogen to make ammonia is reversible:

$$\text{nitrogen} + \text{hydrogen} \rightleftharpoons \text{ammonia}$$
$$N_2 + 3H_2 \rightleftharpoons 2NH_3$$

There is a forward reaction between nitrogen and hydrogen to make ammonia, and a backward reaction in which ammonia decomposes to form nitrogen and hydrogen. In some reversible reactions these two reactions happen at the same time and at the same rate. These reversible reactions may reach **equilibrium**.

A What is the symbol for a reversible reaction?

At equilibrium

When a reversible reaction reaches equilibrium, the rate of the forward reaction will be equal to the rate of the backward reaction. The concentrations of the reactants and products do not change. Note that, even though the concentrations of the reactants and products do not change at equilibrium, the forward and backward reactions are still happening. If the forward reaction is exothermic the backward reaction is endothermic, and vice versa.

The position of equilibrium

The **position of equilibrium** is related to the ratio of the concentration of products to the concentration of reactants:

- It is on the left if the concentration of reactants is greater than the concentration of products.
- It is on the right if the concentration of products is greater than the concentration of reactants.

The position of equilibrium may change if there are changes in temperature, pressure, or the concentration of one of the reacting substances. This change in position of equilibrium will affect the composition of the mixture of substances.

More about equilibrium

Imagine a reversible reaction starting off with just the substances on the left of the equation. These will react quickly because they are at a high concentration. The rate of the forward reaction will then decrease as these substances are used up.

However, as they are used up, the concentration of the substances on the right of the equation will increase. They will react increasingly quickly as their concentration increases. Eventually, the rate of the forward reaction will equal the rate of the backward reaction, and equilibrium is reached.

This works in a **closed system**, such as a stoppered flask or a beaker of liquid in which all the reactants stay in solution. If the system is open, the reacting substances may escape and equilibrium will not be reached.

More about position of equilibrium

The equation shows the reaction to make sulfur trioxide:

$$2SO_2 + O_2 \rightleftharpoons 2SO_3$$

All the substances are gases. In a reversible reaction involving gases at equilibrium, if the pressure is increased the position of equilibrium moves to the side with the lower number of moles of gas molecules. In this example that will be to the right, as there are $(2 + 1) = 3$ mol of gas on the left and only 2 mol on the right.

If the concentration of one of the substances is increased, the position of equilibrium moves to the opposite side. In the example, the position of equilibrium will move to the right if the concentration of oxygen is increased.

If the concentration of one of the substances is decreased, the position of equilibrium moves to its side. In the example, the position of equilibrium will move to the right if the concentration of sulfur trioxide is decreased. This could happen simply by removing the sulfur trioxide as it is made.

If the temperature is increased, the position of equilibrium moves in the direction of the endothermic reaction. The production of sulfur trioxide is an exothermic process. Increasing the temperature moves the position of equilibrium to the left.

Questions

1 How could you tell from its chemical equation that a reaction was reversible?

2 What happens to the concentrations of the reacting substances when a reversible reaction reaches equilibrium?

3 In general, what changes in conditions may change the position of equilibrium?

Questions 4 and 5 are about the reaction to make ammonia:

$$N_2 + 3H_2 \rightleftharpoons 2NH_3$$

4 If the concentration of ammonia is much greater than the concentration of nitrogen and hydrogen, is the position of equilibrium on the right or on the left?

5 Describe the composition of the equilibrium mixture when the position of equilibrium is on the left.

6 Hydrogen can be made by reacting methane with steam: $CH_4(g) + H_2O(g) \rightleftharpoons CO(g) + 3H_2(g)$
Describe and explain the effect on the position of equilibrium of increasing the concentration of methane, and increasing the pressure.

E

C

A*

12: Making sulfuric acid

Learning objectives

After studying this topic, you should be able to:

- ✔ recall the raw materials used to make sulfuric acid
- ✔ recall the conditions used in the Contact Process
- ✔ describe the reactions involved in the Contact Process
- ✔ explain the conditions used in the manufacture of sulfuric acid

Key words

Contact Process

▲ Sulfur deposits are found naturally around volcanoes. Most sulfur today is extracted from crude oil and natural gas, which helps to reduce emissions of sulfur dioxide.

◀ Sulfur burns with a bright blue flame in oxygen, producing clouds of sulfur dioxide gas

Sulfuric acid

Over a million tonnes of sulfuric acid are made in the UK each year, about 20 kg for each person in the country. Car batteries contain it, but most sulfuric acid is used to make other substances. The pie chart shows some of these uses.

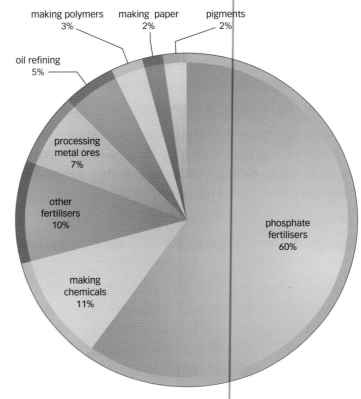

▲ The main uses of the world's sulfuric acid

> **A** What is the main use of sulfuric acid in the world?

The Contact Process

The **Contact Process** is used to make sulfuric acid. Three raw materials are needed:

- sulfur
- air (which provides oxygen)
- water.

There are three stages in the Contact Process. In stage 1, sulfur is burned in air to produce sulfur dioxide gas:

$$\text{sulfur} + \text{oxygen} \rightarrow \text{sulfur dioxide}$$
$$S + O_2 \rightarrow SO_2$$

In stage 2, sulfur dioxide and oxygen react together to produce sulfur trioxide gas:

$$\text{sulfur dioxide} + \text{oxygen} \rightleftharpoons \text{sulfur trioxide}$$
$$2SO_2 + O_2 \rightleftharpoons 2SO_3$$

Notice that the reaction is a reversible reaction. The conditions are chosen carefully to achieve a sufficient daily yield of sulfur trioxide at a reasonable cost. The temperature used is around 450 °C. The pressure used is atmospheric pressure, rather than a high pressure. Vanadium(V) oxide, V_2O_5, is used as a catalyst. It increases the rate of the reaction without being used up in the reaction.

In the final stage, the sulfur trioxide reacts with water to produce sulfuric acid:

$$\text{sulfur trioxide} + \text{water} \rightarrow \text{sulfuric acid}$$
$$SO_3 + H_2O \rightarrow H_2SO_4$$

B State the chemical formula of the catalyst used in the Contact Process.

Choosing suitable conditions

As the second stage in the Contact Process involves a reversible reaction, the conditions needed must be chosen carefully.

The forward reaction, which produces sulfur trioxide, SO_3, is exothermic. This means that a greater yield can be obtained by reducing the temperature. On the other hand, the rate of reaction will be low if the temperature is too low. So an optimum temperature of around 450 °C is used. It is high enough to give a reasonable rate of reaction without decreasing the yield too much.

At atmospheric pressure, the position of equilibrium is far to the right. Almost all the sulfur dioxide is converted into sulfur trioxide. A high pressure would increase the yield of sulfur trioxide. However, the extra cost involved would not be worth it as there would only be a small increase in yield.

The V_2O_5 catalyst does not change the position of equilibrium, but it does increase the rate of reaction.

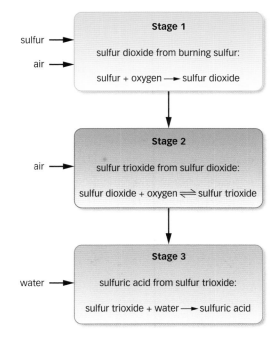

Stage 1
sulfur →
air →
sulfur dioxide from burning sulfur:
sulfur + oxygen ⟶ sulfur dioxide

Stage 2
air →
sulfur trioxide from sulfur dioxide:
sulfur dioxide + oxygen ⇌ sulfur trioxide

Stage 3
water →
sulfuric acid from sulfur trioxide:
sulfur trioxide + water ⟶ sulfuric acid

▲ The three stages of the Contact Process

Questions

1 Name the three raw materials used in the Contact Process.

2 Sulfur trioxide is made in the second stage of the Contact Process.

(a) Write a word equation for the reaction in this stage.

(b) Name the acid made by the Contact Process.

3 State the temperature and pressure used in the Contact Process.

4 What is the function of V_2O_5 in the Contact Process?

5 Write balanced symbol equations for the three stages of the Contact Process.

6 Explain the choice of conditions used in the Contact Process.

Learning objectives

After studying this topic, you should be able to:

- ✔ name some strong and weak acids
- ✔ describe acids in terms of pH, hydrogen ion concentration, and electrical conductivity
- ✔ explain the differences between strong and weak acids

Key words

weak acid, strong acid, hydrogen ions, ionise, electrode, electrolysis, electrical conductivity

▲ Vinegar contains ethanoic acid, a weak acid

A At the same concentration, acid A has a pH of 2 and acid B has a pH of 5. Which one is the weak acid, and why?

Eating acid

Vinegar contains ethanoic acid. This gives vinegar the pleasant, sharp taste that makes it a popular addition to fish and chips. While you can safely consume vinegar, it would be very unwise to swallow hydrochloric acid. This is because ethanoic acid is a **weak acid**, but hydrochloric acid is a **strong acid**. Nitric acid and sulfuric acid are strong acids, too.

Differences in pH

Strong acids and weak acids have different pH values, even if they are at the same concentration. A strong acid will have a lower pH than a weak acid of the same concentration. Its solution will be more strongly acidic. The differences in pH can be measured using universal indicator and a pH colour chart, or using a pH meter. The reason for these differences is due to **hydrogen ions** produced by the acids.

Acids **ionise** in water to produce hydrogen ions, H^+. Strong acids such as hydrochloric acid completely ionise in solution. Weak acids such as ethanoic acid only partially ionise in water. Many of their molecules do not release hydrogen ions. Unlike the reaction for strong acids, the reaction is reversible, and an equilibrium mixture is produced.

Acid strength and concentration

The concentration of an acid is a measure of the number of moles of acid in 1 dm³. The higher the concentration, the more moles of acid are dissolved in the same volume of water. The strength of an acid is a measure of how ionised the acid is in water. The stronger the acid, the more ionised it is. Hydrochloric acid is completely ionised in water, whereas ethanoic acid is only partially ionised in water:

$$HCl \rightarrow H^+ + Cl^- \quad \text{(hydrochloric acid)}$$
$$CH_3COOH \rightleftharpoons CH_3COO^- + H^+ \quad \text{(ethanoic acid)}$$

So, for a given concentration of acid, the concentration of hydrogen ions is greater in hydrochloric acid than it is in ethanoic acid. This is why the pH of a strong acid is much lower than the pH of a weak acid at the same concentration.

Electrolysis of acids

Solutions containing ions conduct electricity because the ions are free to move. They carry charge from one electrode to the other. Acids in solution contain hydrogen ions and other ions, so they conduct electricity. Hydrogen gas is made at the negative **electrode** during the **electrolysis** of either hydrochloric acid or ethanoic acid. This is because the positively charged hydrogen ions are attracted to the negatively charged electrode, where they gain electrons and become hydrogen gas:

$$2H^+ + 2e^- \rightarrow H_2$$

> **B** What gas is produced at the negative electrode during the electrolysis of acids?

However, although the electrolysis of both strong and weak acids produces hydrogen gas, there is a difference in the **electrical conductivity** of the acids. It is more 'difficult' for current to pass through a weak acid than it is through a strong acid at the same concentration. For a given potential difference or voltage, the current will be lower through the weak acid. The electrical conductivity of ethanoic acid is lower than it is for hydrochloric acid at the same concentration, because ethanoic acid solution contains fewer hydrogen ions.

◀ The ammeter on the left is measuring the current through ethanoic acid, and the one on the right is measuring the current through hydrochloric acid at the same concentration

More on conductivity

Ethanoic acid is less conductive than hydrochloric acid at the same concentration because it is a weak acid, whereas hydrochloric acid is a strong acid. There is a lower concentration of hydrogen ions to carry the charge through ethanoic acid than there is in hydrochloric acid.

Questions

1 Which will have the lower pH, 0.1 mol/dm³ ethanoic acid or 0.1 mol/dm³ hydrochloric acid?

2 Which will have the lower electrical conductivity, 0.1 mol/dm³ ethanoic acid or 0.1 mol/dm³ hydrochloric acid?

 E

3 In terms of ions and ionisation, explain why ethanoic acid is a weak acid but hydrochloric acid is a strong acid.

4 Explain why hydrogen is produced at the negative electrode during the electrolysis of acids.

C

5 Explain the difference between acid strength and acid concentration. Include balanced equations referring to ethanoic acid and hydrochloric acid.

 A*

▲ The heating element in this electric kettle is coated with limescale

A Which acid, at the same concentration, will produce the faster reaction with calcium carbonate, ethanoic acid or hydrochloric acid?

Acid attack

Tap water contains dissolved mineral ions. Over time, particularly in hard water areas, **limescale** can build up in washing machines, kettles, and irons. This a deposit of calcium carbonate, which coats the surface of the heating elements in these appliances. Limescale looks unpleasant and it makes the appliances less efficient, wasting electricity.

Luckily, weak acids come to the rescue. Descalers contain a weak acid such as citric acid. This reacts with the limescale without damaging the metal of the heating element. A strong acid such as hydrochloric acid would remove the limescale. Unfortunately, it would also damage the metal. Why do weak and strong acids react so differently?

Rate of reaction

Both ethanoic acid and hydrochloric acid react with magnesium, producing hydrogen. They also react with calcium carbonate, this time producing carbon dioxide. However, the reactions with ethanoic acid are slower than the reactions with hydrochloric acid, even if the two acids are at the same concentration. This is because ethanoic acid is a weak acid, but hydrochloric acid is a strong acid.

At the same concentration, there are fewer hydrogen ions in ethanoic acid. As a result, there are fewer collisions between hydrogen ions and the reactant particles.

◀ The reaction between magnesium and hydrochloric acid produces large bubbles very quickly, keeping the magnesium powder at the surface. The reaction with ethanoic acid is slower and produces more, but smaller, bubbles. These spread through the mixture, giving it a milky appearance.

Volume of gas

You might think that the reactions with ethanoic acid would produce smaller volumes of gas than they would with hydrochloric acid. However, if the volume and concentration of the acids are the same, and the same mass of magnesium or calcium carbonate is used, the same volume of gas is produced. It is just produced faster in reactions with hydrochloric acid, a strong acid. The volume of hydrogen or carbon dioxide produced depends on the amount of reactants present in the reaction mixture. It does not depend on the strength of the acid.

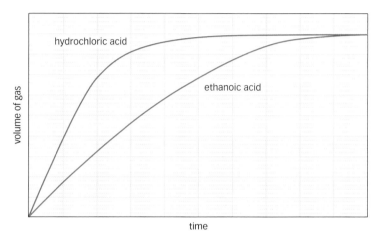

▲ The reactions between magnesium and ethanoic acid or hydrochloric acid produce the same final volume of hydrogen, provided the concentrations, masses, and volumes of reactants are the same

More about rates and volumes

Hydrochloric acid reacts more quickly with magnesium and calcium carbonate than ethanoic acid does because it is a strong acid. At the same acid concentration, hydrochloric acid has a greater concentration of hydrogen ions, so the frequency of collisions between hydrogen ions and reactant particles is greater.

Ethanoic acid is only partially ionised in solution, producing an equilibrium mixture. As hydrogen ions become used up in reactions with reactant particles, the position of equilibrium moves further to the right, releasing more hydrogen ions into solution. This continues until all the acid has reacted, so the volume of gas produced is the same as for a strong acid.

Key words

limescale

B How can you tell from the graph that the rate of reaction between hydrochloric acid and magnesium is different from the rate of reaction between ethanoic acid and magnesium?

Questions

1 Describe a non-food use of weak acids.

2 Ethanoic acid and hydrochloric acid both react with calcium carbonate to produce carbon dioxide. Compare the rates of reaction and volumes of gas produced in each reaction.

3 Explain why a strong acid such as hydrochloric acid might be inappropriate for use as a kettle descaler.

4 What does the volume of carbon dioxide produced in the reaction between calcium carbonate and an acid depend on?

5 Explain why a weak acid reacts with calcium carbonate more slowly than a strong acid does, but still produces the same volume of gas under the same conditions.

↓ E

↓ C

↓ A*

▲ Insoluble yellow lead iodide is formed in a precipitation reaction between lead nitrate solution and potassium iodide solution

A Why is potassium nitrate formed in the reaction between lead nitrate solution and potassium iodide solution?

Precipitation reactions

A **precipitation reaction** happens when two different solutions react together to form an insoluble substance. For example, one happens when lead nitrate solution and sodium iodide solution are mixed together. They react to form potassium nitrate and insoluble lead iodide. The lead iodide forms a bright yellow **precipitate** of tiny particles. Precipitation reactions are a useful way to make insoluble compounds.

Swapping places

Ionic substances, such as lead nitrate and potassium iodide, contain ions. These ions are joined together by strong ionic bonds in solids. They are in fixed positions and are unable to move from place to place. On the other hand, the ions can move from place to place when they are in solution.

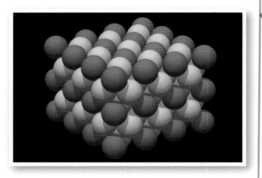

◀ The ions in solid ionic substances are held in fixed positions

Most precipitation reactions involve ions from two different solutions reacting with each other. The ions must collide with other ions so that they can react to form a precipitate. A precipitate will form if the new combination of ions produces an insoluble compound, such as lead iodide. It is as if the ions have swapped places:

lead nitrate + potassium iodide → potassium nitrate + lead iodide

Fast reactions

The collision frequency between ions in solution is very large. There is a high chance that different ions will collide with each other and cause a reaction, so precipitation reactions are extremely fast. Precipitates form as soon as two suitable solutions are mixed together.

State symbols in equations

State symbols are used in balanced symbol equations. They show the state of each substance: (s) means solid, (l) means liquid, (g) means gas, and (aq) means aqueous solution or dissolved in water. Here is the equation for the formation of lead iodide:

$$Pb(NO_3)_2(aq) + 2KI(aq) \rightarrow 2KNO_3(aq) + PbI_2(s)$$

You can tell from the state symbols (s) and (aq) that lead iodide, PbI_2, forms a solid and the other three substances are in aqueous solution.

Making an insoluble salt

Insoluble compounds can be prepared or made by precipitation. There are three main stages:

1. A suitable combination of solutions is mixed together to form a precipitate of the required insoluble compound.
2. The mixture is filtered to separate the precipitate from the other reactants and product.
3. The precipitate is washed with water while it is on the filter paper. It is then dried, for example, in a warm oven.

Questions

1   What is a precipitation reaction?
2   Describe and explain the meaning of the four state symbols.
3   Describe what happens to the ions in a precipitation reaction.
4   Magnesium carbonate is an insoluble compound made by reacting magnesium chloride solution with sodium carbonate solution.
    (a) Write the word equation for the reaction.
    (b) Outline how you could prepare a dry sample of magnesium carbonate using a precipitation reaction.
5   Explain the speed of precipitation reactions.

✓   Take care not to confuse (l) and (aq). For example, NaCl(l) means molten or liquid sodium chloride and NaCl(aq) means sodium chloride dissolved in water.

①
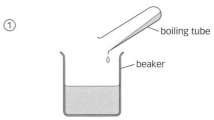

Mix two suitable solutions

②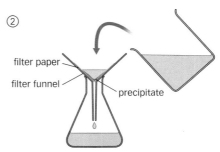

Filter to separate the precipitate

③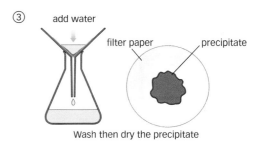

Wash then dry the precipitate

▲ Dry insoluble compounds can be prepared using precipitation reactions

Exam tip   **OCR**

✓   Make sure you can label the apparatus needed to make an insoluble compound by precipitation.

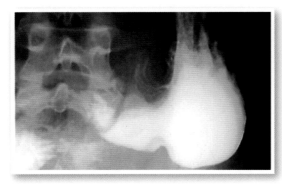

▲ This X-ray image shows a patient's stomach on the right, lined with barium sulfate

A How can you tell from the equations above that barium sulfate forms a precipitate?

◀ A white precipitate when barium chloride solution is added shows the presence of sulfate ions

A medical precipitate

Barium sulfate is an insoluble compound that can be prepared by precipitation reactions. X-rays pass through it with difficulty, making it useful for medical investigations. A patient who needs an X-ray image of their digestive system is given a 'barium meal', a drink containing barium sulfate. The outline of the digestive system shows up in the X-ray image, giving doctors the information they need.

Making barium sulfate

Barium sulfate can be prepared by mixing together solutions of barium chloride and sodium sulfate:

$$\text{barium chloride} + \text{sodium sulfate} \rightarrow \text{sodium sulfate} + \text{barium sulfate}$$

$$BaCl_2(aq) + Na_2SO_4(aq) \rightarrow Na_2SO_4(aq) + BaSO_4(s)$$

The balanced symbol equation can be simplified so that it just shows the ions that react together to make the precipitate:

$$Ba^{2+}(aq) + SO_4^{2-}(aq) \rightarrow BaSO_4(s)$$

This sort of equation is called an **ionic equation**. The barium ions and sulfate ions in this example are the reactants, and the barium sulfate precipitate is the product. Note that barium ions and sulfate ions will make a precipitate together, even if they came from different soluble compounds than barium chloride and sodium sulfate. This is the basis of a simple test to see if a solution contains sulfate ions.

Testing for sulfate ions

A sample of the test solution is placed in a test tube, then acidified with a few drops of hydrochloric acid. A few drops of barium chloride solution are added. If sulfate ions are present, a white precipitate of barium sulfate forms.

Testing for halide ions

Halide ions are ions produced by the halogens, elements in Group 7 of the periodic table. They include chloride ions, Cl^-, bromide ions, Br^-, and iodide ions, I^-. The presence of these ions can be detected using lead nitrate solution:

- Chloride ions give a white precipitate.
- Bromide ions give a cream precipitate.
- Iodide ions give a yellow precipitate.

A sample of the test solution is placed in a test tube, then acidified with a few drops of nitric acid. A few drops of lead nitrate solution are added. If a precipitate forms, its colour lets you identify the halide ion present.

More about ionic equations

You should be able to write the ionic equation for a precipitation reaction, if you are given the ions present and the identity of the products. For example, lead nitrate and sodium chloride react together to form sodium nitrate and a white precipitate of lead chloride. The mixture contains aqueous Pb^{2+}, NO_3^-, Na^+, and Cl^- ions. It must be the aqueous Pb^{2+} and Cl^- ions that react together to make lead chloride, so the ionic equation is:

$$Pb^{2+}(aq) + 2Cl^-(aq) \rightarrow PbCl_2(s)$$

The other ions, Na^+ and NO^{-3}, are called **spectator ions**. They do not take part in the reaction, but instead form the other product, aqueous sodium nitrate.

Questions

1 Describe the colours of the precipitates formed when lead nitrate solution is added to solutions containing chloride, bromide, or iodide ions.

↓ E

2 Describe the test for sulfate ions.

3 A solution produces a cream-coloured precipitate with lead nitrate solution, and a white precipitate with barium chloride solution. Which ions must it contain?

↓ C

4 What is a spectator ion?

5 Lead nitrate and potassium bromide solution react together to form potassium nitrate and a precipitate of lead bromide.

(a) Identify the ions present in the mixture.

↓ A*

(b) Write the ionic equation for the formation of the precipitate, including state symbols.

(c) Explain why potassium nitrate also forms.

B Describe the colours of lead chloride, lead bromide, and lead iodide.

▲ The formation of a yellow lead iodide precipitate when lead nitrate solution is added shows the presence of iodide ions

Exam tip OCR

✓ You may be asked to interpret the results of tests using barium chloride solution and lead nitrate solution.

Module summary

Revision checklist

- The amount of a substance is measured in moles. Molar mass = formula mass in grams.
- Number of moles = $\dfrac{\text{mass}}{\text{molar mass}}$
- Mass is conserved in chemical reactions.
- Reacting masses in reactions are calculated using formula masses and ratios in equations.
- Percentage composition of elements in compounds $= \dfrac{\text{mass of element}}{\text{mass of compound}} \times 100$
- The empirical formula of a compound is the simplest ratio of atoms (or moles) of elements in the compound.
- The concentration of a solution is how much solute is dissolved in $1\,dm^3$ of the solution. In solutions, number of moles = concentration (in mol/dm^3) × volume.
- In titrations, acids are slowly added to alkalis. The pH changes suddenly at the end point of the reaction. Indicators demonstrate this.
- Solutions are measured out using burettes and pipettes. The amount of gas produced as a product of a reaction is measured using a gas syringe.
- Titrations are used to calculate concentrations of solutions.
- Number of moles of a gas = $\dfrac{\text{volume of gas}}{\text{molar volume (24 dm}^3)}$
- Reversible reactions are shown by the ⇋ symbol.
- Reactions reach equilibrium if rate of forward reaction = rate of backward reaction. Changes in concentration, pressure, and temperature affect equilibrium position.
- The Contact Process (forming sulfuric acid from sulfur, air, and water) involves a reversible reaction. A temperature of $450\,°C$, atmospheric pressure, and a V_2O_5 catalyst are used.
- Strong acids completely ionise in water (forming H^+ ions). Weak acids partly ionise and have higher pH values.
- Strong acids have a higher concentration of H^+ ions than weak acids. They react faster with magnesium and carbonates and have greater conductivity.
- In precipitation reactions, two solutions react together to make an insoluble substance.
- Precipitation reactions are used to test for sulfate ions, halide ions, or to prepare insoluble salts.

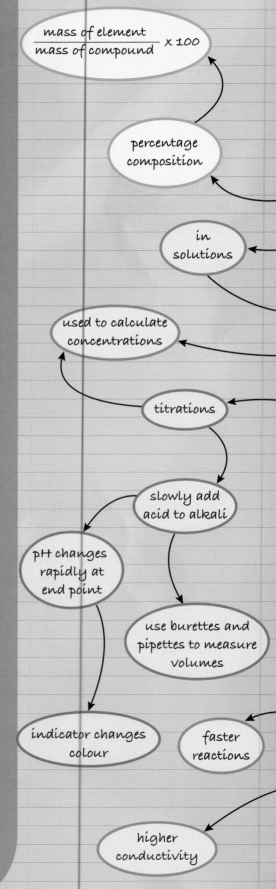

$\dfrac{\text{mass of element}}{\text{mass of compound}} \times 100$

percentage composition

in solutions

used to calculate concentrations

titrations

slowly add acid to alkali

pH changes rapidly at end point

use burettes and pipettes to measure volumes

indicator changes colour

faster reactions

higher conductivity

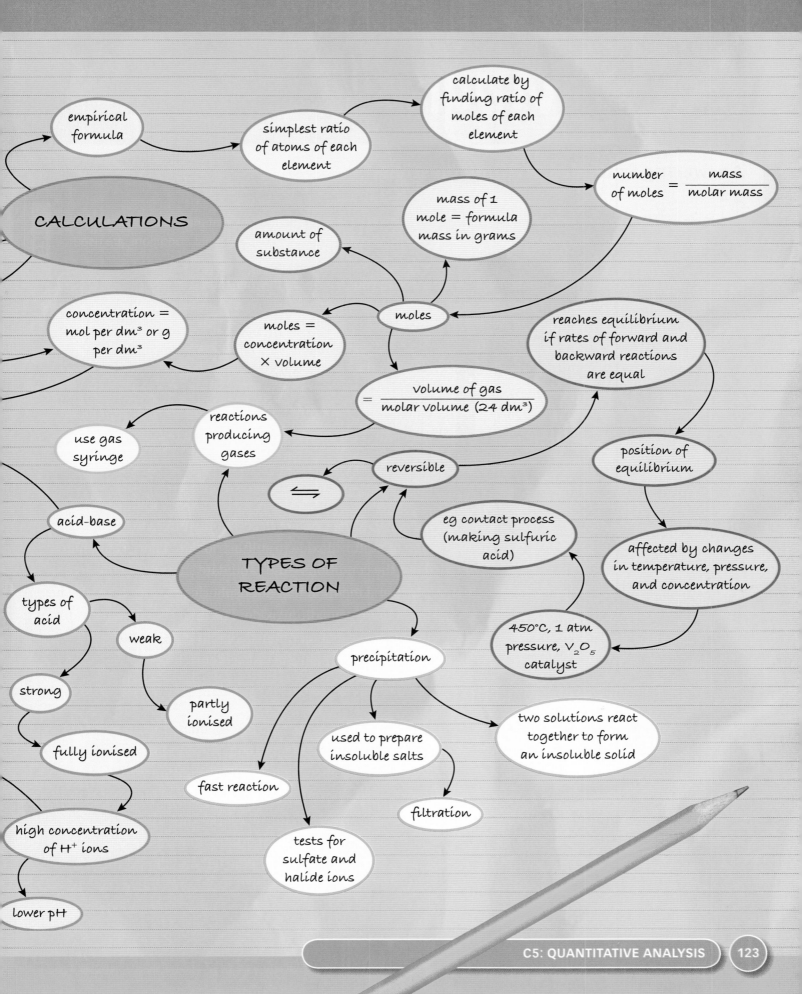

empirical formula

simplest ratio of atoms of each element

calculate by finding ratio of moles of each element

$$\text{number of moles} = \frac{\text{mass}}{\text{molar mass}}$$

CALCULATIONS

amount of substance

mass of 1 mole = formula mass in grams

concentration = mol per dm³ or g per dm³

moles = concentration × volume

moles

reaches equilibrium if rates of forward and backward reactions are equal

$$= \frac{\text{volume of gas}}{\text{molar volume (24 dm}^3\text{)}}$$

use gas syringe

reactions producing gases

reversible

position of equilibrium

$\rightleftharpoons$

eg contact process (making sulfuric acid)

affected by changes in temperature, pressure, and concentration

acid-base

TYPES OF REACTION

types of acid

weak

precipitation

450°C, 1 atm pressure, V_2O_5 catalyst

strong

partly ionised

used to prepare insoluble salts

two solutions react together to form an insoluble solid

fully ionised

fast reaction

filtration

high concentration of H^+ ions

tests for sulfate and halide ions

lower pH

Answering Extended Writing questions

QUESTION

Sulfuric acid is manufactured by the Contact Process, which uses sulfur as the raw material from which to produce sulfuric acid. Describe how sulfur is converted into sulfuric acid and explain what conditions are used in the Contact Process.

The quality of written communication will be assessed in your answer to this question.

As well as sulfur you need air and oxygen. Getting a lot of sulfuric acid is difficult because the reaction is revursable so special conditions are used.

↓ E

Examiner: The answer mentions one other raw material (air), but the second one is water. The candidate has correctly explained the problem about the reversible reaction (note spelling). If the conditions had been listed, this might have been an answer in the D–C band.

Sulfur dioxide reacts to make sulfuric acid in the Contact Process using high temperature and a vanadium catalyst. These help the reaction to be fast, oxygen is also needed for burning the sulfur.

↓ C

Examiner: This is an incomplete answer. The candidate needs to make clear that the Contact Process only refers to the conversion of sulfur dioxide to sulfur trioxide. There is not much detail about the conditions – the candidate should give the actual temperature and mention that atmospheric pressure is used. The catalyst is actually vanadium oxide. The final step (adding water to sulfur trioxide) is not mentioned. Spelling is fine, but a full stop should be used to split the last sentence into two.

First of all sulfur is burnt in air to make sulfur dioxide. This will react with more oxygen to make sulfur trioxide in the Contact Process, but the reaction is in equilibrium. You would expect a high pressure and high temperature to move the position of equilibrium and make the yeald greater but that would be expensive so 450°C and normal pressure is used, also a V_2O_5 catalyst. Finally the sulfur trioxide reacts with water to make sulfuric acid.

↓ A*

Examiner: The candidate includes a lot of correct facts about the conditions and goes some way towards explaining why they are chosen. A full answer would also mention the need for increased rate. However, high temperature actually moves the position of equilibrium to the left and makes the yield smaller, so 450°C is chosen to give the optimum combination of rate and yield.

Exam-style questions

1 Calcium carbonate breaks down when it is heated to make calcium oxide + carbon dioxide.

$$\text{calcium carbonate} \rightarrow \text{calcium oxide} + \text{carbon dioxide}$$

Asif heated 10 g of calcium carbonate. He was left with 5.6 g of calcium oxide.

A02 **a** Calculate the mass of carbon dioxide given off in this experiment.

A02 **b** Is mass conserved in this reaction? Explain your answer.

2 Alkanes are hydrocarbons that are used as fuels. Different alkanes have different formulae.

A01 **a** **i** What is meant by the term empirical formula?

A02 **ii** The chemical formula of butane is usually written as C_4H_{10}. Write down its empirical formula.

A02 **b** 11.6 g of butane (C_4H_{10}) contains 9.6g of carbon. Calculate the percentage by mass of carbon in butane.

3 William has a bottle of sodium hydroxide of unknown concentration. He takes 25 cm³ (0.025 dm³) and titrates it against hydrochloric acid with a concentration of 0.1 mol/dm³.

A02 **a** 18.2 cm³ of hydrochloric acid was the average volume needed to neutralise the sodium hydroxide. The hydrochloric acid and sodium hydroxide react in a 1:1 ratio.

   i Calculate the average amount in moles of hydrochloric acid used in the titration.

   ii What amount in moles of sodium hydroxide reacts with this amount of hydrochloric acid?

   iii Use your result from **ii** and other information from the question to calculate the concentration of the sodium hydroxide in mol/dm³.

Extended Writing

4 Write instructions for a titration to find **A02** out what volume of sulfuric acid is needed to neutralise a solution of sodium hydroxide.

5 Hydrochloric acid (HCl) is a strong acid **A01** and ethanoic acid (CH_3COOH) is a weak acid. Explain the meaning of these terms and describe how the properties of hydrochloric acid are different to those of ethanoic acid.

6 The Contact Process is a method for **A02** manufacturing sulfuric acid. The key stage is a reaction between sulfur dioxide and oxygen:

$$2SO_2 + O_2 \rightleftharpoons 2SO_3$$

A temperature of 450 °C and atmospheric pressure are used, along with a V_2O_5 catalyst. Explain why these conditions are chosen.

A01 Recall the science

A02 Apply your knowledge

A03 Evaluate and analyse the evidence

C6

Chemistry out there

Why study this module?

Chemistry is all around you, at home as well as in industry. Some industrial chemicals have brought us great benefits, while others have caused unforeseen problems. In this module, you will learn about electrolysis and its uses. Fuel cells, used in spacecraft and submarines, hold the promise of cleaner electricity for use in vehicles. You will learn about fuel cells, alternative fuels such as bioethanol, and the chemistry behind them.

CFCs were widely used in the second half of the last century, but were found to damage the ozone layer that protects life on Earth from harmful ultraviolet light. You will discover why they were used, how they cause damage, and the steps taken to reverse this. Closer to home, you will find out about hard and soft water, natural fats and oils, and the chemistry behind keeping yourself clean.

You should remember

1 Electrolysis can be used to purify copper and to make useful chemicals from sodium chloride.

2 Heat energy is released by burning fuels.

3 Rusting is a slow reaction between iron, oxygen and water.

4 Oxidation involves reacting with oxygen, gaining or losing electrons.

5 Alcohols react with acids to make an ester and water.

6 Bromine water is used in a laboratory test for unsaturation in hydrocarbons.

7 Emulsions are mixtures in which one liquid is finely dispersed in another liquid.

8 Emulsifiers are molecules with a water hydrophilic part and a hydrophobic part.

The International Space Station (ISS) can house six astronauts at a time. It orbits 386 km above the Earth at 9000 m/s. Waste water inside the ISS is carefully recovered from sinks, showers, and even perspiration and urine. Oxygen for the astronauts to breathe is produced in a chemical reaction called electrolysis. Electricity is passed through water, breaking it down into hydrogen and oxygen.

Learning objectives

After studying this topic, you should be able to:

- ✔ describe and explain electrolysis
- ✔ predict the products of electrolysis of molten ionic compounds
- ✔ write half equations for electrode processes

Key words

electrolyte, cathode, cation, anode, anion, discharged, half equation

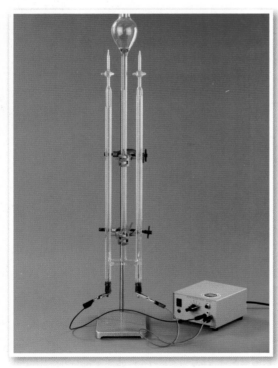

▲ The Hofmann voltameter uses platinum electrodes and a d.c. power pack to electrolyse acidified water

A What is electrolysis?

Splitting water

Alessandro Volta invented the battery in 1800. Scientists were soon keen to build their own 'voltaic pile' and find out what happens when an electric current is passed through a substance. William Nicholson built England's first voltaic pile in 1800 and tested it with water. He discovered bubbles of hydrogen coming from one wire and oxygen from the other wire. The race was on to see what else electrolysis could reveal.

Electrolysis of water

Electrolysis is the decomposition of a liquid by passing an electric current through it. The liquid that is decomposed or broken down is called the **electrolyte**. It must be able to conduct electricity, and this can only happen if its ions are free to move:

- The negative electrode is called the **cathode**. Positively charged ions called **cations** move towards it.
- The positive electrode is called the **anode**. Negatively charged ions called **anions** move towards it.

The potential difference across the two electrodes causes the ions to move and so carry charge through the liquid. When the ions reach the electrodes, they may be **discharged**, releasing elements as products:

- Cations (positively charged ions) are discharged at the cathode, the negative electrode.
- Anions (negatively charged ions) are discharged at the anode, the positive electrode.

Water contains small concentrations of hydrogen ions, $H^+(aq)$, and hydroxide ions, $OH^-(aq)$, discharged at the electrodes during electrolysis. The hydrogen ions are discharged at the cathode, producing hydrogen, $H_2(g)$. The hydroxide ions are discharged at the anode, producing oxygen, $O_2(g)$.

Half equations

A **half equation** describes what happens at an electrode during electrolysis. For example, during the electrolysis of water:

- At the cathode: $2H^+(aq) + 2e^- \rightarrow H_2(g)$
- At the anode: $4OH^-(aq) - 4e^- \rightarrow O_2(g) + 2H_2O(l)$

Notice that the atoms and the charges are balanced.

Molten electrolytes

1807 was an exciting year for Humphry Davy. He passed an electric current through molten potassium hydroxide and was rewarded by being the first person to see potassium metal. Later the same year, Davy discovered sodium in a similar way using molten sodium hydroxide.

When ionic substances are solid, their ions are in fixed positions and cannot move from place to place. The substances cannot be electrolysed. However, they can be electrolysed if they are heated until they melt, because the ions in a molten liquid can move. During electrolysis, metal ions or hydrogen ions move to the negative electrode, and non-metal ions (apart from hydrogen ions) move to the positive electrode. For example, when molten aluminium oxide is electrolysed, aluminium forms at the negative electrode and oxygen at the positive electrode.

> B At which electrode do metals form?

Questions

1 What are anions, cations, and electrolytes?

2 When molten lead bromide is electrolysed, lead forms at the cathode and bromine at the anode. Predict the products formed at each electrode during the electrolysis of molten lead iodide and molten sodium chloride.

3 Explain why there is a flow of charge during electrolysis.

4 Explain why ionic substances can be electrolysed when molten as liquids but not when solid.

5 Write half equations for the electrode reactions that happen when the following are electrolysed:
   (a) $PbBr_2(l)$ (contains $Pb^{2+}(l)$ ions and $Br^-(l)$ ions).
   (b) $PbI_2(l)$ (contains $Pb^{2+}(l)$ ions and $I^-(l)$ ions).
   (c) $NaCl(l)$ (contains $Na^+(l)$ ions and $Cl^-(l)$ ions).

↓ E

↓ C

↓ A*

Did you know...?

Humphry Davy danced around his laboratory in delight when he discovered potassium.

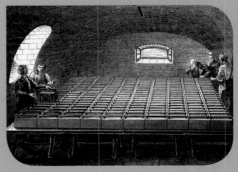

▲ This engraving shows the electric battery built at the Royal Institution in London for Davy's experiments. It was the most powerful battery at the time.

More half equations

Half equations can be written for the electrode reactions during electrolysis of molten compounds. For example, for the electrolysis of molten aluminium oxide:

- At the cathode:
  $$Al^{3+}(l) + 3e^- \rightarrow Al(l)$$
- At the anode:
  $$2O^{2-}(l) - 4e^- \rightarrow O_2(g)$$

2: Electrolysis of solutions

Learning objectives

After studying this topic, you should be able to:

- describe the apparatus needed to electrolyse solutions in school
- describe the electrolysis of copper(II) sulfate solution
- describe the factors affecting the amount of substance formed during electrolysis
- write half equations for electrode processes in solutions
- carry out simple calculations relating amount of substance to current and time during electrolysis

▲ Pencil lead is graphite, so even pencils can be used as electrodes. During the electrolysis of aqueous potassium iodide, yellow-brown iodine is released at the anode and hydrogen is released at the cathode.

◀ Copper(II) sulfate solution can be electrolysed using a d.c. power supply and carbon electrodes. Copper is deposited at the anode, on the left here, and oxygen is released at the cathode.

Simple electrolysis

The electrolysis of molten liquids can be difficult to do because of the high temperatures involved. On the other hand, the electrolysis of aqueous solutions of ionic substances is usually quite easy to do. This is because aqueous solutions are just substances dissolved in water.

The electrolyte is poured into a beaker. Two graphite rods are used as electrodes. Graphite is a form of carbon that conducts electricity and it does not usually react with the electrolysis products. A d.c. power supply, or simply an ordinary battery, supplies the potential difference needed for a current to flow through the electrolyte.

Electrolysis of aqueous copper(II) sulfate

Copper(II) sulfate, $CuSO_4$, is an ionic compound that dissolves in water to form a blue aqueous solution. During the electrolysis of aqueous copper(II) sulfate, copper is formed at the cathode, which becomes coated with copper. Oxygen is formed at the anode, and bubbles of this gas are released from the surface of the anode.

Some other solutions

Copper is less reactive than hydrogen, so it is produced at the cathode during the electrolysis of aqueous copper(II) sulfate. However, if the metal in solution is more reactive than hydrogen, or there is no metal in solution, hydrogen gas is produced instead.

If the aqueous solution contains chloride ions, chlorine is produced at the anode. If not, oxygen gas is produced instead. The table shows five examples of how this works.

Electrolyte	Product at cathode	Product at anode
$CuCl_2$(aq)	copper	chlorine
$CuSO_4$(aq)	copper	oxygen
KNO_3(aq)	hydrogen	oxygen
NaOH(aq)	hydrogen	oxygen
H_2SO_4(aq)	hydrogen	oxygen

A What products would be formed during the electrolysis of hydrochloric acid, HCl?

Key words

directly proportional

More about electrolysis

Water contains H^+(aq) ions and OH^-(aq) ions. It may be easier for these to be discharged during electrolysis than for the ions from the solute to be discharged. This is the case with ions from reactive metals, like Na^+(aq) ions and K^+(aq) ions. Similarly, it is easier for OH^-(aq) ions to be discharged than for NO_3^-(aq) ions and SO_4^{2-}(aq) ions to be discharged.

Copper forms at the cathode during the electrolysis of aqueous copper(II) sulfate, but hydrogen forms there during the electrolysis of aqueous potassium nitrate:
- Cu^{2+}(aq) + 2e$^-$ → Cu(s) . . . and . . . $2H^+$(aq) + 2e$^-$ → H_2(g)

Chlorine forms at the cathode during the electrolysis of aqueous copper(II) chloride, but oxygen forms there during the electrolysis of aqueous copper sulfate:
- $2Cl^-$(aq) – 2e$^-$ → Cl_2(g) . . .
  and . . . $4OH^-$(aq) – 4e$^-$ → O_2(g) + $2H_2O$(l)

How much?

The amount of any product made during electrolysis is affected by the electric current used, and the time taken for the process. The amount made is **directly proportional** to the current, and to the time. For example, during the electrolysis of aqueous copper(II) sulfate, twice as much copper will be made if the current or time is doubled. Four times as much copper will be made if both the current and time are doubled.

How much again?

The amount of charge transferred during electrolysis is equal to the current multiplied by the time. For example, 1 g of hydrogen is produced from acid when 2 A flows for 800 minutes. In the same time, 0.5 g would be made using a current of 1 A. It would take 80 minutes to make 1 g if a current of 20 A is used.

Questions

1 Describe the apparatus needed to carry out electrolysis in the school laboratory.

2 Describe what happens during the electrolysis of aqueous copper(II) sulfate.

3 Describe the products formed during the electrolysis of aqueous sodium hydroxide, NaOH(aq), and dilute sulfuric acid, H_2SO_4(aq).

4 Describe the factors affecting the amount of product formed during electrolysis.

5 Dilute sulfuric acid contains H^+(aq), SO_4^{2-}(aq), and OH^- ions. Write half equations for the electrode reactions that happen when it is electrolysed.

6 In an electrolysis experiment using a current of 1.0 A, 1.0 g of copper was deposited in 60 minutes.

   (a) How long will it take to deposit 3.0 g of copper if a current of 2 A is used?

   (b) What current will be needed to deposit 10.0 g of copper in 4 hours?

Learning objectives

After studying this topic, you should be able to:

- ✔ outline how a hydrogen-oxygen fuel cell works
- ✔ write the word and symbol equations for the overall reaction in a hydrogen-oxygen fuel cell
- ✔ draw and interpret an energy level diagram for the reaction between hydrogen and oxygen
- ✔ explain the changes that take place at each electrode in a hydrogen-oxygen fuel cell

Key words

fuel cell, exothermic reaction, energy level diagram

A What is an exothermic reaction?

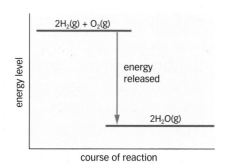

▲ The reactants, hydrogen and oxygen, contain more energy than the product, water. The downwards arrow shows that energy is released to the surroundings during the reaction.

Grove's gaseous voltaic battery

In 1800, William Nicholson passed an electric current through water using platinum electrodes and produced hydrogen and oxygen. This gave scientists an idea. They thought that the process might be reversed. It might be possible to pass hydrogen and oxygen over platinum electrodes and produce an electric current, with water as the waste product. In 1839, the Welsh scientist William Grove invented a device that did this. Grove's 'gaseous voltaic battery' produced an electric current as long as hydrogen and oxygen were bubbled into it. His invention was the first hydrogen-oxygen **fuel cell**.

Hydrogen and oxygen

Hydrogen is a highly flammable gas. It reacts explosively with oxygen if it is ignited with a spark or flame, producing water vapour. The reaction is an **exothermic reaction** because it releases energy to the surroundings. It is difficult to use hydrogen as a fuel in this way. Some vehicles use hydrogen instead of petrol in their engines, but this is less efficient than using a fuel cell.

Energy level diagrams

The energy involved in a chemical reaction can be represented using an **energy level diagram**. This is a graph in which the energy contained in the reactants and products is plotted on the vertical axis, and the course of the reaction on the horizontal axis. Each energy level is shown as a horizontal line. The higher up it is, the more energy the substance contains.

The hydrogen-oxygen fuel cell

A fuel cell produces electrical energy efficiently from an exothermic reaction. There are many different types using different fuels, such as methanol. The hydrogen-oxygen fuel cell uses hydrogen as its fuel. When oxygen or air is supplied, the hydrogen and oxygen react together. The energy released in the reaction is used to produce a potential difference or voltage. This causes a current to flow when the fuel cell is connected in a circuit.

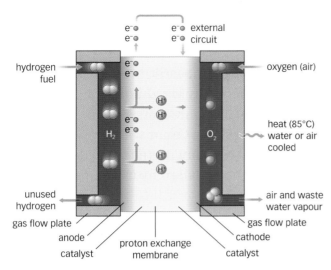

▲ A cross-section through a typical hydrogen-oxygen fuel cell. The potential difference can be increased by stacking several cells together.

The overall reaction that takes place in the hydrogen-oxygen fuel cell is the same as the one that happens when hydrogen explodes in air:

$$\text{hydrogen} + \text{oxygen} \rightarrow \text{water}$$
$$2H_2(g) + O_2(g) \rightarrow 2H_2O(g)$$

However, the design of the fuel cell ensures that the way in which the hydrogen and oxygen react is not the same, but instead happens in a controlled way.

Electrode reactions

Hydrogen molecules lose electrons at the anode and become hydrogen ions:

$$H_2(g) - 2e^- \rightarrow 2H^+(aq)$$

This is an oxidation reaction because the hydrogen molecules lose electrons. The electrons pass through the electrical circuit, and the hydrogen ions pass through a special artificial membrane. This lets hydrogen ions through, but not hydrogen or oxygen gas.

When the hydrogen ions reach the cathode, they combine with oxygen and electrons from the electrical circuit:

$$4H^+(aq) + O_2(g) + 4e^- \rightarrow 2H_2O(g)$$

This is a reduction reaction because electrons are gained. The overall reaction is an example of a redox reaction: reduction happens at the cathode while oxidation happens at the anode.

Exam tip **OCR**

✓ You do not need to be able to explain the detailed working of a fuel cell.

B Name the waste product of a hydrogen-oxygen fuel cell.

Questions

1 Name the fuel used in a hydrogen-oxygen fuel cell, and the type of energy produced.

2 Write the word equation for the reaction between hydrogen and oxygen.

3 Write the balanced symbol equation for the reaction between hydrogen and oxygen.

4 What is created from the energy released by the reaction between the fuel and oxygen in a fuel cell?

5 Draw an energy level diagram to represent the decomposition of calcium carbonate to form calcium oxide and carbon dioxide, which is an endothermic reaction.

6 Write half-equations for the reactions in a hydrogen-oxygen fuel cell, and explain whether they represent reduction or oxidation.

↓E

↓C

↓A*

4: Uses of fuel cells

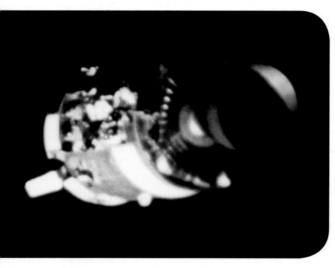

▲ This is Apollo 13's damaged CSM. The explosion blew an entire panel off the side of the module and nearly cost the lives of the astronauts.

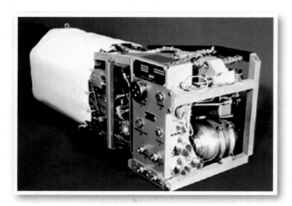

▲ A fuel cell used in NASA's Space Shuttle. It measures just 35 cm × 38 cm × 114 cm, and has a mass of 118 kg. It is over 70% efficient and can supply 12 kW of electricity continuously.

Apollo 13

A near-disaster in space in April 1970 kept millions of people around the world anxiously watching their television sets for the latest news. Two days into a mission to the Moon, an oxygen tank on Apollo 13's Command Service Module (CSM) exploded because of a fault with the electrical wiring. Vital oxygen needed for the on-board hydrogen-oxygen fuel cells was lost.

The three astronauts had to escape into the Lunar Module, attached to the CSM. This was only intended to carry two people for two days, rather than three people for four days. Its design had been changed four years earlier, and it now relied on batteries for its electricity rather than fuel cells. This meant that electricity, and water for drinking and for cooling the spacecraft's systems, was limited. The astronauts had a cold and miserable journey home, but landed safely six days after blast off. Fuel cells are very important for providing electrical power in spacecraft.

Fuel cells in space

Satellites and the International Space Station in orbit above the Earth usually get their electricity from solar panels. These convert sunlight into electricity, and on-board batteries store it so that enough electrical energy is always available. This is not practical for spacecraft like Apollo and the Space Shuttle. They rely on hydrogen-oxygen fuel cells for their electricity. Fuel cells have several advantages that make them suited to use on spacecraft. They

- are lightweight
- are compact
- have no moving parts
- provide drinking water for the astronauts.

> A Give three reasons why a fuel cell might be used on a spacecraft.

Fuel cells on Earth

There is a lot of interest in hydrogen-oxygen fuel cells from the car industry. Most vehicles use petrol or diesel. These hydrocarbon fuels are made from crude oil, which is a **non-renewable resource**: it takes a very long time to make and it is being used up faster than it can form. In addition, the combustion of hydrocarbon fuels produces carbon dioxide. This is a **greenhouse gas** that has been linked with **global warming** and climate change. Vehicles using hydrogen-oxygen fuel cells, rather than petrol or diesel engines, have several advantages:

- Water vapour is the only waste product.
- There are no emissions of carbon dioxide from the car.
- There is a large potential source of hydrogen – water can be decomposed by electrolysis.

> B Give two advantages of using a fuel cell in a car.

▲ This bus uses a hydrogen-oxygen fuel cell to generate electricity. The electricity charges batteries and powers an electric motor.

Key words

non-renewable resource, greenhouse gas, global warming

Some drawbacks

Conventional methods of generating electricity rely on using a fuel to turn water into steam. The steam spins turbines, which turn generators. These stages make the process less efficient than a fuel cell, which has fewer stages. A fuel cell transfers electrical energy directly as needed, whenever fuel and oxygen are supplied to it. The hydrogen-oxygen fuel cell is less polluting than, for example, a coal-fired power station.

> C Give two advantages of using a fuel cell to generate electricity, compared to conventional methods.

At the moment, most hydrogen production involves fossil fuels. Hydrogen can be produced by reacting steam with coal or natural gas. The electrolysis of water produces hydrogen, too, but fossil fuels are used to generate most of the world's electricity. Fuel cells often contain poisonous catalysts. These have to be disposed of safely at the end of the useful life of the fuel cell.

Questions

1. Give two important uses of hydrogen-oxygen fuel cells on spacecraft.
2. Explain why the use of fossil fuels is linked with climate change. ↓ E
3. Describe the advantages of using a fuel cell to provide electrical energy on a spacecraft.
4. Explain why the car industry is developing fuel cells. ↓ C
5. To what extent is it true that hydrogen-oxygen fuel cells do not produce pollution? Explain your answer. ↓ A*

Learning objectives

After studying this topic, you should be able to:

- ✔ recall the reactivity of magnesium, zinc, iron, and tin from most to least reactive
- ✔ describe oxidation and reduction in terms of gain or loss of oxygen
- ✔ predict and explain displacement reactions between metals and metal salt solutions
- ✔ explain oxidation and reduction in terms of loss or gain of electrons
- ✔ explain displacement reactions as examples of redox reactions

Key words

redox reaction, reduction, oxidation, oxidising agent, reducing agent, displacement reaction, reactivity series

▲ The reaction between powdered aluminium and iron oxide is very vigorous. So much heat is released in the exothermic reaction, called the thermite reaction, that the iron which is produced melts.

Reduction and oxidation

A mixture of aluminium and iron(III) oxide is often called a thermite mixture. When it is heated strongly enough, a very vigorous exothermic reaction happens:

aluminium + iron(III) oxide → aluminium oxide + iron

This is an example of a **redox reaction**. Reduction and oxidation happen at the same time.

- Iron(III) oxide loses oxygen and is reduced to iron.
- Aluminium gains oxygen and is oxidised to aluminium oxide.

Reduction is the removal of oxygen from a substance. **Oxidation** is the gain of oxygen by a substance, or the reaction of a substance with oxygen.

> **A** In the following reaction, which substance is reduced and which is oxidised?
>
> copper oxide + magnesium → copper + magnesium oxide

Redox and electrons

Oxidation and reduction can happen even when oxygen is not involved. In these reactions, electrons are lost or gained:

- Oxidation is loss of electrons.
- Reduction is gain of electrons.

These processes happen in electrode reactions during electrolysis or the operation of a fuel cell, but they can also happen in test tube reactions.

An **oxidising agent** is a substance that can remove electrons from other substances, oxidising them. On the other hand, a **reducing agent** is a substance that can give electrons to other substances, reducing them. Look at this example of a redox reaction involving electrons:

$$Cl_2(g) + 2Fe^{2+}(aq) \rightarrow 2Cl^-(aq) + 2Fe^{3+}(aq)$$

chlorine + iron(II) → chloride + iron(III)
reduced   oxidised
oxidising agent reducing agent

Chlorine gains electrons and is reduced to chloride ions, while iron(II) ions lose electrons and are oxidised to iron(III) ions.

> **B** Aluminium is a powerful reducing agent. In the following reaction, which substance is reduced and which is oxidised?
>
> aluminium + iodine → aluminium iodide

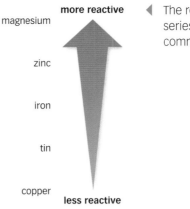

more reactive

magnesium

zinc

iron

tin

copper

less reactive

◄ The reactivity series for five common metals

Displacement reactions

When a strip of zinc foil is dipped into copper(II) sulfate solution, it becomes coated in copper and the blue colour of the solution gradually fades. This is because of a type of redox reaction called a **displacement reaction**:

zinc + copper(II) sulfate → zinc sulfate + copper

The temperature rises because it is an exothermic reaction. One way of understanding displacement reactions involves the **reactivity series** of metals. A more reactive metal can displace a less reactive metal from its compounds. In this example, zinc is more reactive than copper, so it displaces or pushes out copper from copper(II) sulfate. The sulfate has swapped places from the less reactive metal to the more reactive one.

> **C** Will a displacement reaction happen between magnesium and tin nitrate solution? Explain your answer.

Displacement as redox

Displacement reactions can also be explained in terms of redox reactions involving electrons. For example, consider again the reaction between zinc and copper(II) sulfate solution:

$Zn(s) + CuSO_4(aq) \rightarrow ZnSO_4(aq) + Cu(s)$

The sulfate ions act as spectator ions. You can write two half equations, one for what happens to zinc, and one for what happens to the copper(II) ions:

$Zn(s) - 2e^- \rightarrow Zn^{2+}(aq)$ zinc atoms are oxidised
$Cu^{2+}(aq) + 2e^- \rightarrow Cu(s)$ copper(II) ions are reduced

Questions

1 In terms of oxygen, what are oxidation and reduction?

↓ E

2 For each of the following mixtures, explain whether a displacement reaction will happen. Write a word equation for each reaction.

  (a) Zinc + tin chloride solution, $SnCl_2(aq)$.

  (b) Zinc + magnesium chloride solution, $MgCl_2(aq)$.

↓ C

3 A pale green solution containing iron(II) ions $Fe^{2+}(aq)$ gradually turns orange-brown as iron(III) ions $Fe^{3+}(aq)$ form. Explain whether iron(II) ions are oxidised or reduced.

4 Magnesium displaces tin from tin chloride solution.

  (a) Write a balanced symbol equation for the reaction.

↓ A*

  (b) Explain which reactant is reduced and which reactant is oxidised.

Learning objectives

After studying this topic, you should be able to:

- ✔ recall the requirements for iron and steel to rust
- ✔ understand that rusting is a redox reaction
- ✔ describe and explain methods of rust prevention
- ✔ explain why rusting is a redox reaction
- ✔ explain how sacrificial protection and tin plating work

▲ The Pontcysyllte Aqueduct in Wales

B Give the chemical name for rust.

Did you know...?

It has been estimated that rusting costs national economies around the world up to 5% of the value of their goods and services. In the US alone, this means at least $270 billion a year.

Rusting

The Pontcysyllte Aqueduct on the Llangollen Canal in Wales is an amazing structure. It has carried canal traffic in a 307 m cast iron trough over the River Dee 38 m below since 1805. Cast iron contains around 4% carbon. This makes the metal hard, and too brittle for most uses. However, the carbon protects the iron from rusting away. It reacts to form insoluble products that keep air and water away from the metal.

Iron and steel rust when they react with both water and oxygen. Air contains oxygen, so the metal will rust in damp air. Rusting is a redox reaction because the iron atoms are oxidised to iron(III) ions, and the oxygen atoms are reduced to oxide ions. Rusting damages iron and steel objects, so various ways to prevent it happening have been developed.

A What two substances are needed for iron and steel to rust?

Hydrated iron(III) oxide

Rust is hydrated iron(III) oxide:

iron + oxygen + water → hydrated iron(III) oxide

During rusting, the iron atoms lose electrons to become iron(III) ions, Fe^{3+}. This means that they are oxidised. On the other hand, the oxygen atoms gain electrons to become oxide ions, O^{2-}. This means that they are reduced.

Preventing rust

Many methods of rust prevention rely on stopping air and water reaching the surface of the iron. These include:

- coating the metal part with oil or grease
- painting the surface of the metal part
- plating the surface with zinc (galvanising)
- plating the surface with tin.

It is important to choose the correct method. For example, it is sensible to oil a bicycle chain rather than painting it, but it is not sensible to oil car bodywork instead of painting it.

Some iron alloys are resistant to rusting. Stainless steel contains chromium. This oxidises to chromium oxide when exposed to the air, forming a thin film on the surface of the steel. The layer stops air and water reaching the metal below.

▲ Stainless steel is used in kitchen sinks because it does not rust

> **C** Describe two ways in which steel can be coated to protect it from rusting.

Sacrificial protection

Galvanising involves coating the surface of the iron or steel object with a layer of zinc. The zinc coating stops air and water reaching the metal below, but it also does something else. Zinc is more reactive than iron, so it is more likely to be oxidised. It sacrifices itself to protect the iron below. Galvanising is used to protect car body panels before painting, and to protect metalwork sited outdoors.

▲ This farm gate is made from galvanised steel to prevent it rusting

More about sacrificial protection

Sacrificial protection does not just work with zinc. It works with other metals that are more reactive than iron, such as magnesium. The more reactive metal loses electrons more readily than iron does, so it is more readily oxidised. This even works if the reactive metal is just attached to the iron or steel. Ships have zinc or magnesium blocks bolted onto their hulls under the waterline. These protect the hull but they gradually corrode away and have to be replaced.

> **D** Put iron, tin, and zinc into an order of reactivity, starting with the most reactive.

Tin plating is used to protect the inside of steel food cans from rusting. Just like zinc plating, the layer of tin stops air and water reaching the surface of the iron. However, unlike zinc, tin is less reactive than iron. This means that tin loses electrons less readily than iron does, so it is less readily oxidised. Unfortunately, the result is that the iron rusts even faster if the tin layer is broken or scratched.

Key words

galvanising

Questions

1 Explain why rusting involves oxidation.

2 Why do oil, grease, and paint prevent iron from rusting?

3 Explain how galvanising works.

4 Explain why rusting is a redox reaction.

5 Zinc plating and tin plating both protect iron from rusting. Explain how they do this, and describe any differences between the two methods.

↓ E

↓ C

↓ A*

Key words

alcohol, ethanol, fermentation, yeast, fractional distillation, denatured

$$H-\underset{\underset{H}{|}}{\overset{\overset{H}{|}}{C}}-\underset{\underset{H}{|}}{\overset{\overset{H}{|}}{C}}-O-H$$

▲ This is the displayed formula of ethanol

Exam tip | OCR

- ✔ Make sure you can recall the main uses of ethanol.

Did you know...?

In 2010 divers discovered bottles of beer and champagne in a shipwreck off the Finland coast. The corks were still intact and no seawater had got into the bottles. At around two hundred years old, the bottles contain the world's oldest drinkable alcoholic drinks.

Alcohol

Alcoholic drinks such as wine and beer contain an **alcohol** called **ethanol**. Although most people just call it alcohol, ethanol is just one of a family of similar substances. These all contain carbon, hydrogen, and oxygen bonded together. The alcohols are not hydrocarbons, because they contain oxygen atoms in addition to carbon and hydrogen atoms. They often burn well, and ethanol is used as fuel for cars. It is also used as a solvent in perfumes and aftershaves.

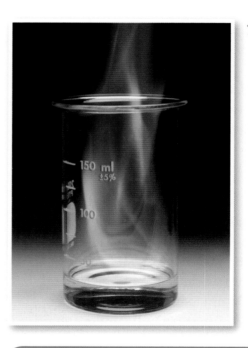

◀ Ethanol burns well and is used as a fuel for cars. Modern cars can run on a mixture of 95% petrol and 5% ethanol without any modifications to the engine.

> **A** How many carbon, hydrogen, and oxygen atoms does a molecule of ethanol contain?

Making alcohol

Fermentation is an ancient method of making ethanol. People have been using it for thousands of years to produce alcoholic drinks. It is still used for this purpose, but nowadays it is also used to make ethanol on an industrial scale.

Fermentation relies on microscopic single-celled fungi called **yeast**. Yeast contains enzymes that can convert glucose to carbon dioxide and ethanol, as long as oxygen is kept out:

$$\text{glucose} \rightarrow \text{carbon dioxide} + \text{ethanol}$$
$$C_6H_{12}O_6 \rightarrow 2CO_2 + 2C_2H_5OH$$

It is easy to make ethanol in the school laboratory. Glucose is dissolved in a conical flask of warm water to make glucose solution. Yeast is added, and a bung and delivery tube fitted. The end of the delivery tube is dipped into a test tube of water or limewater to act as an airlock. It is important to keep the temperature between 25 °C and 50 °C, so the apparatus should be left in a warm place.

As fermentation begins, carbon dioxide bubbles out of the airlock and eventually all the original air inside is replaced with carbon dioxide.

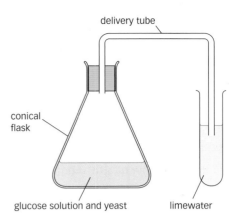

▲ Apparatus used to demonstrate fermentation. The limewater turns milky as carbon dioxide bubbles through it.

> **B** Describe the conditions needed for fermentation.

Fermentation is a slow reaction, so several days at least are needed to make sufficient ethanol to investigate. The ethanol eventually kills the yeast, which sinks to the bottom. Ethanol is separated from the mixture by **fractional distillation**. This works because water boils at 100 °C, but ethanol boils at only 78 °C.

▲ Wine is made by fermentation on a huge scale at this vineyard in California

Choosing the conditions

Yeast is made up of living organisms. They will become inactive if the temperature is too low, so it should not fall below about 25 °C. Enzymes are natural catalysts. They are proteins that need to maintain a particular shape, otherwise they will not work. If enzymes become too hot, their shape changes irreversibly. They become **denatured** and stop working, so the temperature should not rise above about 50 °C. If air gets inside during fermentation, the oxygen causes the ethanol to oxidise to ethanoic acid, the acid found in vinegar.

Exam tip — OCR

✔ Make sure you can describe the conditions needed for fermentation.

Questions

1 Explain why the alcohols are not hydrocarbons.

2 Give three main uses of ethanol.

↓ E

3 Write the molecular formula of ethanol, and draw its displayed formula.

4 Describe how ethanol can be made by fermentation. Include the word equation for the reaction in your answer.

↓ C

5 Explain the range of temperatures chosen for fermentation, and why air must be kept out. Include the balanced symbol equation for fermentation in your answer.

↓ A*

Learning objectives

After studying this topic, you should be able to:

✔ describe how ethanol can be made by the hydration of ethene

✔ evaluate the merits of making ethanol by fermentation or hydration

✔ recall the general formula for alcohols

✔ draw the displayed formulae for alcohols containing from one to five carbon atoms

▲ This huge chemical plant produces ethene, used to make poly(ethene) and ethanol

▲ Ethanol can be made by hydration of ethene

> **A** Which method produces ethanol that is non-renewable?

Making ethanol

Fermentation is not the only way to make ethanol. It can also be made by reacting ethene with steam. The two gases are passed over a hot phosphoric acid catalyst, causing a **hydration reaction** to happen:

$$\text{ethene} + \text{water} \rightarrow \text{ethanol}$$
$$C_2H_4 + H_2O \rightarrow C_2H_5OH$$

This method of producing ethanol is used for ethanol intended for industrial use, rather than ethanol intended for alcoholic drinks.

Ethanol made by fermentation is a renewable fuel. The sugars needed for the process come from plants, including sugar cane and sugar beet. As long as new crops are planted after other crops have been harvested for use in fermentation, we should not run out of ethanol. However, ethanol made by hydration of ethene is a non-renewable fuel. The ethene needed for the process comes from cracking crude oil fractions. Since crude oil itself is a non-renewable resource, ethanol made in this way is also non-renewable.

More about making ethanol

The two methods of making ethanol, fermentation and hydration, each have different advantages and disadvantages. The table summarises the main differences between them.

Feature	Fermentation of sugars	Hydration of ethene
conditions	low temperatures and normal pressure	high temperatures and high pressures
raw materials	sugars from plants	ethene from crude oil
purity of product	low – needs filtering and distillation	high – no by-products are made
percentage yield	low – about 15%	high – around 100%
atom economy	51%	100%
type of process	batch	continuous

Fermentation is a more sustainable process than the hydration of ethene: it requires renewable raw materials and relatively little energy. On the other hand, its percentage yield, atom economy (the percentage of atoms in the reactants that become atoms in the desired product), and purity of the product are all lower than for the hydration process. In addition, fermentation is a batch process, which makes it more labour-intensive and means automation is more difficult.

More alcohols

Ethanol is just one example from a family of compounds called the alcohols. All alcohols contain a hydroxyl group, –OH. The alcohols are named after the number of carbon atoms they contain, just as the alkanes and alkenes are. Their names usually end in 'anol'. The table shows the names and formulae of some alcohols.

Name of alcohol	Number of carbon atoms	Molecular formula	Displayed formula
methanol	1	CH_3OH	
ethanol	2	C_2H_5OH	
propanol	3	C_3H_7OH	
butanol	4	C_4H_9OH	
pentanol	5	$C_5H_{11}OH$	

Notice that that all the molecular formulae have this general formula:

$$C_nH_{2n+1}OH$$

Key words

hydration reaction

B   What does 'atom economy' mean?

C   Write the molecular formula for eicosanol, an alcohol with 20 carbon atoms.

Questions

1   Write the word equation for the hydration of ethene.

2   Describe how ethanol is produced by the hydration of ethene.

3   Ethanol can replace petrol. What method should be used to make ethanol so that the use of fossil fuels is reduced? Explain your answer.

4   Write the balanced symbol equation for the hydration of ethene.

5   Worldwide production of ethanol is around 80 billion litres per year. Around 95% of this is made by fermentation rather than by hydration of ethene. Suggest why fermentation is the preferred way to make ethanol.

6   Write the molecular formula for hexanol, an alcohol with six carbon atoms, and draw its displayed formula.

Learning objectives

After studying this topic, you should be able to:

- ✔ explain what ozone is and how it forms
- ✔ describe the uses of CFCs
- ✔ describe how CFCs can deplete the ozone layer
- ✔ describe, with the help of equations, how chlorine radicals react with ozone

▲ These scientists are carrying out research to do with the ozone layer in the Antarctic. The large helium balloon will take scientific equipment 20 km up into the atmosphere. Airliners typically cruise 9 km to 12 km up.

▲ Ozone molecules contain three oxygen atoms

◀ The displayed formula of a typical CFC

$$Cl$$
$$|$$
$$F-C-Cl$$
$$|$$
$$Cl$$

> **A** What is ozone?

Ozone

Ozone is a form of oxygen with the formula O_3 rather than the more usual O_2. It is a pale blue gas with a choking smell similar to bleach. Ozone can cause breathing problems when it is in the air at ground level. However, ozone high up in the atmosphere is vital to the health and survival of living things.

The ozone layer

Ozone is found throughout the atmosphere, but it is most concentrated in the stratosphere. This is a part of the atmosphere 10 km to 50 km above the Earth's surface, also called the **ozone layer**. However, there is not really a layer of ozone, just a region where it is most concentrated.

Sunlight contains ultraviolet light, as well as visible light. Ultraviolet light causes oxygen, O_2, to react to form ozone, O_3. This happens in stages, but overall three oxygen molecules produce two ozone molecules:

$$3O_2 \rightarrow 2O_3$$

The ozone layer absorbs most of the ultraviolet light in sunlight, stopping it from reaching the Earth's surface.

CFCs

CFC is the shortened name for **chlorofluorocarbon**. CFCs contain carbon atoms with chlorine and fluorine atoms attached. There are many different types of CFC, and they were used in refrigerators and aerosol cans in the past. Unfortunately, CFCs damage the ozone layer.

Damaging the ozone layer

CFC molecules spread out in the atmosphere after release. Ultraviolet light in the stratosphere breaks carbon-chlorine bonds in CFC molecules. For example:

$$CCl_3F \rightarrow CCl_2F + Cl$$

Highly reactive chlorine atoms called chlorine radicals are released. These react with ozone molecules and break them down to form oxygen, O_2. Chlorine atoms are formed in this reaction, and they can go on to react with even more ozone molecules. The reactions reduce the concentration of ozone in the ozone layer, letting more ultraviolet light reach the Earth's surface.

Increased levels of ultraviolet light can cause medical problems, including:

- skin cancer
- an increased risk of sunburn
- an increased risk of eye cataracts
- faster ageing of skin, causing more wrinkles and age spots.

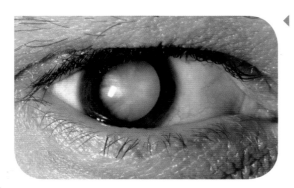

◀ This person has an eye cataract. The proteins in the lens of the eye have become damaged, causing the lens to go cloudy.

Key words

ozone, ozone layer, chlorofluorocarbon (CFC), chlorine radical, chain reaction

B What is the ozone layer?

C Give two medical problems caused by increased levels of ultraviolet light.

More about ozone and chlorine radicals

A covalent bond consists of a shared pair of electrons. Ultraviolet light can break a covalent bond in such a way that each atom from the bond gets one of the electrons. This produces highly reactive radicals. The extra electron is shown as a dot in formulae. For example, this equation shows how a CFC molecule can form a chlorine radical:

$$CCl_3F \xrightarrow{\text{UV light}} \cdot CCl_2F + \cdot Cl$$

Exam tip   OCR

✔ Remember to show a free radical with a dot in chemical equations.

$$F-\underset{\underset{Cl}{|}}{\overset{\overset{Cl}{|}}{C}}\div Cl \longrightarrow F-\underset{\underset{Cl}{|}}{\overset{\overset{Cl}{|}}{C}}\cdot + \cdot Cl$$

▲ Radicals can form when covalent bonds break

Once formed, these chlorine radicals can go on to damage many ozone molecules. There are two steps:

Step 1 Chlorine radical reacts with ozone
$$\cdot Cl + O_3 \rightarrow \cdot ClO + O_2$$

Step 2 New radical reacts with more ozone
$$\cdot ClO + O_3 \rightarrow + 2O_2 + \cdot Cl$$

Notice that a chlorine radical goes in at step 1 and another one comes out at step 2. This sets up a **chain reaction** in which a lot of ozone is destroyed. Steps 1 and 2 can be combined to give an overall equation:

$$2O_3 \rightarrow 3O_2$$

Questions

1 Give two uses of CFCs.

2 What is a chlorine radical?

3 Describe the effect of ultraviolet light on CFCs. What happens as a result?

4 What happens if the concentration of ozone in the ozone layer decreases?

5 Explain how a radical forms.

6 Describe how a chain reaction is set up between chlorine radicals and ozone. Include symbol equations in your answer.

E

↓

C

↓

A*

Key words

refrigerant, propellant, HFC

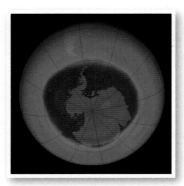

▲ The CFCs in old refrigerators must be removed before the refrigerator can be recycled. The insulating foam may also contain CFCs.

More about CFCs

There are many different types of chlorofluorocarbon or CFC, but they all have similar properties. These include:

- low boiling points, so they are usually gases
- they are insoluble in water
- they are chemically inert, so they do not react easily with other substances.

These properties make CFCs very versatile. In the last century, CFCs were widely used as **refrigerants**. These are the substances in refrigerators and air conditioning systems that carry the heat away. CFCs were also widely used as aerosol **propellants**, the substances that push the can's contents out as a spray when the button is pressed. Unfortunately, the properties that make CFCs so useful also made them a big problem for the ozone layer.

The Montreal Protocol

The inertness of CFCs means that they are removed from the stratosphere only very slowly. Experiments, calculations, and observations made in the 1970s showed that CFCs were destroying ozone and depleting the ozone layer. At a meeting in Montreal in Canada in 1987, 24 countries signed a treaty that placed strict limits on the production and use of CFCs. Since then, almost all countries have signed it. The treaty has been revised several times. Now all but the most vital uses of CFCs have been banned. As a result, the ozone layer is beginning to show signs of recovery.

◄ This satellite image shows the concentration of ozone over the Antarctic in 2008. The purple 'hole' in the ozone layer was one of the largest recorded, even though the concentration of CFCs has decreased steadily since 2000.

A Give one property of a CFC.

B What did the 1987 treaty signed in Montreal agree to?

CFCs everywhere

An unusual discovery was made in 1973. A very sensitive device had just been invented to measure the concentration of compounds in the atmosphere. Wherever it was used, it detected CCl_3F, a commonly used CFC. Calculations showed that the total amount in the atmosphere was similar to the total amount ever made. Once they had been released into the air, CFCs were not breaking down very quickly at all. In fact, they were being removed only very slowly. The very lack of chemical reactivity that made CFCs attractive meant that they might cause problems.

At around the same time as this discovery was made, scientists realised that CFCs could break down ozone. They calculated that a single chlorine radical could cause the breakdown of 100 000 ozone molecules. With around a million tonnes of CFCs being made every year, there was huge potential to deplete the ozone layer within decades. Things were about to get even worse.

The unusual conditions over the poles mean that ozone levels there vary naturally with the seasons. Measurements in 1985 revealed a startling discovery. The concentration of ozone in the ozone layer had decreased far more than anyone expected. A link had been shown between the use and release of CFCs, and the depletion of the ozone layer. It was clear to scientists and the wider public that something had to be done urgently.

Replacements for CFCs

Society at large has now agreed with the scientists' views about the ozone layer and the role of CFCs in depleting it. Chemists have developed safer alternatives to CFCs. They include alkanes, and compounds called hydrofluorocarbons or **HFCs**. These do not contain chlorine atoms and they do not damage the ozone layer.

▲ The displayed formula of trifluoromethane, an HFC used to replace CFCs in refrigerators and air conditioning units

Did you know...?

The concentration of ozone in the stratosphere is measured in Dobson units, named after Gordon Dobson. He was the scientist at the University of Oxford who built the first instrument to measure total ozone from the ground in the 1920s.

C How many ozone molecules can one chlorine radical destroy?

Questions

1 Why are CFCs usually gases?

2 What replacements have been developed for CFCs?

3 Explain why the use of CFCs in the UK and elsewhere has been banned.

4 Explain why CFCs disappear from the atmosphere very slowly.

5 Describe how the attitude of scientists to CFCs has changed over time.

6 Explain why CFCs will carry on depleting ozone for long time to come.

11: Water hardness

▲ Soapless detergents lather just as well in hard water as they do in soft water, but ordinary soap does not lather well in hard water

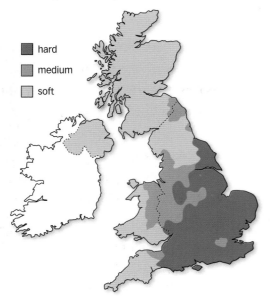

■ hard
■ medium
□ soft

▲ How hard or soft the water from your taps is depends upon where you live

Hard and soft water

The water that flows from your taps is not pure. It contains chlorine to kill harmful bacteria, and various dissolved mineral ions. These ions may be good for your health. For example, calcium ions help to maintain healthy bones and teeth. However, they can make it difficult to get a lather with soap. **Soft water** contains low concentrations of calcium ions and magnesium ions, and easily forms a lather with soap. **Hard water** contains higher concentrations of these ions, which stops the soap forming a lather easily.

Acid attack

Rainwater is naturally slightly acidic. Carbon dioxide in the air dissolves in the rain, producing a weak acid. Chalk and limestone consist mainly of calcium carbonate. Rain falling on these rocks reacts with the calcium carbonate to form calcium hydrogencarbonate:

$$\text{calcium carbonate} + \text{water} + \text{carbon dioxide} \rightarrow \text{calcium hydrogencarbonate}$$

Calcium carbonate is insoluble in water, but calcium hydrogencarbonate is not. The rock gradually erodes away as water from rain, rivers, lakes, and reservoirs stays in contact with it.

> **A** Why is rainwater naturally slightly acidic?

The rocks in some parts of country are mostly igneous rocks like granite. These are not so susceptible to acid attack and the water there is usually soft. Chalk and limestone in other parts of the country are susceptible to acid attack, and the water there is hard. The degree of hardness depends upon the rocks the water has flowed over and through.

Types of hardness

There are two types of hardness:

- **permanent hardness** – caused by dissolved calcium sulfate
- **temporary hardness** – caused by dissolved calcium hydrogencarbonate.

When water with permanent hardness is boiled, the hardness is not removed. However, when water with temporary hardness is boiled, the hardness is removed. This happens because calcium hydrogencarbonate decomposes when heated:

calcium hydrogencarbonate $\rightarrow$ calcium carbonate + water + carbon dioxide

This is essentially the reverse of the process that produced the hard water in the first place. It can lead to deposits of calcium carbonate as limescale in kettles, irons, and heating systems.

Symbol equations

These are the symbol equations for the formation of hard water from calcium carbonate in rocks, and the decomposition of calcium hydrogencarbonate when water with temporary hardness is boiled:

$$CaCO_3 + H_2O + CO_2 \rightarrow Ca(HCO_3)_2$$

$$Ca(HCO_3)_2 \rightarrow CaCO_3 + H_2O + CO_2$$

Limescale

Limescale is calcium carbonate. It damages equipment that uses hot water and increases the amount of energy used in them. Limescale removers are weak acids, like citric acid. Weak acids will not react with the metal of the equipment, but they will react with the limescale to form a calcium salt, water, and carbon dioxide. For example:

calcium carbonate + citric acid $\rightarrow$ calcium citrate + water + carbon dioxide

C   Why are weak acids used as limescale removers?

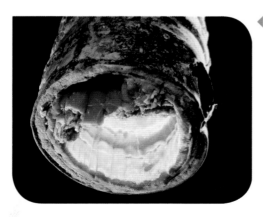

◀ This copper hot water pipe is almost completely blocked by a thick layer of limescale, calcium carbonate

B   Which type of hardness can be removed by boiling?

Did you know...?

It has been estimated that hard water costs British industry around £1 billion per year. Limescale damages pipes, boilers, and other equipment that involves hot water. It also increases energy costs. A layer just 1 mm thick can increase energy costs by around 8%.

Questions

1   Why can you tell from the lather formed by soap that water is hard or soft? Why would this not work with a soapless detergent?

2   Why does water hardness vary across the UK?

3   Describe, with the help of an equation, how hard water forms.

4   Suggest why some people use boiled water in their steam irons.

5   Describe, with the help of a balanced symbol equation, how boiling removes temporary hardness.

Key words

washing soda, ion-exchange resin

A What is washing soda?

▲ Washing soda can soften hard water

Washing soda

Temporary hardness in water can be removed by boiling, but this is not the only way to soften hard water. **Washing soda** is sodium carbonate, white crystals that dissolve in water to make an alkaline solution. It has several uses in the home, including removing grease from cookers and pans, and unblocking sinks and drains. Washing soda is added to water to soften it when washing clothes. Both temporary and permanent hardness are removed by washing soda. Without it, extra detergent would be needed in hard water areas.

More about washing soda

Most carbonates are insoluble, including calcium carbonate and magnesium carbonate, but sodium carbonate is soluble in water. When washing soda is added to hard water, a precipitation reaction happens. For example:

calcium hydrogen-carbonate + sodium carbonate → calcium carbonate + sodium hydrogen-carbonate

$$Ca(HCO_3)_2(aq) + Na_2CO_3(aq) \rightarrow CaCO_3(s) + 2NaHCO_3(aq)$$

The hard water is softened because the calcium ions and magnesium ions are removed as a precipitate.

Ion-exchange

There is another way to remove both temporary and permanent hardness from water. Ion-exchange columns contain **ion-exchange resins**, tiny beads packed into a plastic or metal tube. Hard water is softened as it passes through an ion-exchange column. This is ideal as a permanent solution to hard water in the home. The ion-exchange column is usually plumbed into the home's water supply so that all the water used in the home is softened.

Ion-exchange resins work by swapping ions in the water for ions from the resin. As the hard water passes through, calcium ions and magnesium ions from the water attach to the resin and sodium ions leave it. The water is softened because the calcium ions and magnesium ions are removed.

Eventually, all the sodium ions in the resin are replaced by calcium ions and magnesium ions. When this happens, the resin is regenerated by flushing sodium chloride solution through the column. Sodium ions are swapped back into the resin. Calcium ions and magnesium ions are pushed out and washed away in waste water. Domestic water softeners may carry out this process automatically.

Water experiments

Hardness in water can be investigated using soap solution. This is added drop by drop from a teat pipette to a fixed volume of water. The more drops needed to get a permanent lather, the harder the water. The table shows the results of an experiment involving three different samples of water.

Sample	Drops of soap solution needed
A	4
B	12
C	8

Sample A was the softest because it needed the least amount of soap solution to get a permanent lather.

> **B** Which sample of water was the hardest?
>
> **C** Why is dishwasher salt needed?

Questions

1 Give two ways in which temporary and permanent hardness can be removed.

2 The three water samples in the table were evaporated to dryness. Explain why water B left a lot of white solid behind.

3 Explain how an ion-exchange resin works.

4 In the table, water sample C was produced by boiling sample B. What do the results show about water sample B?

5 Explain how washing soda can soften hard water.

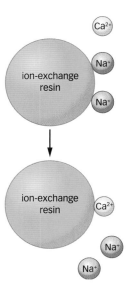

▲ Ion-exchange resins work by swapping calcium ions and magnesium ions in water for sodium ions in the resin

Did you know...?

Dishwashing machines contain an ion-exchange column to soften the water. This stops white streaks of calcium carbonate and other precipitates being left on the clean plates as they dry. Dishwasher salt has to be added regularly to regenerate the ion-exchange resin.

▲ Salt granules being added to the ion-exchange resin in a dishwasher

Learning objectives

After studying this topic, you should be able to:

- ✔ describe some of the properties and uses of oils and fats
- ✔ describe the differences between saturated and unsaturated fats
- ✔ explain why bromine can be used to test for unsaturation
- ✔ explain why unsaturated fats are healthier options in the diet

▲ Edible fats and oils

▲ Glycerol and a fatty acid. Most natural fatty acids contain 4–28 carbon atoms.

Exam tip   OCR

- ✔ Unsaturated fats and oils have at least one C=C bond in their displayed formula.

Fats and oils

Animals and plants contain fats and oils. For example milk, cheese, and butter contain animal fats, while margarine and cooking oils contain vegetable oils. All these substances have a very similar chemical structure. Whether the substance is called a fat or an oil depends upon its state at room temperature:

- fats are solid at room temperature
- oils are liquid at room temperature.

Vegetable oils are not only an important part of a healthy diet, they are also important raw materials for the chemical industry. Biodiesel is an alternative to diesel made from crude oil. It is made from vegetable oils such as rapeseed oil. Unlike ordinary diesel, biodiesel is a renewable resource. Soap is also made from vegetable oils.

> **A** What is the difference between a fat and an oil?

Esters

Fats and oils are **esters**. These compounds form when a carboxylic acid reacts with an alcohol. Some esters are used in perfumes and as solvents. These are simple esters like ethyl ethanoate, made from ethanoic acid and ethanol. Fats and oils are more complex. They consist of **fatty acids** chemically joined to **glycerol**, which is an alcohol. Fatty acids have long chains of carbon atoms. Glycerol has three hydroxyl groups, –OH, unlike many other alcohols that only have one.

> **B** What are the two components of a fat or oil molecule?

Saturated or unsaturated?

Fats and oils can be saturated or unsaturated:

- in a **saturated** fat or oil, all the carbon-carbon bonds in the fatty acid parts are single covalent bonds
- in an **unsaturated** fat or oil, one or more of the carbon-carbon bonds in the fatty acid parts is a double covalent bond.

This is similar to alkanes and alkenes. Both these types of compound are hydrocarbons, but alkanes have all single bonds and are saturated, while alkenes have one or more double bonds and are unsaturated. Unsaturation in alkenes, fats, and oils can be shown using bromine water:

- bromine water stays orange when mixed with a sample of a saturated alkene, fat, or oil
- bromine water goes colourless when mixed with enough unsaturated alkene, fat, or oil.

> C What colour is bromine water?

More about unsaturation

Bromine reacts with the carbon-carbon double bonds in unsaturated fats and oils. An **addition reaction** happens there, producing a dibromo compound that is colourless. Saturated fats and oils do not contain carbon-carbon double bonds, so they cannot react with bromine to produce a colourless compound.

◀ Part of an unsaturated fatty acid, showing how bromine reacts with the carbon-carbon double bond. This addition reaction produces a colourless dibromo compound.

Fats and oils are an important part of a healthy diet, but too much of them can cause health problems and make us overweight. Saturated fats, found mainly in meat and dairy products, can raise the level of cholesterol in the blood. High levels of cholesterol increase the risk of blocked arteries and heart disease.

Unsaturated fats and oils, found mainly in vegetables, fruits and nuts, tend to be more healthy choices. For example, omega-3 oils from oily fish such as mackerel are thought to help reduce the risk of heart disease.

Key words

ester, fatty acid, glycerol, saturated, unsaturated, addition reaction

Exam tip OCR

- ✔ You do not need to know any detail about the structure of glycerol and fatty acids, except that fats and oils are esters, and have chains of carbon atoms that can contain single bonds and double bonds.
- ✔ For a given mass of fat or oil, the more unsaturated it is, the greater volume of bromine water it can decolourise.

Questions

1 Give two uses of natural fats or oils in the chemical industry.

2 What type of compound are fats and oils?

3 In terms of carbon-carbon bonds, what is the difference between a saturated fat and an unsaturated fat?

4 Describe how bromine water can be used to distinguish between a saturated fat and an unsaturated fat.

5 Explain how the bromine test for unsaturation works.

6 Explain why unsaturated fats are regarded as healthier for us than saturated fats.

▲ Vegetable oil and water are immiscible liquids

Emulsions

If vegetable oil and water are poured into a beaker, the vegetable oil forms a layer on top of the water. This is because vegetable oil is less dense than water, and the two liquids are **immiscible** – they do not dissolve into one another. However, if they are vigorously shaken together, they form a mixture called an **emulsion**.

In an emulsion, tiny droplets of one of the liquids are dispersed throughout the other liquid. The two liquids in an emulsion will eventually settle out into separate layers again, unless the emulsion is stabilised by an emulsifier.

> **A** What does immiscible mean?

Different emulsions

There are two types of emulsion, depending on which liquid forms droplets and which liquid surrounds the droplets:

- **oil-in-water emulsions** consist of tiny droplets of oil dispersed in water
- **water-in-oil emulsions** consist of tiny droplets of water dispersed in oil.

Milk is an oil-in-water emulsion. It contains tiny droplets of butterfat dispersed throughout a watery liquid. Full fat and semi-skimmed milk eventually separate into two layers, with the butterfat forming a creamy layer at the top of the container.

Butter is a water-in-oil emulsion. It contains tiny droplets of watery liquid dispersed throughout the butterfat.

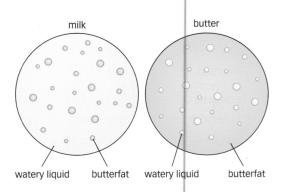

▲ Milk is an oil-in-water emulsion and butter is a water-in-oil emulsion

Margarine

Margarine is a water-in-oil emulsion. It consists of a blend of different vegetable oils, mixed with water. It is important that margarine from the refrigerator is soft enough to spread easily on bread and toast, but not be so soft that it runs everywhere. Unsaturated vegetable oils tend to have relatively low melting points, so they must be blended with saturated vegetable oils to achieve the desired consistency. Unsaturated vegetable oils are turned into saturated vegetable oils by reacting them with hydrogen. The hydrogen reacts at the carbon-carbon double bonds, turning them into single bonds.

◀ Margarine is a water-in-oil emulsion containing a mixture of vegetable oils and fats

▲ Sodium hydroxide solution reacts with oils and fats to make soap

Making soap

Soap is made when oils or fats react with hot sodium hydroxide solution. Vegetable oils such as olive oil, coconut oil, and palm oil are often used to make soap. The reaction splits the oil into glycerol, and sodium salts of the fatty acids. These sodium salts are the soap. This process of splitting up natural fats and oils using sodium hydroxide solution is called **saponification**.

More about saponification

Saponification is an example of a **hydrolysis reaction**. This is a type of reaction in which a compound is broken down by its reaction with water. During saponification, the hydroxide ions from the sodium hydroxide solution break down the oil or fat molecule in a similar way to a water molecule. They cause the bonds between the fatty acids and glycerol to break. Here is the word equation for the overall process:

fat + sodium hydroxide → soap + glycerol

B What is saponification?

Questions

1 Describe how an emulsion is formed.

2 Give an example of an oil-in-water emulsion and a water-in-oil emulsion.

3 Describe how margarine is manufactured.

4 Describe how soap is made from natural fats and oils.

5 Explain, with the help of an equation, what happens during saponification.

↓ E

↓ C

↓ A*

Learning objectives

After studying this topic, you should be able to:

- describe the function of each ingredient in a washing powder and a washing-up liquid
- explain the advantages of washing clothes at low temperatures
- describe the chemical nature of a detergent
- explain how detergents can remove fat or oil stains

This scientist is carrying out research into the effectiveness of washing powder. The sheet has been deliberately stained with different substances to see how well the powder removes them without damaging the fabric.

Ingredient	Function
active detergent	does the cleaning
bleaches	remove coloured stains by destroying the dye
optical brighteners	give white fabrics a 'whiter than white' appearance
water softener	softens hard water to avoid 'scum' on the clothes
enzymes	remove food stains in low-temperature washes

Detergents

Detergents are ingredients of washing powders and washing-up liquids. They are substances that can surround fat or oil molecules in stains and remove them from the clothes or plates. Some washing powders contain soap, but most do not. They are soapless and contain synthetic detergents. They have the advantage that they form a lather in hard water, as well as in soft water. However, soaps are more suited to handwashing and cause less damage to delicate fabrics.

Detergent molecules are similar in structure to emulsifier molecules. They have a **hydrophilic** or water-loving head, and a **hydrophobic** or water-hating tail.

The displayed formula of a typical synthetic detergent molecule. The charged hydrophilic head forms bonds with water molecules, and the hydrophobic tail forms bonds with oil and fat molecules.

More about detergents

The hydrophilic end of the detergent molecule forms strong intermolecular forces with water molecules in the wash, but not with the molecules in greasy stains. Meanwhile, the hydrophobic end of the detergent molecule forms strong intermolecular forces with the fat or oil molecules in greasy stains, but not with the water molecules in the wash. The detergent molecules can surround the fat or oil molecules in the stain, lifting them from the fabric and into the washing water.

Washing powders

Washing powders are used to clean fabrics including clothes, sheets, and towels. They have several ingredients to improve their cleaning performance. The table on the left shows the main ones and what they do.

Washing powders that contain enzymes are called biological powders. Those that do not are called non-biological powders or just non-bio powders. Biological powders must be used in low-temperature washes in which the water is at 40 °C or less. This is because the enzymes will be denatured at higher temperatures and so will stop working. However, the ability to clean clothes in cooler water means that less energy is used to heat water for the washing machine. Some fabrics are damaged by high temperatures, so a greater range of clothing can be cleaned using biological powders.

A What does a biological powder have that a non-bio powder does not have?

Washing-up liquid

Washing-up liquids are used to clean plates, cutlery, and pans without using a dishwashing machine. They also have several ingredients to improve their cleaning performance. The table below shows the main ones and what they do.

Ingredient	Function
active detergent	does the cleaning
water	makes the liquid thinner and less viscous, so it pours easily
colouring agent and fragrance	make the washing-up liquid more attractive to use
rinse agent	helps the water drain from the crockery

Key words

detergent, hydrophilic, hydrophobic

Did you know...?

The enzymes in biological powders include lipases to break down fats and oils, and proteases to break down proteins. It is important that washing machines rinse the clothes thoroughly as part of the washing cycle, otherwise the enzymes may irritate your skin.

▲ Washing-up liquids contain several ingredients to make washing up more efficient

B What does the rinse agent do?

Questions

1 Describe the function of each of the five main ingredients in washing powders.

2 Describe the function of each of the four main ingredients in washing-up liquids.

3 Explain the advantages of using low temperature washes for clothes.

4 Describe the structure of detergent molecules.

5 Explain how detergents can remove fat or oil stains.

E

C

A*

Exam tip   OCR

✔ You do not need to know the detailed structure of a detergent molecule, but you should recognise that it has a hydrophilic head and a hydrophobic tail.

16: Cleaning and washing

Learning objectives

After studying this topic, you should be able to:

- ✔ identify the correct solvent to remove a particular stain
- ✔ describe dry cleaning
- ✔ interpret data from experiments on the effectiveness of washing powders and washing-up liquids
- ✔ explain how dry cleaning works
- ✔ deduce from experimental data which detergent contains an enzyme

▲ Silk will be damaged in a washing machine so it is best to hand wash it or have it dry cleaned

▲ These clothes have been dry cleaned

The S words

If a substance is **insoluble** in a particular liquid, the substance will not dissolve in it. However, if a substance is **soluble** in a particular liquid, the substance will dissolve in it to form a **solution**. In a solution, the dissolved substance is called the **solute** and the liquid that does the dissolving is called the **solvent**. For example, sugar is soluble in water. Sugar dissolves in water to form sugar solution, in which sugar is the solute and water is the solvent.

Water is a very good solvent for many different substances, but it is not the only solvent. For example, nail polish is insoluble in water but it is soluble in ethyl ethanoate and propanone. Different solvents will dissolve different substances. This is very useful for cleaning clothes made with fabrics that would be damaged by being washed in water. The label on these clothes may show 'dry clean only'.

Dry cleaning

Dry cleaning is a way to clean clothes without using water. A different solvent such as tetrachloroethene is used instead. Solvents like this are good at dissolving greasy stains, and other stains that do not dissolve in water.

$$\underset{Cl}{\overset{Cl}{}}C=C\underset{Cl}{\overset{Cl}{}}$$

▲ Tetrachloroethene is used as a dry cleaning solvent

At the dry cleaners, the clothing is carefully checked for anything that might dissolve in the solvent or be damaged by it. This can include plastic pens left in pockets, which may dissolve and release their ink all over the clothing. The clothes are cleaned in a machine rather like a large washing machine, but with equipment to stop solvent fumes escaping. The clothes are washed in the dry-cleaning solvent, rinsed with fresh solvent, and dried in warm air. Used solvent is distilled so that it can be reused.

> **A** What are the solute and solvent in salty water?
>
> **B** Name a solvent for nail polish.
>
> **C** Name a solvent used in dry cleaning.

More about dry cleaning

Removing stains using dry cleaning solvent involves a balance between intermolecular forces. There are weak intermolecular forces between molecules of grease in a stain, and also weak intermolecular forces between solvent molecules. However, the solvent molecules can also form intermolecular forces with grease molecules.

The solvent molecules surround the grease molecules, lifting them off the fabric and into the bulk of the solvent. The solvent itself becomes dirty during the cleaning cycle as the stains dissolve in it, which is why the clothes must be rinsed with fresh solvent.

Using clothes labels

Clothes have wash labels sewn in them. These have various symbols to explain how the clothes should be washed. It is wise to follow the instructions if you do not want to damage your clothes. The labels include information such as:

- the water temperature to use in the washing machine
- whether the clothes should be hand washed
- the correct drying conditions, including whether to tumble dry or not
- the correct ironing temperature, including whether the item can be ironed
- the correct dry-cleaning conditions to use.

These are some symbols found on clothes labels

Questions

1   What do the words soluble and insoluble mean?
2   What information does a wash label on clothing give you?
3   Describe what dry cleaning involves, including an example of the solvent used and the type of stain removed.
4   Suggest why used dry-cleaning solvent is distilled rather than disposed of.
5   Explain, in terms of intermolecular forces, how dry cleaning works.

Module summary

Revision checklist

- In electrolysis, positive ions in a liquid move to the cathode and gain electrons. Negative ions move to the anode and lose electrons.
- Molten substances decompose into elements during electrolysis.
- Hydrogen and oxygen can be formed from solutions because of the H+ and OH– ions in water.
- Fuel cells use the reaction between hydrogen and oxygen to release electrical energy.
- Fuel cells produce clean energy efficiently, but need expensive catalysts and a hydrogen supply.
- In redox reactions, reduction (gain of electrons) and oxidation (loss of electrons) happen in the same reaction.
- More reactive metals will displace less reactive metals from solutions.
- Rusting is prevented by covering iron with a protective layer or by sacrificial protection using more reactive metals.
- Ethanol is an alcohol made by fermenting sugar or by reacting ethene with steam.
- Alcohols contain an OH group.
- CFC (chlorofluorocarbon) molecules deplete the ozone layer by means of reactions involving chlorine radicals.
- Ozone absorbs damaging ultraviolet light, preventing it reaching the Earth's surface.
- Most countries have agreed to ban CFCs and replace them with less damaging alternatives.
- Hard water is caused by calcium and magnesium ions that dissolve when rainwater containing carbon dioxide flows through rocks.
- Temporary hardness is removed by boiling and is caused by dissolved calcium hydrogencarbonate. Permanent hardness is caused by calcium sulfate and isn't removed by boiling.
- Washing soda or ion-exchange resins also soften water.
- Fats and oils are naturally occurring esters.
- Fats and oils are split up by alkalis to form soap and glycerol. They can also be made into biodiesel.
- Unsaturated fats and oils contain C=C double bonds.
- Emulsifiers cause oils and water to mix as an emulsion.
- Washing powders use synthetic detergents to remove fats and oils. Enzymes and bleaches remove other stains.
- Dry cleaning uses solvents other than water to remove grease stains.

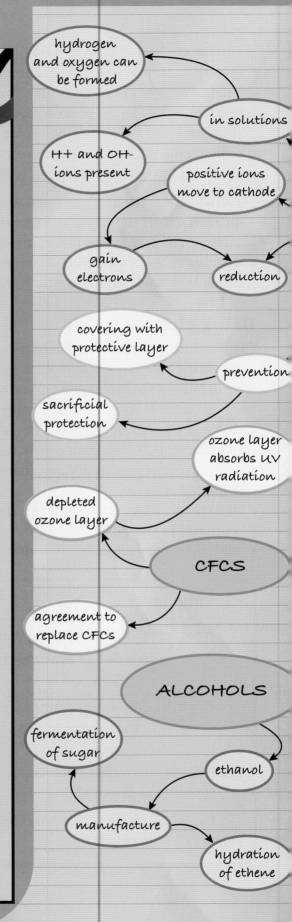

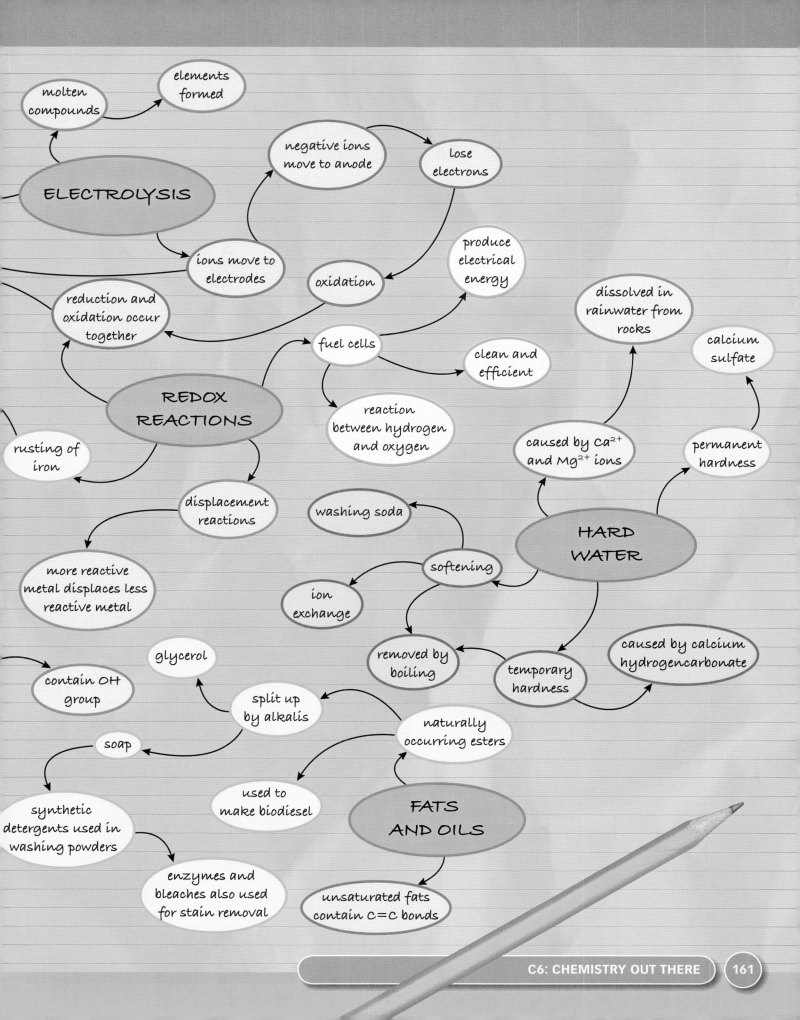

molten compounds

elements formed

ELECTROLYSIS

negative ions move to anode

lose electrons

ions move to electrodes

oxidation

produce electrical energy

reduction and oxidation occur together

fuel cells

clean and efficient

dissolved in rainwater from rocks

calcium sulfate

REDOX REACTIONS

reaction between hydrogen and oxygen

caused by Ca^{2+} and Mg^{2+} ions

permanent hardness

rusting of iron

washing soda

HARD WATER

displacement reactions

softening

more reactive metal displaces less reactive metal

ion exchange

removed by boiling

caused by calcium hydrogencarbonate

glycerol

contain OH group

split up by alkalis

temporary hardness

naturally occurring esters

soap

used to make biodiesel

FATS AND OILS

synthetic detergents used in washing powders

enzymes and bleaches also used for stain removal

unsaturated fats contain C=C bonds

OCR gateway *Upgrade*

Answering Extended Writing questions

QUESTION

Explain what happens when iron rusts. Describe two ways of preventing rusting and explain how they work

The quality of written communication will be assessed in your answer to this question.

Water and air make iron rust. If you stop the air and water getting to the iron you can stop iron rusting greasing and painting are used to do this.

E

Examiner: This answer contains several correct points and the candidate has answered all of the requirements of the question at a basic level. The spelling is good, although the last sentence should be divided into two with a full stop after 'rusting'.

Rust is iron oxide so it happens in a redox reaction with oxygen. Galvanising is a good way of protecting iron. The zinc covers the iron and prevents air reaching it.

C

Examiner: The candidate uses some good vocabulary here, such as 'galvanising' and 'redox'. Water is also involved in rusting, but this isn't mentioned. Only one method of protecting iron is included, and although the description is partly correct, the candidate should also mention that zinc is a sacrificial metal. Spelling, punctuation, and grammar are good.

Rusting happens when iron reacts with water and oxygen to make hydrated iron oxide. This is an oxidation reaction. It can be prevented by painting the iron to stop the oxygen getting to the iron or by sacrificial protection. Iron is covered in zinc and the zinc losses electrons because it is reactive.

A*

Examiner: This a reasonably full and correct answer, although the full name of rust is hydrated iron(III)oxide. Redox would have been a better description than just oxidation. Sacrificial protection is described well, although it is important to actually compare the reactivity of iron and zinc. 'Loses' is spelt incorrectly.

Exam-style questions

1 Here is the apparatus needed to carry out electrolysis on a solution of copper(II) sulfate.

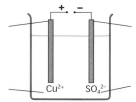

A02 **a** Complete the diagram by adding labels. Use the following words:
anode   anion   cathode   cation

A02 **b** Give two observations that you would expect to see when the power supply is turned on.

2 Many parts of Britain have hard water due to the presence of calcium and magnesium ions.
Calcium ions get into water because of the action of rainwater on limestone rocks.

A02 **a** Complete this equation for the reaction that dissolves the calcium ions:
$$CaCO_3 + H_2O + \_\_\_\_ \rightleftharpoons Ca(HCO_3)$$

A02 **b** Name the product of the reaction.

A01 **c** This process produces temporary hardness in water. How is this different from permanent hardness?

3 Iron rusts when it is exposed to air and water.

A01 **a i** Give the chemical name for rust.

    ii Rusting is a redox reaction. Explain the meaning of this term.

A01 **b** Sometimes iron is coated with a layer of zinc. This is called sacrificial protection. Explain how sacrificial protection works.

A02 **c** When zinc is added to a solution of copper(II) sulfate, a brown colour develops on the surface of the zinc.

    i Name the brown colouring.

    ii Complete the equation for the reaction that occurs:
$$Zn\ (s) + Cu^{2+} \rightleftharpoons _____$$

    iii Which substance is oxidised? Explain your answer.

Extended Writing

4 Ethanol is a chemical substance with several important uses. Describe some of these uses and explain two ways in which ethanol is manufactured.
A01

5 CFCs have been banned in most countries because scientific research has shown that they deplete the ozone layer. Describe how this depletion is thought to occur and why it has consequences for human health at the Earth's surface.
A01

6 Car manufacturers are developing cars powered by fuel cells in which hydrogen and oxygen react and release electrical energy. Some people suggest that we should use fuel cells rather than the combustion of fossil fuels because it will be more environmentally friendly. Discuss the arguments for and against this.
A02
A03

A01 Recall the science
A02 Apply your knowledge
A03 Evaluate and analyse the evidence

C6: CHEMISTRY OUT THERE   163

P5

Space for reflection

Why study this module?

We have only started to use satellites in the last 50 years. They are now an essential part of communication, scientific research, navigation, and even home entertainment. As part of this module you will learn about forces and motion. You will study how satellites stay in orbit, learning about some of their uses, and you will find out what happens to the path of a tennis ball or a bullet fired from a gun.

In this module you will also learn more about how electromagnetic waves travel through our atmosphere, how they reflect off invisible layers, and how we communicate with satellites. You will find out why at the bottom of a valley you can still get a good radio signal but not a clear picture on your television.

Finally you will learn more about light, how it is refracted by different materials, how rainbows are formed, and how simple lenses can focus light into a point. You will learn the history of ideas about the nature of light and how the most famous physicist of all time, Sir Isaac Newton, was wrong!

You should remember?

1 The meaning of speed, velocity, acceleration, and momentum.

2 How the forces acting on an object effect its motion.

3 How waves can be used to communicate.

4 The properties of electromagnetic waves.

5 How waves are refracted when they travel from one medium to another.

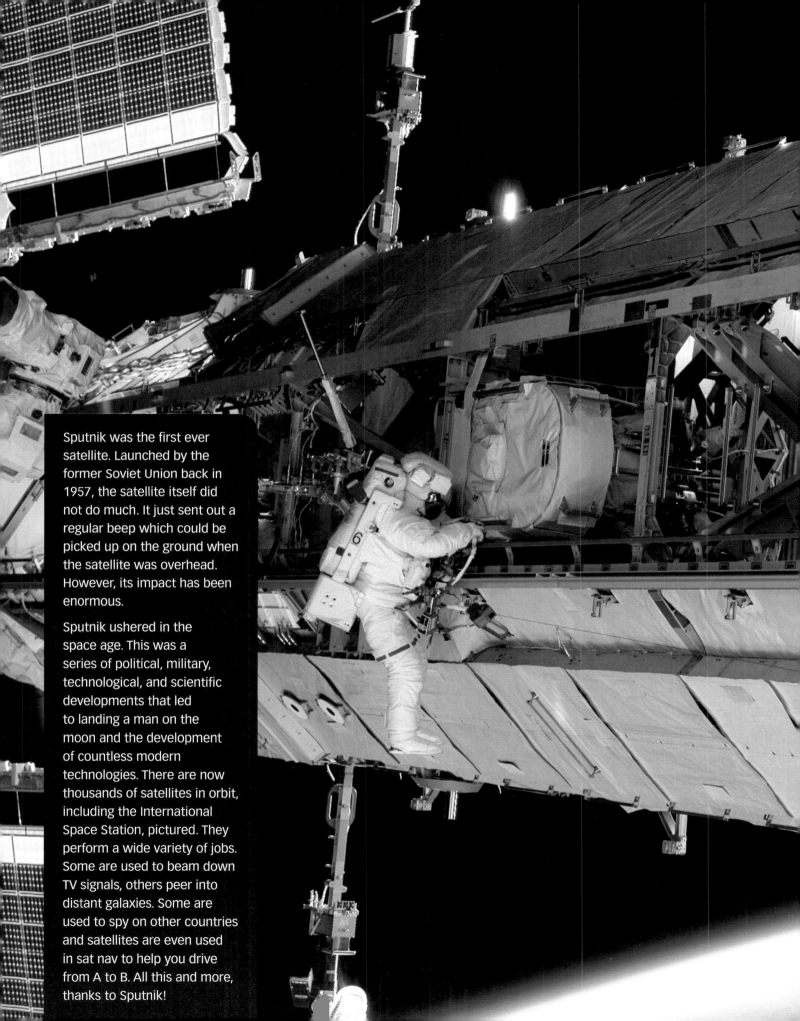

Sputnik was the first ever satellite. Launched by the former Soviet Union back in 1957, the satellite itself did not do much. It just sent out a regular beep which could be picked up on the ground when the satellite was overhead. However, its impact has been enormous.

Sputnik ushered in the space age. This was a series of political, military, technological, and scientific developments that led to landing a man on the moon and the development of countless modern technologies. There are now thousands of satellites in orbit, including the International Space Station, pictured. They perform a wide variety of jobs. Some are used to beam down TV signals, others peer into distant galaxies. Some are used to spy on other countries and satellites are even used in sat nav to help you drive from A to B. All this and more, thanks to Sputnik!

Learning objectives

After studying this topic, you should be able to:

✔ explain what a satellite is

✔ describe how satellites stay in their orbits

✔ state some uses of artificial satellites

✔ explain how the speed of a comet varies in its orbit

Key words

satellite, natural satellite, orbit, artificial satellite, gravitational attraction, gravity, weight, inverse square law

▲ The International Space Station is an artificial satellite

A What kind of satellite is the Hubble Space Telescope?

◄ The moon is a natural satellite of the Earth

Natural and artificial satellites of the Earth

A **satellite** is an object that orbits a larger object in space. For example, the Moon is a satellite of the Earth. It is a **natural satellite**.

Along with the Moon, the Earth has over 20 000 man-made objects in **orbit**. These are called **artificial satellites**. Some are very small, just a few metres across. Others are much larger commercial or military satellites, perhaps the size of buses. The Hubble Space Telescope and the International Space Station are examples of larger artificial satellites. If you look up at night you can often see them passing overhead.

Artificial satellites perform a number of very important roles, including:

- telecommunications (eg satellite TV)
- weather prediction
- military uses (eg spy satellites)
- satellite navigation systems (eg GPS found in some cars and mobile phones)
- scientific research (eg Hubble Space Telescope)
- producing images of the Earth.

What keeps satellites in orbit?

As you may recall, any two masses attract each other. The force between them is called **gravitational attraction** or **gravity**.

Satellites are kept in orbit by this universal force of attraction. The Moon stays in orbit around the Earth because of the gravitational attraction between them – otherwise it would fly off into space! The Earth and other planets stay in orbit around the Sun because of the gravitational force between them and the Sun.

The bigger the masses of any two objects, the bigger the attraction between them. The Earth is more massive than the Moon, so the force of attraction between you and the Earth would be greater than the attraction between you and the Moon.

The gravitational attraction force is called **weight**.

B Give two examples of uses of artificial satellites.

C What is the name of the force that keeps satellites in orbit?

Orbit and distance

The gravitational force of attraction varies with the distance between two objects. It varies in proportion to an **inverse square law**. This means that if the distance between the objects is trebled, for example, the force between them is nine times smaller (3^2). It is reduced to one-ninth of what it was previously.

Comets have highly elliptical orbits around the Sun. The furthest distance of a comet from the Sun can be more than 50 times its closest distance from the Sun. The change in the distance means that the gravitational force of attraction between a comet and the Sun also varies enormously. It is higher when the comet is closer to the Sun. This means that the speed of the comet in its orbit also varies. It is higher when it is closer to the Sun.

The time taken for a planet to orbit the Sun depends on its distance from the Sun. The further away a planet is from the Sun, the longer its time period to orbit the Sun.

The times for some objects to complete an orbit are shown in the table.

Object	Time to orbit the Sun	Distance from Sun
Halley's comet	75 years	Between 88 million km (closest) and 5270 million km (furthest)
Mercury	116 days	Between 46 million and 70 million km
Earth	1 year	150 million km
Jupiter	11.9 years	780 million km

Exam tip **OCR**

✓ Learn the examples of uses of satellites – this can be an easy way to pick up marks.

✓ You may remember that you can calculate an object's weight using this equation: weight = mass × gravitational field strength.

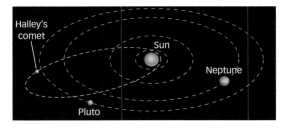

▲ The orbit of Halley's comet

Questions

1 What is the difference between a natural satellite and an artificial satellite?

2 How does the International Space Station stay in orbit around the Earth?

3 Explain why the Moon is in orbit of the Earth, not the other way around.

4 Explain how the speed of a comet varies in its orbit of the Sun.

5 How much stronger is the gravitational force of attraction on Halley's comet when it is closest to the Sun than when it is furthest away from the Sun?

Learning objectives

After studying this topic, you should be able to:

- ✔ link how a satellite is used to the height of its orbit
- ✔ explain a geostationary orbit
- ✔ explain how artificial satellites continually accelerate towards the Earth

Key words

time period, trajectory, polar orbit, geostationary orbit, centripetal force

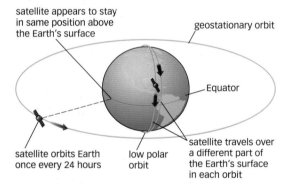

satellite appears to stay in same position above the Earth's surface

geostationary orbit

Equator

satellite orbits Earth once every 24 hours

low polar orbit

satellite travels over a different part of the Earth's surface in each orbit

▲ Different types of satellite orbit

A What type of orbit is used for a satellite that takes pictures of the Earth's surface?

B What force is needed to keep a satellite in orbit?

How high are satellites above the Earth?

Satellites are carefully placed into different orbits at different heights, depending on their use. They can be as low as just a few hundred kilometres above the Earth's surface, or tens of thousands of kilometres high. The International Space Station (ISS) is just 340 km above the Earth. Satellites used for satellite television are 36 000 km up (over 100 times further away).

The height of a satellite affects its orbital **time period**. This is how long it takes to orbit once around the Earth. The higher a satellite is above the Earth, the longer its time period. The ISS takes just 90 minutes to complete one orbit. Satellites used for television take 24 hours. Satellites used in satellite navigation systems (such as GPS) have low orbits, so they can easily send and receive signals. Their low orbit means they travel very fast. There are normally 5 or 6 navigational satellites overhead at once.

Types of orbit

Satellites are placed in different orbits as well as at different heights. The **trajectory** of a satellite is the name given to the path it follows around the Earth. There are two main trajectories followed by artificial satellites:

- low **polar orbit**
- **geostationary orbit**.

Satellites in low polar orbit have a short time period. As the Earth rotates, satellites in low polar orbit can observe any part of the planet over a few days. This makes them ideal for taking pictures of the Earth's surface, and for military purposes. They are closer to the Earth than satellites in geostationary orbit, so can produce much clearer images of the surface and need less powerful communications systems to send and receive signals.

Satellites in geostationary orbit are much further away. A satellite in geostationary orbit:

- orbits the Earth once in 24 hours
- remains in a fixed position above the Earth's surface
- orbits the Earth above the Equator.

As they stay fixed above the same position on Earth, geostationary satellites are always overhead in certain places. This makes them useful for communications (TV and radio broadcasts) and weather forecasting.

They are always pointing at the same place, so they don't miss anything. Satellite dishes on Earth can be directed straight at the satellite and don't need to move.

Whatever orbit a satellite is in, it moves in a circle. Any object following a circular path requires a **centripetal force** to keep it moving in a circle. For satellites this centripetal force is provided by gravity, which pulls the satellite towards the centre of the Earth.

Exam tip

✓ Remember that the closer to the Earth the satellite is, the shorter the time period of its orbit.

✓ Don't say that geostationary satellites do not move. They are moving very fast!

More on satellite orbits

The centripetal force acting on an artificial satellite is always at right angles to its motion and is always directed towards the centre of the Earth. As the direction of the satellite is continually changing, its velocity is also changing, so it is accelerating (although it continues to travel at a steady speed). The satellite is continually accelerating towards the Earth.

Despite being pulled towards the Earth, a satellite stays in orbit because it is moving so fast. At point A, the satellite's velocity is at right angles to the acceleration and the centripetal force. The force causes the satellite to change direction, but it stays at the same height. This happens at all points in the orbit and leads to a circular path. The satellite's high velocity keeps it in a stable orbit. If it were to stop, it would accelerate towards the Earth.

Earth

B

direction of travel at this point

A
acceleration towards Earth, at right angles to motion

distance from Earth is greater, so gravitational force of attraction is smaller

▲ The direction of motion at B has changed, but is still at right angles to the acceleration

The distance between the Earth and artificial satellites in lower orbits is smaller, so the gravitational attraction is greater. This means that they travel faster. Low polar orbit satellites orbit the Earth with a time period of about 2 hours. Geostationary satellites orbit with a period of 24 hours. The satellites in low polar orbit have a much shorter time period because the gravitational force on them is larger, so they travel much faster than those in geostationary orbit.

Questions

1 How does the height of a satellite above the Earth's surface affect its period of orbit?

2 What are the differences between a geostationary orbit and a low polar orbit?

3 Why are TV satellite dishes in a fixed position?

4 Why does a satellite in a geostationary orbit travel more slowly than one in a low polar orbit?

5 Explain how the force of gravity keeps artificial satellites in orbit around the Earth.

E

C

A*

Learning objectives

After studying this topic, you should be able to:

- ✔ describe the difference between scalar and vector quantities
- ✔ add up parallel vectors to find the vector sum
- ✔ find the resultant of vectors that are at right angles to each other

Key words

size, scalar, direction, vector, velocity, resultant

Relative speed

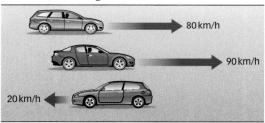

▲ These three cars are travelling on a straight road. The speed of the green car relative to the red car is 10 km/h to the right. The speed of the blue car relative to the red car is 100 km/h to the left.

A Give two examples of scalar quantities.

B What two things does a vector quantity have?

C Is weight a scalar or a vector quantity?

What direction?

Some quantities only tell us how big something is. For example, a bag of flour may have a mass of 1 kg, or the temperature outside might be 16 °C. A quantity that only has a **size** is called a **scalar** quantity. Time is another example.

For some quantities, the **direction** is just as important. For instance, with a force we need to know the direction and the size of the push or pull. A quantity that has a direction as well as a size is called a **vector**. Acceleration is vector quantity.

A car is travelling at 50 km/h. This tells us how fast the car is moving, but not which direction it is travelling in. The speed of the car is 50 km/h and it is a scalar quantity.

Now imagine a car travelling north at 50 km/h. We know how fast the car is moving and we know what direction it is going in. The **velocity** of the car is 50 km/h northwards and this is a vector quantity.

Vector sums

Worked example 1

Sam is walking at 1.75 m/s. He steps on a moving walkway that is going in the same direction, but carries on walking as before. The moving walkway is travelling at 1.25 m/s. What is Sam's total velocity?

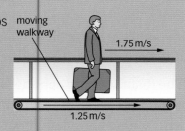

The velocities are parallel, so we can add them together.

total velocity = 1.75 m/s + 1.25 m/s = 3.0 m/s

Worked example 2

What is the total force on the box?

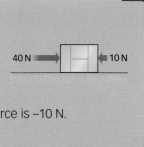

The forces are parallel, so we can add them together. Assume that the positive direction is left to right, so the right-hand force is –10 N.

Add forces together: 40 N + (–10 N) = 30 N

Finding a resultant vector

Sometimes vectors are at an angle to each other. For example, if an aircraft is flying in a cross wind, there are two velocity vectors at an angle to each other. The **resultant** velocity of the plane is the sum of the two velocities.

When the two velocities are at right angles to each other, you can calculate the resultant of the two vectors by drawing a scale diagram or by calculation.

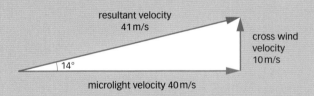

Questions

1   What is the difference between a scalar and a vector?

2   Calculate the vector sum for each diagram:

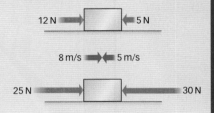

3   A boat is going across a river at 4 m/s. The current in the river is moving the boat downstream at 3 m/s.

(a) Draw a scale diagram to work out the resultant velocity.

(b) Calculate the resultant velocity using Pythagoras' theorem and trigonometry.

4   A force of 6 N is acting downwards and a force of 7 N is acting to the right.

(a) Draw a scale diagram to work out the resultant force.

(b) Calculate the resultant force using Pythagoras' theorem and trigonometry.

Learning objectives

After studying this topic, you should be able to:

✔ use the equations of motion
$s = \dfrac{(u + v)}{2}$ and $v = u + at$

✔ use the equations of motion
$v^2 = u^2 + 2as$ and $s = ut + \frac{1}{2}at^2$

▲ You can use the equations of motion to calculate distances, speeds, and other quantities

Exam tip   OCR

✔ When answering questions involving the equations of motion, write down all the quantities that you know, and the one you are trying to find. Then select the equation that contains all of these quantities.

Average speed and distance

During a journey, speed can change. If acceleration is constant we can easily calculate the average speed. If the initial speed is u and the final speed is v, then:

$$\text{average speed} \ = \ \frac{(u + v)}{2}$$

Distance travelled is speed × time, so if the distance travelled is s, and the length of time of the journey is t, then:

$$s \ = \ \frac{(u + v)}{2} \quad \text{or} \quad s \ = \ \tfrac{1}{2}(u + v)t$$

If the steady acceleration is a and the time the acceleration lasts for is t, then the initial and final speeds are connected by the equation:

$$v \ = \ u \ + \ at$$

These equations work when something is moving in a straight line and any acceleration is constant (steady).

Worked example 1

An aeroplane accelerates to a final velocity of 200 m/s over 20 s. Its acceleration is 4 m/s².

i   What was the initial velocity of the aeroplane?

ii   How far did it travel?

i $v = u + at$

$v = 200$ m/s, $t = 20$ s, $a = 4$ m/s²

200 m/s $= u + 4$ m/s² $\times 20$ s

Rearranging the equation:

$u = 200$ m/s $- 4$ m/s² $\times 20$ s

$= 200$ m/s $- 80$ m/s

$= 120$ m/s

ii $s = \frac{1}{2}(u + v)t$

$s = \frac{1}{2}(120$ m/s $+ 200$ m/s$) \times 20$ s

$= 160$ m/s $\times 20$ s

$= 3200$ m

A   Which equation would you use to calculate the distance an object travels?

B   A train accelerates at 2 m/s² for 20 seconds. Its final velocity is 40 m/s. What was its initial velocity?

More equations of motion

We can combine and rearrange the two equations of motion to get two more:

$$v^2 = u^2 + 2as$$
$$s = ut + \tfrac{1}{2}at^2$$

Worked example 2

A car travels 216 m. Its final velocity is 12 m/s and initial velocity is 6 m/s. What is its acceleration?

$s = 216$ m

$v = 12$ m/s

$u = 6$ m/s

We use the equation $v^2 = u^2 + 2as$

$$(12 \text{ m/s})^2 = (6 \text{ m/s})^2 + 2 \times a \times 216 \text{ m}$$

Rearranging the equation:

$$a = \frac{(144 - 36)}{(2 \times 216) \text{ m/s}^2} = \frac{108}{432 \text{ m/s}^2} = 0.25 \text{ m/s}^2$$

Worked example 3

A train travels 200 m while it accelerates at –2 m/s² for 5 seconds. What was the train's initial velocity?

$s = 200$ m

$a = -2$ m/s² (the minus sign tells us the train is slowing down or decelerating)

$t = 5$ s

Use the equation $s = ut + \tfrac{1}{2}at^2$

$$200 \text{ m} = u \times 5 \text{ s} + \tfrac{1}{2} \times -2 \text{ m/s}^2 \times (5 \text{ s})^2$$

Rearranging the equation:

$$u = \frac{200 \text{ m} - (\tfrac{1}{2} \times -2 \text{ m/s}^2 \times (5 \text{ s})^2)}{5 \text{ s}} = \frac{225 \text{ m}}{5 \text{ s}} = 45 \text{ m/s}$$

C The initial velocity of a car is 5 m/s. It accelerates at 1.5 m/s² for 8 seconds. How far does it travel?

D An aeroplane is stationary. It accelerates down a runway at 2 m/s². It travels 900 m. What is its final velocity?

Questions

1 A car's initial velocity is 5 m/s. It accelerates at 1.5 m/s² for 6 seconds. What is its final velocity?

2 An aeroplane's initial velocity is 120 m/s. It accelerates at –3 m/s² for 10 seconds. What is its final velocity?

3 An object is dropped from the top of a cliff. It takes 2 seconds to reach the bottom. The acceleration due to gravity is 10 m/s².

   (a) What is the object's final velocity?

   (b) What is the height of the cliff?

4 A train travels 168 m as it accelerates from an initial velocity of 5 m/s over 12 s. What is the acceleration of the train?

5 An aeroplane travels 1200 m while it accelerates at 2 m/s². Its final velocity was 150 m/s. What was its initial velocity?

▲ The aircraft is accelerating down the runway

Learning objectives

After studying this topic, you should be able to:

- ✔ describe what a projectile is
- ✔ explain the motion of a projectile

Key words

projectile, trajectory, parabolic, range, optimum angle

▲ The long jumper is a projectile and his path, or trajectory, is parabolic in shape

▲ The range of this football depends on the launch angle

A Give three examples of projectiles.

B What is meant by the range of a projectile?

The path of a projectile

When you kick a football, it takes a curved path through the air. The path of the football has this curved shape because of the Earth's gravitational field.

Anything that is thrown (or 'projected') through the air has a curved path, and is called a **projectile**. Other examples of projectiles are missiles and cannonballs, and all balls that are hit, thrown, or kicked in sports. A dart is a projectile when it has been thrown. Long jumpers are projectiles from the moment when their feet leave the ground.

The curved path of a projectile is called its **trajectory**. The shape of the path of a projectile is said to be **parabolic**.

When a projectile is moving through the air, gravity is the only force acting on it, apart from air resistance.

The diagram below shows a football that is kicked horizontally off a cliff. If air resistance is ignored, the football has a constant horizontal velocity. The football is accelerated downwards towards the sea by the force of gravity. This acceleration only affects the vertical velocity of the football. Its vertical velocity increases steadily while the horizontal part of its motion stays the same.

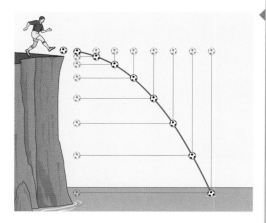

◀ After this football has been kicked, the only force acting on it is gravity

How far a ball travels when it is hit – its **range** – depends on the angle at which it leaves the ground. This is called the launch angle. If the launch angle is high, the ball will not travel as far, because the horizontal velocity will be smaller. If the launch angle is low, the ball will fall back to the ground in less time. The greatest range is achieved when the launch angle is 45° – this is the **optimum angle**.

Horizontal and vertical velocity vectors

The horizontal and vertical velocities of a projectile are vectors. The resultant velocity of a projectile is the resultant vector of these horizontal and vertical components.

> **C** Why are the vertical and horizontal velocities vectors?

You can use the equations of motion from spread P5.4 to work out how long it will take for a projectile to hit the ground and work out how far it has travelled. You use the equations separately for the horizontal and the vertical parts of the motion.

Worked example

A stunt car drives horizontally off a small cliff with a velocity of 12 m/s. The cliff is 1.25 m high.

i How long does the car take to hit the ground?

ii How far from the base of the cliff will the car land?

i Looking at the vertical part of the motion, height of the cliff, $s = 1.25$ m, initial vertical velocity, $u = 0$ m/s (as the car is travelling horizontally when it leaves the cliff, it has no vertical velocity), and vertical acceleration, $a = 10$ m/s² (just acceleration due to gravity).

$$s = ut + \tfrac{1}{2}at^2$$
$$1.25 \text{ m} = 0 \text{ m/s} \times t + \tfrac{1}{2} \times 10 \text{ m/s}^2 \times t^2$$
$$t^2 = \frac{1.25 \text{ m}}{5 \text{ m/s}^2} = (0.25) \text{ s}^2$$
$$t = \sqrt{(0.25)5^2} = 0.5 \text{ s}$$

ii Looking at the horizontal part of the motion, horizontal velocity of the car = 12 m/s (and this stays the same), and the car lands at the foot of the cliff after 0.5 s (from calculation above).

Distance car lands from the base of the cliff = horizontal velocity × time
= 12 m/s × 0.5 s
= 6 m

Exam tip   OCR

✔ Remember to read the question properly. In a recent exam, students were asked to identify the projectile in a photo – many identified the sport instead!

Questions

1 What is a projectile?

2 Explain why a long jumper is a projectile.

3 Explain why the horizontal velocity of a projectile remains constant (ignoring air resistance).

4 What is the vertical velocity of the car in the worked example when it hits the ground?

5 A stone is fired horizontally from a catapult off the top of a building, with a horizontal velocity of 25 m/s. The stone takes 2.5 seconds to hit the ground.

  (a) What is the height of the building?

  (b) What is the stone's vertical velocity when it hits the ground?

  (c) How far from the base of the building does the stone hit the ground?

  (d) Calculate the resultant velocity of the stone as it hits the ground.

Learning objectives

After studying this topic, you should be able to:

- ✔ explain that every action has an equal and opposite reaction
- ✔ describe reactions involving gravity
- ✔ apply Newton's third law of motion to collisions

Key words

action, reaction

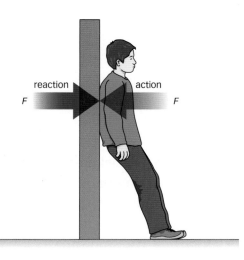

▲ The wall pushes against Tom with an equal and opposite force

A In the example of Tom and the wall, which force is the action?

B What pairs of forces act on a book sitting on a table?

C What is the reaction to the pull of the Earth's gravity on the person in the diagram on the right?

Simple actions and reactions

Tom is leaning against a wall with a force F. He does not fall over because the wall pushes back on Tom with an equal force F that acts in the opposite direction. There is a pair of forces – the force exerted on the wall by Tom and the force the wall exerts on Tom. This is an important principle of physics – forces always appear in pairs. Each **action** has an equal and opposite **reaction**. It is known as Newton's third law of motion.

When a person stands on the ground, there are two forces acting: a pair of contact forces between the person's feet and the ground, and a pair of forces due to the gravitational attraction between the Earth and the person. The push of the person's feet on the ground is equal and opposite to the push of the ground on the person's feet. The pull of Earth's gravity on the person is equal and opposite to the pull of the person's gravity on the Earth.

The action forces are the push of the person's feet on the ground and the pull of the Earth's gravity on the person. The reaction forces are the push of the ground on the person's feet and the pull of the person's gravity on the Earth.

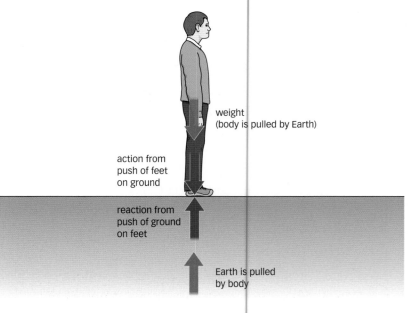

▲ Pairs of forces acting on a person standing on the ground

When an object is hanging from a crane, there are two pairs of forces acting on the object. The first pair of forces involves tension in the wire that is lifting the object. The object is pulling on the wire. There is an equal and opposite force from the pull of the wire on the object.

The second pair of forces involves the gravitational attraction between the Earth and the object. The pull of the Earth on the object is equal and opposite to the pull of the object on the Earth.

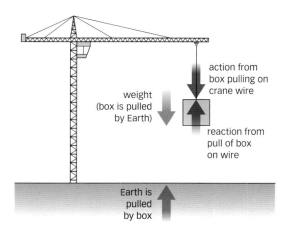

▲ There are pairs of action and reactions acting on the object the crane is lifting

> **D** What is the reaction force to the weight of the object on the crane?

Collisions

When two objects collide, they exert equal and opposite forces on each other. This is another example of Newton's third law. For example, when this car collided with the post, the car exerted a force on the post. The post exerted a force on the car that was equal and opposite to the force the car exerted on the post.

▲ The car and post exerted equal and opposite forces on each other

Questions

1 What is the direction of a reaction force?

2 (a) What forces are acting on a parked car?

   (b) Which of these forces are reactions?

3 A light is suspended from the ceiling.

   (a) Draw a diagram to show the pairs of forces acting on the light.

   (b) The weight of the light is 15 N. What is the size of the reaction force?

4 (a) Describe what happens when a car collides with a wall in terms of the action and reaction forces.

   (b) The car exerts a force of 7500 N to the right on the wall. What is the size and direction of the reaction force?

Exam tip **OCR**

✓ When explaining something in an answer, remember to use the correct scientific language – if you don't, you could lose marks.

Learning objectives

After studying this topic, you should be able to:

- ✔ give examples of collisions
- ✔ explain the change in motion of objects in a collision
- ✔ explain how rockets work

Key words

recoil, rocket

▲ Equal and opposite forces act on the football and the foot

◀ There is a collision between the cricket bat and the ball

Simple collisions

When two things collide they exert equal and opposite forces on each other.

Collisions happen all the time in sporting activities. For example, there is a collision between a footballer's foot and a football when the ball is kicked. The force exerted by the footballer's foot on the ball is equal and opposite to the force exerted by the ball on the footballer's foot.

The action of these forces changes the motion of the objects. When kicked, the football moves at a different speed in a different direction: its velocity changes. The momentum of the football is its mass multiplied by its velocity. The force applied during the collision changes the momentum of the football.

> **A** Give three other examples of sporting activities where there are collisions.

Recoil, explosions, and rockets

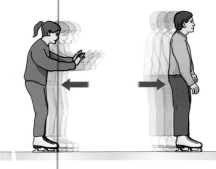

▲ The skater on the right recoils when the skater on the left pushes on them

The diagram shows two ice skaters. At first the skaters are not moving. Then Sadie pushes Ben in the back and Ben moves forwards. But Ben's back exerts an equal and opposite force on Sadie's hands, so Sadie will **recoil** backwards. Both skaters now have momentum, but in opposite directions.

Similarly when you fire a gun, the bullet travels out of the gun barrel at high speed, and the gun recoils in the opposite direction to the bullet.

Rockets work on the same principle. Rocket fuel is burned in the combustion chamber, which means that the particles have a high energy and move very fast.

Inside the chamber the particles crash into the sides, causing a high pressure. The hotter the gas gets, the faster the particles move and the higher the pressure (the pressure can also be increased by reducing the volume of the gas, but this is not practical). Some of the particles escape out of the bottom of the chamber. The force pushing these particles out is the same as the force pushing the rocket up, so the rocket accelerates upwards.

> **B** What is recoil?
>
> **C** How does a rocket move?

Inside the combustion chamber of large rockets, the pressure is very high. As the particles strike the walls of the chamber they bounce off, changing their momentum. There are a large number of collisions each second. This high frequency of collisions leads to a high rate of change of momentum, so a large force is created. In order to ensure that this force is large enough to lift the massive rockets carrying satellites into orbit, the exhaust must contain a large number of gas particles moving at very high speeds. This is achieved by rapidly burning a large volume of fuel at very high temperatures.

Questions

1 What are the action and the reaction forces when a cricketer hits a ball?

2 How do action and reaction forces help to explain why a tennis ball changes direction when it is hit?

3 Explain how a gun recoils when it is fired.

4 Explain how a rocket motor works.

5 Explain why large numbers of particles moving at high speed are needed to put a rocket into orbit.

E

C

A*

Did you know...?

For rockets that take people and objects into space, the mass of fuel is a very large proportion of the total mass of the rocket. The total mass of the Space Shuttle at take-off is about 2030 tonnes. The total mass of fuel is about 1750 tonnes.

Gas particles leave a shuttle's engine at over 4000 m/s at temperatures of over 3000 °C, and the shuttle burns over 1000 litres of fuel per second!

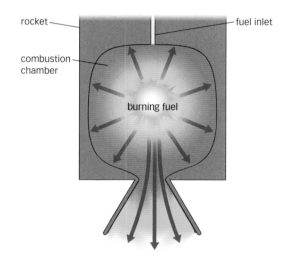

rocket — fuel inlet

combustion chamber

burning fuel

▲ The fast moving particles collide with the walls of the combustion chamber. Some particles escape backwards.

◄ At take-off over 85% of the mass of the Space Shuttle is fuel

Learning objectives

After studying this topic, you should be able to:

- ✔ explain the law of conservation of momentum
- ✔ apply the law to the collision of two objects

Key words

law of conservation of momentum, coalesce

Did you know...?

The law of conservation of momentum can be used to predict how the balls in a game of pool will behave when the cue ball hits them.

Law of conservation of momentum

The total amount of momentum stays the same. For example, if two moving objects collide, their total momentum does not change. This is the **law of conservation of momentum**.

$$\begin{array}{c}\text{total momentum before} \\ \text{collision (or explosion)}\end{array} = \begin{array}{c}\text{total momentum after} \\ \text{collision (or explosion)}\end{array}$$

The law only applies if the forces involved come from the objects themselves. If any external forces act on the objects, such as friction, then momentum is not conserved.

You can use the law of conservation of momentum to describe explosions, the recoil of a gun, and rocket propulsion:

Before you fire a gun, the total momentum of the gun and bullet is zero. When you fire a gun, the gun moves in the opposite direction to the bullet. The momentum of the gun is equal and opposite to the momentum of the bullet. As the gun has a much larger mass than the bullet, its velocity is much less than that of the bullet, and in the opposite direction.

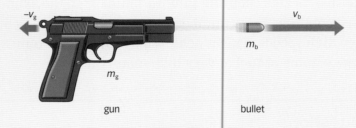

gun   bullet

▲ The total momentum of the gun and bullet is zero

Similarly, you can use the law of conservation of momentum to explain how rockets work. The momentum of the gases coming out of the rocket is equal and opposite to the momentum of the rocket. The total momentum of the rocket and exhaust gases is zero.

> **A** Why is the velocity of the gun much less than that of the bullet?

Momentum calculations

You can use the law of conservation of momentum to solve problems involving, for example, the collision of two cars. When two objects moving in the same direction collide, and then **coalesce** (join together) after the collision, you can use the following equation:

$$m_1 u_1 + m_2 u_2 = (m_1 + m_2)v$$

where m_1 and m_2 are the masses of the two objects in kg, u_1 and u_2 are the velocities of the two objects before the collision in m/s, and v is the velocity of the two objects after the collision in m/s.

> **B** How does the law of conservation of momentum help in solving the worked example?

Worked example

A car of mass 1250 kg is travelling at 20 m/s. It collides with a car in front of it of mass 1000 kg that is travelling at 10 m/s in the same direction. The two cars coalesce after the collision and move at the same velocity. What is the velocity of the two cars after the collision?

before

1250 kg   1000 kg

after

$$m_1 u_1 + m_2 u_2 = (m_1 + m_2)v$$

m_1 = 1250 kg, m_2 = 1000 kg, u_1 = 20 m/s, u_2 = 10 m/s

1250 kg × 20 m/s + 1000 kg × 10 m/s = (1250 kg + 1000 kg)v

Rearranging the equation:

v = (1250 kg × 20 m/s + 1000 kg × 10 m/s)/(1250 kg + 1000 kg)

= (25 000 kg m/s + 10 000 kg m/s)/2250 kg

= 15.6 m/s

So the two cars move in the positive direction (to the right) at 15.6 m/s.

Questions

1 What is the law of conservation of momentum?

2 A model car of mass 0. 3kg is moving at 5 m/s. It collides with a second model car of mass 0.2 kg that is stationary. The two cars move off together. What is the speed of the two cars?

3 A car has a mass of 750 kg and is travelling at 20 m/s. A second car is travelling in the same direction and has a mass of 1250 kg. The two cars collide and coalesce. They move on at 14 m/s. What was the initial velocity of the second car?

4 Use the law of conservation of momentum to explain how a rocket works.

5 A ball of mass 0.5 kg is moving at 4 m/s. Another ball of mass 0.5 kg is moving with a velocity of –4 m/s. The balls collide head on and come to a stop.
Show that momentum is conserved in the collision.

Learning objectives

After studying this topic, you should be able to:

✔ understand how only some frequencies of radio waves pass through the atmosphere

✔ describe how information is transmitted to and from satellites

Key words

atmosphere, electromagnetic wave, microwave, aerial

A Give an example of a type of electromagnetic wave that cannot travel through our atmosphere.

B Which part of the electromagnetic spectrum is used for both terrestrial and satellite TV signals?

A satellite dish receives microwaves beamed down from a satellite in orbit. Why do all satellite TV dishes in the UK point southwards? Which way do they point in Australia?

Waves and our atmosphere

We've already learnt how parts of the **atmosphere** protect us from high energy ultraviolet radiation from the Sun. This thin layer of air surrounding our planet is essential for life. It acts like a shield, not only protecting us from ultraviolet, but also stopping higher energy parts of the electromagnetic spectrum, such as X-rays and gamma rays, from reaching the surface.

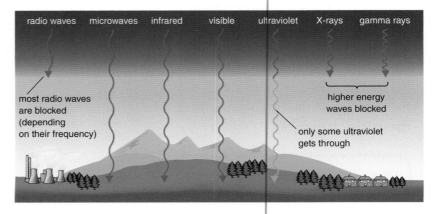

radio waves   microwaves   infrared   visible   ultraviolet   X-rays   gamma rays

most radio waves are blocked (depending on their frequency)

higher energy waves blocked

only some ultraviolet gets through

▲ Only certain frequencies of electromagnetic waves can pass through our atmosphere

Only some **electromagnetic waves** are able to pass through our atmosphere. Some waves are absorbed by one of the many gases, others by water droplets. Whether an electromagnetic wave passes through depends on its wavelength and its frequency.

If you don't have cable TV at home then the pictures you receive are all beamed through the air. The TV signal might consist of **microwaves** sent from your local transmitter. This is called a 'terrestrial' TV signal. These waves travel at the speed of light through the air and are received by your TV **aerial**. For the best quality image, your aerial needs to be pointing towards the transmitter.

Satellite TV works in a similar way, but there is one crucial difference. Instead of the TV signal being sent from a transmitter tower to your aerial, the signal is beamed down from a satellite in orbit. For this, higher frequency microwaves are used: they have a shorter wavelength than normal TV signals.

To receive a signal from a satellite you need a satellite dish. A normal TV aerial is not sensitive enough to pick up the signal. The satellite dish has to be very carefully aligned. A few millimetres out and it won't be able to pick up the signal.

Communicating with satellites

All signals sent to and from satellites are digital. This allows the signal to be processed by computers and any interference can be removed. The signal is sent as a series of microwave pulses. Relatively low frequency microwaves are used to communicate with nearby satellites. To communicate with satellites much further away, higher frequency microwaves are used.

Satellites can be used to bounce a signal around the world. The signal is sent up to a satellite. The satellite then processes the signal, before it re-transmits it to another receiver. The signal can be made to travel further by using more than one satellite. Instead of transmitting the signal to another receiver on the ground, the satellite could transmit it to another satellite, then another, then another. Finally, the signal is sent back to a receiver on Earth.

More on microwaves

Microwaves have a shorter wavelength than radio waves. As a result they don't spread out, or diffract, as much as radio waves. This is the reason the dishes need such careful alignment. The microwave beam travels in a straight line, not spreading out very much at all. The dish needs to be at precisely the correct angle to reflect the signal onto the receiver.

▲ Satellite dishes must be carefully aligned. The signal from the satellite does not spread out very much.

To increase the quality of the signal, dishes with sizes many times that of the wavelengths of microwaves are used. They reflect the signal to a central receiver. This signal is then processed by your TV.

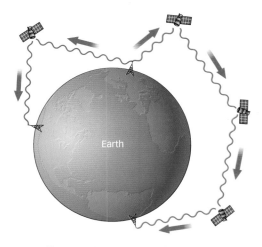

▲ Satellites can be used to relay signals around the world

Did you know...?

Satellites that transmit satellite TV signals are in a geostationary orbit. They beam the signal from a height of over 30 000 km from the Earth's surface. If you could drive to one, the journey would take around four weeks, driving for 10 hours every day.

Questions

1 List the parts of the electromagnetic spectrum whose waves are able to pass through the atmosphere.

2 What type of signal is used to communicate with satellites?

3 Describe how a satellite might be used to transmit a signal from the UK to the other side of the world.

4 Explain, in terms of diffraction, why a satellite dish needs to be very carefully aligned.

Learning objectives

After studying this topic, you should be able to:

✔ describe the effect of the ionosphere on radio waves of different wavelengths

✔ explain the effect of diffraction on the transmission of radio waves

✔ describe the meaning of amplitude modulation

Key words

ionosphere, amplitude modulation, diffraction

Did you know...?

Information is sent in most longer wavelength radio waves by a technique called **amplitude modulation** (or AM for short). The amplitude of the 'carrier' radio wave is changed according to the amplitude of the original signal. The information is encoded in the height of the wave transmitted.

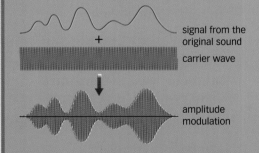

signal from the original sound

carrier wave

amplitude modulation

▲ Long wavelength radio waves carry information by changing the amplitude of the 'carrier' radio wave. This is called amplitude modulation (AM).

The ionosphere

Our atmosphere is made up of several different layers. Each layer has different properties. One of these is the **ionosphere**, and it is very important for longer range communications.

The ionosphere is at a height of around 400 km from the surface of the Earth. It is unusual as it contains a large number of ionised gases.

Radio waves are part of the electromagnetic spectrum. They have the longest wavelength and the lowest frequency. When radio waves approach the ionosphere they are reflected back from it, like light reflecting off a mirror.

Radio waves with a frequency lower than 30 million Hz (30 MHz) are reflected back towards the Earth. Some higher frequency electromagnetic waves, such as microwaves, are able to pass through the ionosphere unaffected.

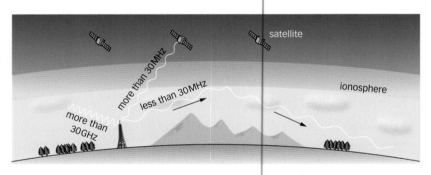

▲ Lower frequency waves such as radio waves are reflected by the ionosphere, but higher frequency waves pass through

It's not just low frequencies that meet obstacles. Higher frequency microwaves above 30 GHz (30 000 MHz) also have difficulty passing through the atmosphere. They are scattered and absorbed by dust and rain. This reduces the signal strength and results in a poor quality connection over long distances.

The problems caused by the ionosphere and the dust, rain and other particles in the atmosphere limit the radio waves and microwaves that can pass all the way through it. Waves between 30 MHz and 30 GHz are able to pass through all parts of the atmosphere. This makes them very valuable for communication.

Diffraction and radio waves

You might remember that waves spread out whenever they pass through a gap or around an obstacle. This is called **diffraction**.

In general, the smaller the gap or the longer the wavelength, the stronger the diffraction. Waves with longer wavelengths passing through small gaps spread out more than waves with shorter wavelengths passing through wider gaps.

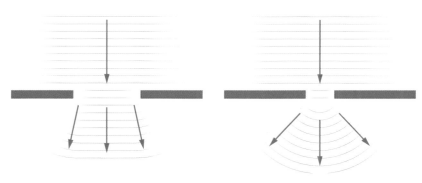

▲ The smaller the gap, the greater the diffraction

Diffraction is not always a bad thing. Radio waves diffract over hills and between buildings, allowing you to pick up signals. Longer wavelength radio signals diffract more than shorter wavelength microwaves. This allows the house in the picture above to receive a radio signal but not one for their TV.

> In general, the strongest diffraction occurs when the wavelength of the wave is the same size as the gap it passes through.

Some radio waves have such a long wavelength that they diffract around the curvature of the Earth. This allows them to be transmitted over very long distances – they diffract over the horizon. Some submarines use extremely low-frequency radio waves (between 3 and 30 Hz). This allows the submarine to send and receive signals from anywhere on the planet.

▲ Submarines can communicate using extremely long radio waves. These can diffract over the horizon and travel around the world.

A Which part of the electromagnetic spectrum has the longest wavelength?

B Radio waves below what frequency are reflected off the ionosphere?

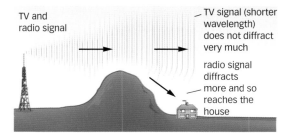

TV and radio signal

TV signal (shorter wavelength) does not diffract very much

radio signal diffracts more and so reaches the house

▲ Longer wavelength radio waves diffract more than shorter wavelength TV signals

Questions

1 Name which type of wave in the electromagnetic spectrum:
   (a) is reflected off the ionosphere
   (b) is able to pass through the ionosphere.

2 Draw a diagram to show how waves are diffracted.

3 Explain why the house in the picture can pick up a radio signal but not a TV signal.

4 Explain why frequencies between 30 MHz and 30 GHz are useful for longer distance communication.

5 Describe how the size of the gap affects the diffraction of waves.

Learning objectives

After studying this topic, you should be able to:

- ✔ describe how waves interfere
- ✔ describe some examples of interference
- ✔ explain how an interference pattern might be formed from coherent wave sources
- ✔ understand the importance of path difference, and what is needed for two wave sources to be coherent

▲ Water waves at sea can reach large heights because of constructive interference

A Two waves overlap and create a single wave with a different amplitude. What is this called?

B What is the name given to the interference where two waves cancel each other out?

Key words

Interference, constructive interference, destructive interference, coherent, monochromatic, path difference

When waves combine

If you stand on a pier looking at the water waves beneath you, you might notice that they are not all the same height. Some are much higher than others. This is because two or more water waves pass over one another and produce a single wave with a new amplitude. This effect is called **interference**.

Interference causes the reinforcement of some waves (also called **constructive interference**). This happens if the crests and troughs of two waves line up. This creates a wave with even greater amplitude. In the case of water waves, this would produce an even taller wave with deeper troughs.

Interference can lead to the cancellation of some waves (also called **destructive interference**). If a crest from one wave lines up with the trough of another they cancel out. If this happens to two water waves, you get a calm area.

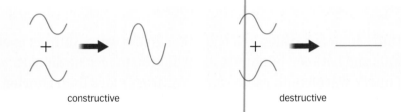

constructive   destructive

▲ Interference can be constructive or destructive

This effect happens with all types of wave, not just water waves. Interference happens with sound waves, radio waves, microwaves, and even light waves. When two waves reinforce each other you get a louder sound, stronger radio or microwave signal, or a brighter area of light. If the waves cancel out then the reverse happens. You get a darker region, a weaker signal, or a quieter sound (if the cancellation is perfect it would be silent).

Forming an interference pattern

The water waves that you see from a pier interfere in a fairly random way. However, the water waves in the ripple tank on the next page are interfering to form a stable interference pattern. This is because the dippers forming the two sets of waves are vibrating in the same way. Both dippers are fixed to the same moving beam. When two wave sources are vibrating in the same way like this, they are said to be **coherent**.

A ripple tank shows an interference pattern. The two dippers are coherent wave sources, so they can produce a stable interference pattern

To get coherent sources of light waves, we need to use light of a single frequency. This is called **monochromatic** light. Lasers produce monochromatic light.

Two coherent wave sources will have the same frequency. The two sets of waves produced by the two sources will be in step with each other – they are said to be in phase. They also need to have the same amplitude to produce an interference pattern that can be seen.

Interference patterns are caused by the waves from each source travelling a different distance. This is referred to as **path difference**. If one wave travels half a wavelength further than the other one, this is a path difference of half a wavelength. For waves to produce constructive interference the path difference must be an *even* number of half wavelengths. For destructive interference the path difference must be an *odd* number of wavelengths.

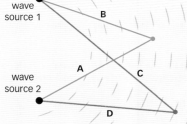

path **A** from wave source 2, is $\frac{1}{2}$-wavelength longer than path **B**, from wave source 1 (destructive interference)

wave source 1

wave source 2

path **C** from wave source 1, is $2 \times \frac{1}{2}$-wavelengths longer than path **D**, from wave source 2 (constructive interference)

The type of interference at different positions depends on the path difference between the two waves

Questions

1 Describe the effect of interference on the volume of sound heard by an observer.

2 Draw a diagram to show how two waves can:
   (a) interfere constructively
   (b) interfere destructively.

3 Use a diagram to show how the path difference at different distances from two sources produces an interference pattern.

4 The path difference between two waves is measured at 3 cm. The wavelength of the waves is 2 cm. Explain what type of interference would be observed at this point.

↓ E

↓ C

↓ A*

Some modern headphones use interference to cancel out background noise

> **A** Did Newton believe light was a stream of particles or a wave?

▲ Newton and Huygens had very different ideas about the nature of light

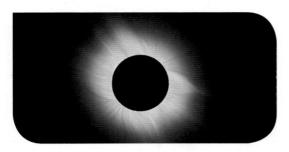

▲ The sharp shadows formed by a solar eclipse led scientists to believe that light was made up of a stream of particles

Ideas about light

Over time, ideas about the nature of light have changed. We now know that light is an electromagnetic wave, but different theories of light have caused some of the fiercest debates in the history of science. Perhaps the most well-known was between the famous English physicist, Sir Isaac Newton, and the Dutch astronomer, Christiaan Huygens.

Newton thought light was a stream of particles; Huygens thought light was a wave. There was good evidence to support both sides of the argument and there were several other scientists on both sides.

Newton stated that the evidence that light travels in straight lines was proof of its particle nature. Waves, like sound and water waves, spread out, but light doesn't. A good example of this is the formation of shadows. Each shadow has a clear edge. If light was a wave it would spread out (diffract) around the obstacle and form a blurry shadow. Newton stated that the shadows formed by a solar eclipse were indisputable proof of that light was a particle.

Evidence for light as a wave

Newton was able to explain both refraction and reflection in terms of particles. Throw a bouncing ball at the ground and it bounces back up at the same angle. Newton used a similar model to explain reflection: particles of light would bounce off surfaces.

> **B** How did Newton explain the reflection of light in terms of particles?

However, as more evidence was collected it became clear that not all phenomena could be explained using the model of light as a particle. Newton was wrong, and the model of light had to be changed.

The first key piece of evidence for light as a wave is diffraction. It had appeared that light did not diffract. However, light has such a short wavelength that the gap needed to see this effect has to be very, very small. If a tiny single slit is used, light can be diffracted. It spreads out from a narrow beam when it passes through the gap.

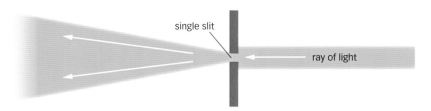

A ray of light can be diffracted through a narrow slit

If two slits are used, the light diffracts through both slits and overlaps. This forms an interference pattern. Particles do not form interference patterns. The fact that light does was the final key piece of evidence that light must be a type of wave.

For light to diffract, a tiny slit about the same size as the wavelength of light is needed.

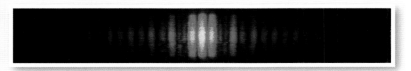

Light forms an interference pattern of light and dark bands

At different places, the light from each slit has travelled a slightly different distance. Where the path difference is an even number of wavelengths, as described on spread P5.11, the waves interfere constructively. Where it is an odd number of wavelengths, they interfere destructively. This leads to the formation of bright and dark bands on a screen.

All electromagnetic waves can be polarised. **Polarisation** only happens to transverse waves. The polarisation of light confirms that light is not only a wave but a **transverse wave**. Like all transverse waves the vibrations are at right angles to the direction of wave motion. These vibrations might take place in any plane as the wave travels forwards (eg up and down, side-to-side). Light from most sources, such as light bulbs or the Sun, is not polarised. The vibrations take place in all possible planes. Plane-polarised light has vibrations in one plane only.

A **Polaroid filter** only lets through light that is polarised in a certain plane. If you have a pair of filters and slowly rotate one in front of the other, eventually all of the light is blocked.

Key words

polarisation, transverse wave, Polaroid filter

Did you know...?

Some sunglasses contain Polaroid filters. Light reflected off the surface of roads, snow, and even water becomes partly polarised. Polaroid glasses block this light, reducing the glare from the surface.

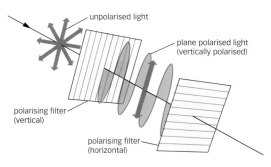

Light can be plane-polarised, confirming that it is a transverse wave

Questions

1   What evidence was there for light behaving like a stream of particles?

2   Give three examples of effects that show light must be a wave.

3   Describe how to form an interference pattern with light.

4   Explain the meaning of the term polarisation and describe the effect of a Polaroid filter.

Learning objectives

After studying this topic, you should be able to:

- ✔ describe refraction as the bending of a light wave when it travels from one medium to another
- ✔ explain the meaning of the term refractive index

Key words

refraction, medium, refractive index

▲ Refraction can lead to some strange optical effects!

> **B** What happens to the direction of light when it passes from a medium into one that has a lower density?

Bending rays of light

The **refraction** of light leads to some unusual optical effects. Mirages in deserts are caused by refraction, swimming pools look shallower than they actually are, and fish that are seen from above the surface of the water are not where they appear to be.

> **A** Give an example of an unusual optical effect caused by refraction.

As you will remember, refraction is the bending of light (or any wave) when it travels from one **medium** to another. When light moves from one medium to another its speed changes, depending on the density of the material. This speed change causes a change in the direction of the light.

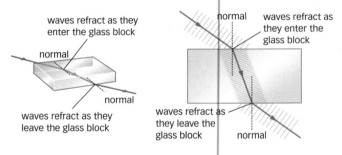

▲ Light refracts as it passes through a glass block

The direction that the light bends in depends on the relative density of the two media. If the light enters a denser material, such as travelling from air to glass, the light slows down. This makes the light bend towards the normal. The angle of incidence is greater than the angle of refraction.

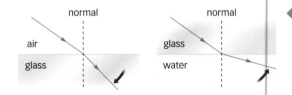

◀ Light either refracts towards or away from the normal depending on the relative density of the two media

If the light goes from a denser medium to one that is less dense, such as travelling from glass to water, the light speeds up. This makes the light bend away from the normal.

Refractive index

The **refractive index** of a material is a measure of the speed of light through the material compared with the speed of light in a vacuum. The more slowly the light travels through the material, the higher its refractive index. The denser the material, the higher its refractive index. Water has a refractive index of 1.3 and the refractive index of glass is around 1.4 (depending on the type of glass).

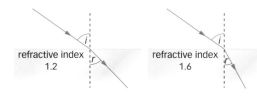

refractive index 1.2   refractive index 1.6

▲ The greater the refractive index, the more the light ray bends when it enters the material

Materials with a higher refractive index cause the light to slow down more and bend more towards the normal.

The refractive index of a material can be calculated using this equation:

$$\text{refractive index} = \frac{\text{speed of light in vacuum}}{\text{speed of light in the medium (material)}}$$

Worked example

Light travels at 300 000 000 m/s (3×10^8 m/s) through a vacuum. It travels at 200 000 000 m/s (2×10^8 m/s) through a piece of glass. Find the refractive index of the glass.

$$\text{refractive index} = \frac{\text{speed of light in vacuum}}{\text{speed of light in the medium (material)}}$$

speed of light in vacuum = 3×10^8 m/s = 300 000 000 m/s

speed of light in glass = 2×10^8 m/s = 200 000 000 m/s

$$\text{refractive index} = \frac{300\,000\,000 \text{ m/s}}{200\,000\,000 \text{ m/s}}$$

$$= 1.5$$

When light passes into a block of material with a higher density, it slows down. This also has the effect of reducing the wavelength of the light passing through the block. When the light exits the block, both its speed and wavelength return to what they were previously.

Questions

1 Describe what happens to the direction of light when it passes from a low density medium into one with a higher density. E

2 Explain what causes a ray of light to change direction when it passes from one material to another.

3 Explain the meaning of refractive index and describe how it might be calculated. C

4 Light travels at 3.0×10^8 m/s through a vacuum. It slows to 2.3×10^8 m/s when it enters water. Find the refractive index of water.

5 A piece of glass has a refractive index of 1.6. Find the speed of light through the glass.   A*

Learning objectives

After studying this topic, you should be able to:

- ✔ describe how light is made up of different component colours
- ✔ explain how a spectrum of colours is formed when light passes through a prism
- ✔ understand that the blue end of the visible spectrum has a higher refractive index compared with the red end

Key words

dispersion, prism, visible spectrum

The prism is splitting white light into the colours of the visible spectrum

Did you know...?

The English poet John Keats is believed to have felt that Newton had destroyed the poetry and beauty of the rainbow by using science to explain it. Others would argue from the opposite point of view: that learning how light is refracted inside water droplets to form a rainbow enhances the sense of wonder and beauty.

Unweaving the rainbow

White light is a mixture of all of the colours of the rainbow. When white light is refracted in a certain way it is split into its component colours. This is called **dispersion**.

> **A** What is the name given to the effect of splitting white light into its component colours?

▲ A rainbow is formed by a combination of refraction, Total Internal Reflection, and dispersion inside water droplets

A rainbow is formed by the refraction of light as it passes through tiny water droplets in the air. The light is split into the colours that we see.

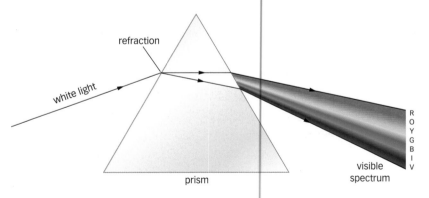

▲ The refraction of white light by a prism splits it into colours

The same effect can be seen when light passes through a **prism**. When it enters the glass, it slows down and refracts. The light bends towards the normal. However, different colours are refracted by different amounts. When the light leaves the prism it is refracted again. This causes the light to disperse far enough for us to see the separate colours.

The visible spectrum

The range of colours we can see is called the **visible spectrum**. It ranges from deep red to the blues and purples at the violet end of the spectrum.

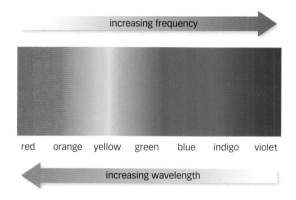

▲ The visible spectrum

The different colours have different wavelengths. Violet has the shortest wavelength, and red light has the longest. The order from longest wavelength to shortest is:

red, orange, yellow, green, blue, indigo, violet

All the colours travel at the same speed through a vacuum, but they travel at slightly different speeds when they travel through other materials (media). The shorter the wavelength, the more slowly the light travels through the medium. When light is refracted through glass, violet slows down more than red and is bent more towards the normal.

As the different colours travel at different speeds through glass, they all have different refractive indices. The shorter the wavelength, the higher the refractive index. Violet has the largest refractive index and red the smallest.

Colour	Typical refractive index in glass
red	1.520
orange	1.523
blue	1.530
violet	1.538

Exam tip   OCR

✓ The shorter the wavelength, the higher the refractive index. Remember 'Blue Bends Best'. The blue/violet part of the spectrum refracts the most.

✓ You need to learn the order of the visible spectrum. From longest to shortest wavelengths: **R**ichard **O**f **Y**ork **G**ave **B**attle **I**n **V**ain.

B State the colours of the visible spectrum from longest wavelength to shortest.

Questions

1 Which part of the spectrum is refracted the most when white light is passed through a prism?

2 Draw a diagram to show how a visible spectrum can be formed from a prism.

3 Explain why white light splits into colours when it is dispersed through a prism.

4 Describe the relationship between the wavelength of a certain colour and its refractive index.

5 Calculate the speed of red and violet light through a piece of glass using the values given in the table.

Learning objectives

After studying this topic, you should be able to:

✓ describe how Total Internal Reflection (TIR) happens, in terms of refractive index and critical angle

✓ state some uses of Total Internal Reflection

✓ describe the relationship between refractive index and critical angle

Key words

Total Internal Reflection, critical angle

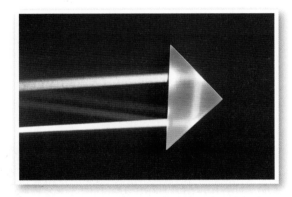

▲ Total Internal Reflection inside a glass block

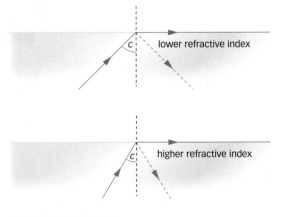

▲ The critical angle

Total Internal Reflection (TIR)

When light travels from one medium to another it refracts (bends), but there is also a small amount of internal reflection. For example, if light travels from glass to air it bends away as it leaves the glass, but a small amount is reflected back into the glass.

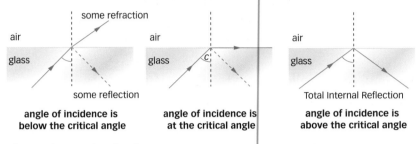

some refraction		
air	air	air
glass	glass	glass
some reflection		Total Internal Reflection
angle of incidence is below the critical angle	angle of incidence is at the critical angle	angle of incidence is above the critical angle

▲ Total Internal Reflection

If light hits the boundary between the glass and air at a big enough angle of incidence, all of the light stays within the glass; it is all reflected internally. This is **Total Internal Reflection**. It happens if the angle is above the **critical angle** for the material.

This effect can be seen whenever light travels from an optically dense material to a less dense one (for example, from water to air, glass to air, or Perspex to air). Two things are needed for Total Internal Reflection to happen:

• the light must be travelling in the more optically dense of the two materials

• the angle of the light must be greater than the critical angle.

Different media have different critical angles.

> **A** What is name given to the angle above which Total Internal Reflection occurs?

The critical angle of a medium depends on its refractive index. An optically denser medium has a higher refractive index and so a lower critical angle.

Using Total Internal Reflection

You might remember how Total Internal Reflection is used in fibre optics. Optical fibres are very fine glass cables. They can be used to provide superfast broadband by sending information as pulses of light totally internally reflected along the fibre.

Optical fibres are not only used for communication. A laparoscope is a medical instrument that is inserted through a tiny keyhole incision to get an image of the inside of the body without having to cut the patient open. An endoscope also uses optical fibres, but in this case there is no incision; the long tube is often passed through the patient's mouth down to the stomach to obtain images.

Binoculars contain a pair of prisms that are specially shaped so that light is totally internally reflected. This is used to produce a magnified view of the object. The image is also turned the right way up.

An important safety use of Total Internal Reflection is in the 'cat's eyes' found in the centre of main roads. Light from the headlights of cars enters the cat's eye and is totally internally reflected. The light then exits back the way it came. This allows the driver see the path of the road in front of them over a much greater distance.

Exam tip   **OCR**

✔ Remember that there are two conditions for Total Internal Reflection: the light must be travelling in the denser of the two materials, and the angle of the light from the normal must be above the critical angle of the material.

B What is an endoscope?

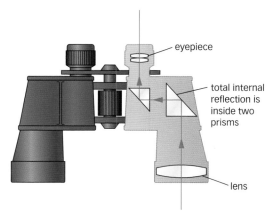

▲ Light is totally internally reflected in prisms inside binoculars

▲ Light is totally internally reflected inside cat's eyes in the road

Questions

1. State the two requirements for Total Internal Reflection.

2. Draw a diagram to show what happens to a ray of light inside a glass block when it hits the edge of the block:
   (a) below the critical angle
   (b) at the critical angle
   (c) above the critical angle.

3. Give three uses of Total Internal Reflection.

4. Describe an experiment that could be carried out to determine the critical angle of a glass block.

5. Describe the relationship between the refractive index and critical angle of a material.

Learning objectives

After studying this topic, you should be able to:

- ✔ describe what happens to light passing through a convex lens
- ✔ explain that that a convex lens can bring parallel rays of light to a focus
- ✔ complete the path of a ray of light passing through a convex lens

Key words

converging, convex, principal axis, focus, optical centre, focal length

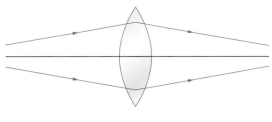

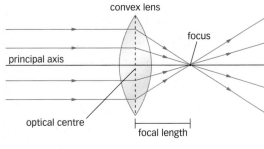

convex lens

focus

principal axis

optical centre

focal length

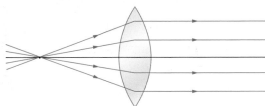

▲ A converging lens refracts the light passing through it. All rays of light passing through a convex lens are converged to some extent.

Life through a lens

Lenses are found in cameras, telescopes, glasses and in the eyes of most animals. There are lots of different types of lens, but they all work exactly the same way. A lens is used to refract the light that passes through it. The lens then forms an image.

◄ Like most eyes, the eyes of a shark contain a lens to focus the light

A Give two examples of where lenses can be found.

The most commonly used type of lens is a **converging** one. A **convex** lens is an example of a converging lens.

▲ A simple convex, converging lens

When rays of light parallel to the **principal axis** pass through a convex lens, they are focussed to a single point called the **focus**.

The distance from the **optical centre** of the lens to the focus is called the **focal length**. In general, the fatter the lens, the shorter the focal length.

Rays of light that are diverging (spreading out) from the focus on one side are refracted so that they come out parallel.

B What type of lens can be used to bring light to a focus?

▲ The converging lens used in a magnifying glass focusses the sunlight. This can create a hot spot.

Constructing ray diagrams

We often draw (or construct) ray diagrams showing the path of light through a lens. In these examples an arrow is used to represent the object. Light is reflected from all parts of the object, but we just consider the light that is being reflected from the tip of the object.

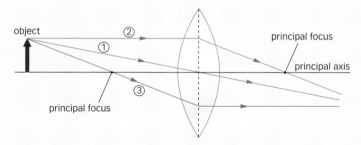

▲ The three rules for rays of light passing through a convex lens

Light is being reflected from the tip in many directions, but we can find out where the image will be by considering light that follows one of three paths.

1. *Light passing through the optical centre of the lens.* The light that passes through the centre of a lens continues through in a straight line.
2. *Light travelling parallel to the principal axis.* The light that is travelling parallel to the principal axis is refracted by the lens so that it passes through the focus.
3. *Light passing through the focus.* The light that passes through the focus is refracted by the lens so that it comes out travelling parallel to the principal axis.

Questions

1. What happens to light passing through the optical centre of a converging lens? E

2. Draw a diagram to show how a converging lens can focus rays of light. Label the focal length, optical centre, and focus. C

3. Describe what happens to the focal length if a fatter lens is used.

4. Draw a diagram showing the paths taken by light passing through a lens if the light:
   (a) passes through the optical centre of a lens A*
   (b) is travelling parallel to the principal axis
   (c) passes through the focus.

Learning objectives

After studying this topic, you should be able to:

✔ state some uses of convex lenses

✔ calculate the magnification of an image

✔ describe how convex lenses can be used to produce real images

✔ construct ray diagrams for lenses, including one for a magnifying glass

A Give two examples of optical instruments that use lenses to form images.

Forming an image

We use lenses to form images of a wide variety of objects. From looking at distant planets right down to microscopic cells, lenses are used to help us make sense of the world around us.

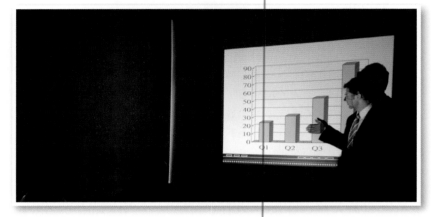

▲ A projector contains a converging lens that focuses an image on a screen

Convex lenses are used in cameras, projectors, some spectacles and in magnifying glasses. A digital projector produces an image on a big screen that is much larger than the tiny screen inside the projector. The lens inside a camera produces a smaller image on film or on a light-sensitive chip.

Images from a convex lens

A convex lens can be used to produce a **real image**. This is a type of image that can be focussed to form upon a screen or piece of film. For the image to be in focus, rather than blurry, the distances from object to lens and lens to screen must be just right. Changing the distance from the object to the lens changes the nature of the image produced.

Using the three paths for rays of light that are shown on spread P5.16, we can construct a ray diagram showing how images are formed.

Where the rays cross shows where the image forms. If an object is far away, the image formed is smaller than the object, upside down (inverted), and a real image.

If the object is closer to the lens, then a different image is formed.

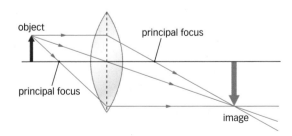

▲ Using a convex lens to form an image of an object that is far away from the lens

▲ If the object is closer to the lens, the image formed is very different

When a lens is used to magnify an object, the **magnification** can be calculated using the equation:

$$\text{magnification} = \frac{\text{image height}}{\text{object height}}$$

Any magnification greater than 1 means the image is larger than the object. A magnification of 5 would mean the image is 5× larger than the object. A 2 cm object would produce a 10 cm image.

A convex lens can be used in a magnifying glass. As the light passes through the lens, it is refracted in such a way to produce a larger image. This allows the observer to see miniscule details usually invisible to the naked eye.

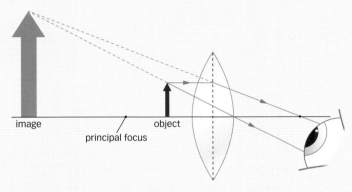

image   object

principal focus

▲ Using a convex lens as a magnifying glass produces a magnified, virtual image

Using a convex lens in this way produces a **virtual image**. This kind of image cannot be formed on a screen, but, unlike other images from a convex lens, the image is the right way up (upright). The observer must look through the lens to see the image.

◀ A magnifying glass is a single convex lens

B What is meant by a magnification of 3?

Questions

1 What type of lens is used in a magnifying glass?

2 Light from a 2.0 cm high object is projected through a lens onto a screen, producing an image 56 cm high. Calculate the magnification.

3 An image 4.8 cm high is focussed by a lens onto a piece of film. The object being photographed is 19.2 cm tall. Calculate the magnification.

4 Describe the difference between a real and a virtual image.

5 Use graph paper to carefully produce your own lens diagrams for the three examples shown and calculate the magnification in each case.

E

C

A*

Module summary

Revision checklist ✔

- Satellites may be natural or artificial. Gravitational force (weight) causes a satellite's curved path.
- Artificial satellites are used for telecommunications, weather, GPS, and photography in low polar or geostationary orbit.
- Centripetal force keeps satellites moving in a circular orbit.
- Scalar quantities (eg mass, temperature) indicate size. Vector quantities (eg force, acceleration) indicate size and direction.
- Projectiles have a parabolic trajectory. They have a constant horizontal velocity and an increasing vertical velocity.
- Every action has an equal and opposite reaction.
- Force applied in a collision changes the momentum of an object. Action and reaction affect both objects in a collision.
- Total momentum before collision (or explosion) = total momentum after collision (or explosion).
- Higher-energy parts of the electromagnetic spectrum cannot pass through the atmosphere.
- Microwaves are used for satellite communication. Digital signals are passed from satellite to satellite as a series of microwave pulses.
- Radio waves of less than 30 MHz are reflected by the ionosphere, while higher frequency waves pass through it.
- Radio waves diffract around obstructions. Very low-frequency radio waves diffract around the curvature of the Earth.
- Wave interference can be constructive or destructive. Coherent wave sources can form interference patterns.
- Monochromatic light is light of a single frequency (eg lasers).
- Diffraction (causing interference patterns) and polarisation are evidence for the wave nature of light. Newton originally believed light was a stream of particles.
- Refraction is the bending of light as it passes from one medium into another.
- The component colours of the visible spectrum are refracted when passing through a prism, causing dispersion.
- Total Internal Reflection is used in optical fibres, endoscopes, binoculars, and cat's eyes.
- Lenses refract light. A converging (convex) lens brings rays of light parallel to the principal axis to a focus.
- Images produced by lenses may be real or virtual.

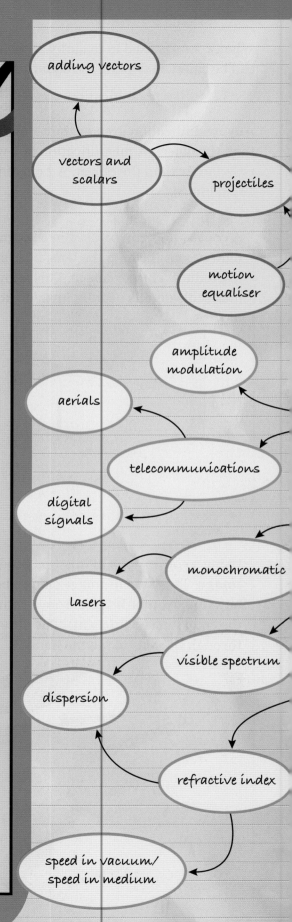

adding vectors

vectors and scalars

projectiles

motion equaliser

amplitude modulation

aerials

telecommunications

digital signals

monochromatic

lasers

visible spectrum

dispersion

refractive index

speed in vacuum/ speed in medium

NOW USE THE P5 GRADE CHECKER ON PAGE 248

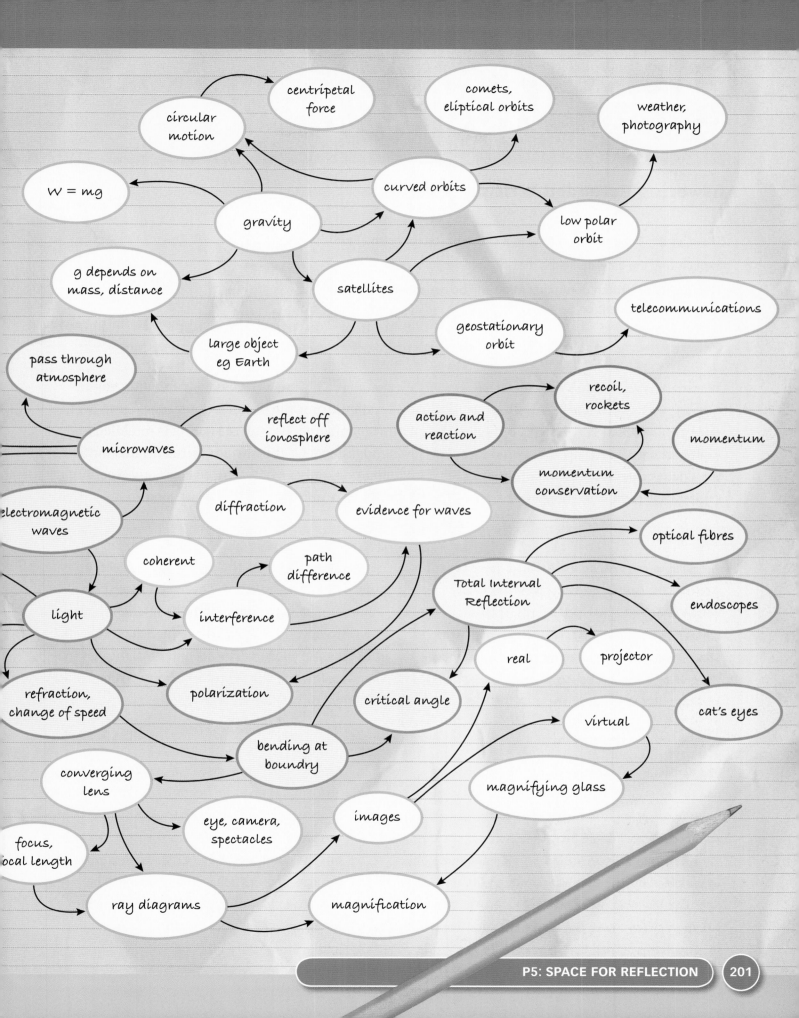

centripetal
force

circular
motion

comets,
eliptical orbits

weather,
photography

w = mg

gravity

curved orbits

low polar
orbit

g depends on
mass, distance

satellites

telecommunications

pass through
atmosphere

large object
eg Earth

geostationary
orbit

recoil,
rockets

reflect off
ionosphere

action and
reaction

momentum

microwaves

momentum
conservation

electromagnetic
waves

diffraction

evidence for waves

optical fibres

coherent

path
difference

Total Internal
Reflection

endoscopes

light

interference

real

projector

refraction,
change of speed

polarization

critical angle

cat's eyes

bending at
boundry

virtual

converging
lens

magnifying glass

focus,
ocal length

eye, camera,
spectacles

images

ray diagrams

magnification

OCR gateway *Upgrade*

Answering Extended Writing questions

The diagram illustrates a satellite in a circular orbit round the Earth.

Explain why the satellite keeps moving in its circular path.

The quality of written communication will be assessed in your answer to this question.

The path curves because of gravity. if gravity was swixchd off centrifugl force (which dosnt realy exist would make the satelite fly off sideways. the satelite carries on because of the rokket that fired it at the lornch.

↓ E

Examiner: This answer demonstrates only vague understanding of the physics. Some ideas have been half-remembered, but the reasoning is muddled and misunderstood. Of the physics words needed for a full explanation, only gravity is used correctly. Spelling, punctuation, and grammar are not good.

The path is curved, so a sideways force is needed. The earth's gravity provides this, which is called centripetle force. If this wasn't there the satelite would fly off into space and go on for ever. Its like a conker on the end of a string being whirled round, the string pulls it towards the middle.

↓ C

Examiner: Most of the physics is correct, but there are ideas missing. There is no mention of changing velocity, acceleration, or unchanging forward speed and KE. The sequence of ideas is not structured well. The second half, though true, is not relevant. There are occasional errors in spelling, punctuation, and grammar.

The direction of movement of the satellite is continuously changing. That means its velocity is changing, so it is accelerating. The direction of its acceleration is towards the centre of the Earth. This requires a force, called centripetal force. This is provided by the Earth's gravity, pulling on the satellite towards the centre of the Earth. There is no air resistance; so the KE of the satellite, originally provided by the rocket, is not reduced.

↓ A*

Examiner: This answer is well ordered and accurate. It gives an account of why the speed of the satellite doesn't change, as well as why the path is curved. The word vector isn't used, but the concepts of velocity, acceleration, and force as vectors are well expressed. The physics explanations and the use of technical terms are all correct. Spelling, punctuation, and grammar are all good.

Exam-style questions

1 a *A01* Draw a diagram showing a beam of white light entering a prism, passing through it, then leaving again after it has been split into its colours.

b *A01* Label the seven colours correctly.

c *A01* What is this splitting of the light into its colours by the prism called?

2 a *A01* Explain how a converging lens affects light.

b *A01* Explain the meaning of focal length for a converging lens.

c *A01* Explain the meaning of real image.

d *A02* Using a particular projector, a transparency of width 15 cm produces an image 1.8 m wide on a screen. Calculate the magnification achieved.

e *A01* What is a virtual image?

3 a *A02* An object 4 cm tall is 8 cm from a converging lens with focal length 5 cm. Draw a ray diagram at actual size on a sheet of A4 graph paper to find the size and nature of the image. Show all three possible construction rays. (Hint: use the paper in landscape orientation, and put the lens about 10 cm from the left edge of the paper.)

b *A02* Describe how the image changes if the object is brought gradually closer to the lens.

4 A stuntman takes a running jump off the roof of a building, to be caught in a net at ground level. He leaves the roof horizontally at 8 m/s. The roof is 10 m above ground level.

a *A02* Calculate the time taken by the man to reach the ground.

b *A02* Calculate how far from the base of the building he lands.

c *A02* Calculate the man's resultant velocity when he lands.

Extended Writing

5 *A01* Describe two examples of artificial satellites. For each of your examples, explain how the use of the satellite dictates what orbit is chosen for it.

6 *A01* Explain how Total Internal Reflection (TIR) occurs. Why is TIR not possible if light is travelling in air towards a glass surface?

7 *A01* Explain what is meant by interference when discussing waves. What evidence does interference give about the nature of light?

A01   Recall the science
A02   Apply your knowledge
A03   Evaluate and analyse the evidence

P6

Electricity for gadgets

Why study this module?

Electricity is a fundamental part of our lives. We use many electronic devices that need a supply of electrical energy to operate. We can control these devices, and many of them store information. Electronic devices are also used to control things automatically – for example a cooling fan in a computer switching on automatically when the computer gets too hot, or turning on central heating when it gets too cold. Engineers need to understand the physics behind these devices so that they can design new ones and repair existing ones when they go wrong.

In this module you will learn about other components of electronic circuits such as resistors, thermistors, transistors, diodes, and capacitors. You will also learn about how transistors can be combined to form logic gates, and how logic gates can be used to control devices. You will learn about motors and dynamos. You will also learn about how transformers are used to increase and decrease voltages to minimise power losses in transmission lines.

You should remember

1 That the power used by an electrical device depends on the potential difference across it and the current flowing through it.

2 How electricity is conducted through a metal.

3 How the electrical resistance of a component is connected to the potential difference across the component and the current flowing through it.

4 How electricity is generated and that it is transmitted around the country by the National Grid.

5 What a transformer is.

The capacity of silicon chips has been getting greater and greater as the transistors on them have been getting smaller and smaller. The number of transistors that can be put on a single silicon chip has been doubling approximately every 18 months. In the 1960s, manufacturers were able to get a few hundred transistors on a silicon chip. Manufacturers can now get up to 500 million transistors on a single chip with an area of 350 mm^2!

Learning objectives

After studying this topic, you should be able to:

- ✔ use standard circuit symbols
- ✔ calculate resistance from voltage and current
- ✔ use a voltage–current graph

Key words

switch, cell, battery, resistor, variable resistor, power supply, resistance

Did you know...?

Circuit symbols are an almost universal language. This means that when you draw a circuit diagram, most electricians around the world could understand it.

A Draw the symbols for a variable resistor and a cell.

B A variable resistor is connected in series with a bulb and a cell. How could you use the variable resistor to change the brightness of the bulb?

C How could you use the variable resistor to change the speed of a motor in a circuit?

Circuit symbols

Symbols for some components of circuits are shown in the table.

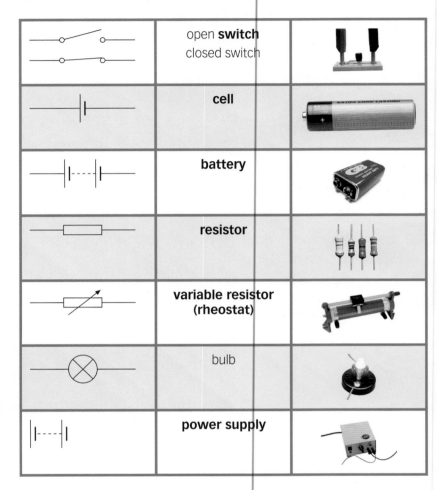

	open **switch** closed switch	
	cell	
	battery	
	resistor	
	variable resistor (rheostat)	
	bulb	
	power supply	

Resistance, voltage, and current

You may remember that you can calculate **resistance** using the equation:

$$\text{resistance (ohms, }\Omega\text{)} = \frac{\text{voltage (volts, V)}}{\text{current (amperes, A)}}$$

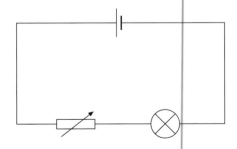

▲ Circuit with a variable resistor

How a variable resistor works

The resistance of a length of wire depends on its length. The longer the piece of wire, the higher its resistance is. A variable resistor consists of a long piece of wire that is often in a coil. Its resistance is changed by altering the length of the resistance wire in the circuit.

Voltage–current graphs

The diagram below shows voltage–current graphs for three different resistors. Resistor C has the lowest current for a particular voltage. Therefore it has the highest resistance of the three resistors.

Remember that when the resistance goes up, the current comes down.

These resistors are ohmic resistors: their voltage–current graphs are straight lines.

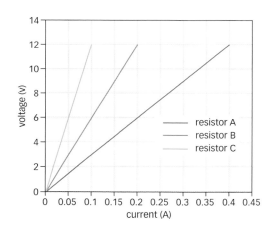

▲ Voltage–current graphs for three resistors

> **D** How do you know that resistor C has the highest resistance?

Finding the resistance from a voltage–current graph

You can calculate the resistance from a voltage–current graph by reading off the values of voltage and current at a point and substituting them into the equation for resistance.

Exam tip **OCR**

✓ Take care with the units of current and resistance when using them in calculations. Always make sure you convert kilo-ohms (kΩ) and milliamps (mA) to ohms and amps.

Questions

1 Name each of the components shown in the circuit diagram.

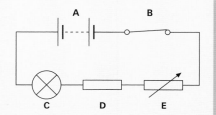

2 What does a variable resistor do in a circuit?

3 Calculate the resistance for the following values of voltage and current:

   (a) 12 V, 6 A

   (b) 6 V, 0.05 A

   (c) 3 V, 2 mA.

4 Calculate the resistance of resistors A, B, and C from the graph.

5 The voltage across a resistor is 12 V. Calculate the current through the resistor for the following resistances:

   (a) 6 Ω

   (b) 24 Ω

   (c) 1.2 kΩ.

2: Resistance and non-ohmic conductors

Resistance in a wire

The current in a wire conductor is a flow of free electrons that carry charge. These electrons collide with the atoms of the conductor. This makes the flow of charge more difficult, and is called the resistance of the conductor

When there are fewer collisions with atoms (lower resistance), the electrons flow more easily through the conductor, and the current is higher. When there are more collisions (higher resistance) it is more difficult for the electrons to flow, and the current is lower.

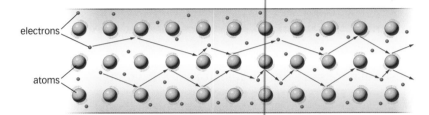

electrons

atoms

▲ Electrons moving through a metal conductor

> **A** What is happening to electrons in a wire when the resistance is higher?

Why do resistance and temperature increase?

The atoms in a conductor are vibrating. When the electrons moving through the conductor collide with the atoms, some energy is transferred to the atoms. The atoms vibrate more, and the number of collisions increases. This means that the resistance increases – it becomes more difficult for the electrons to move through the metal. The increased vibration of the atoms also means that the temperature of the conductor increases.

Conductors whose resistance changes

A bulb has a thin coil of wire that is usually made of a metal with a high melting point such as tungsten. When a current flows through the wire, it glows brightly and becomes hot.

When you plot a graph of current against voltage for the bulb, you find that it is not a straight line. It is a curve.

As the graph is not a straight line, this shows that the resistance is not constant. As the current increases, the resistance is also increasing.

Devices that have a voltage–current graph that is not a straight line are called **non-ohmic**.

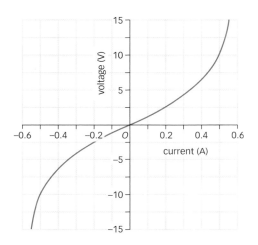

▲ Voltage–current graph for a filament lamp

▲ A filament lamp

Exam tip   **OCR**

✔ Remember that when a graph of voltage against current is a straight line, this means that the resistance is constant.

B What happens to the resistance of a bulb as the temperature increases?

C What does non-ohmic mean?

Why the voltage–current graph curves

When the voltage increases, this means that the electrons are carrying more energy. So when they collide with the atoms they transfer more energy, making the atoms vibrate even more. The greater vibration of the atoms means that the temperature and the resistance increase. So as the voltage goes up, so does the resistance. The current still increases for a while, but not as much as at lower voltages.

Questions

1 What is the current in a wire?

2 What happens to resistance when a wire gets hot?

3 Why is the voltage–current graph for a bulb not a straight line?

4 Describe how a voltage–current graph shows the changing resistance in a non-ohmic device.

5 Explain what happens to the charge carriers in a metal conductor as the voltage increases.

Key words

series, potential divider

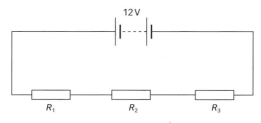

▲ Three resistors connected in series

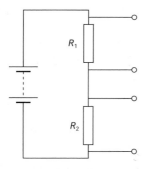

▲ Simple potential divider circuit

B What is a potential divider?

In electronic circuits, the supply voltage usually needs to be varied. This is done by splitting the voltage across two resistors connected in series.

Resistors in series

When resistors are connected in **series**, they increase the total resistance of the circuit. The total resistance is given by:

$$R_T = R_1 + R_2 + R_3$$

This equation is true for any number of resistors connected in series.

Worked example 1

Three resistors are connected in series. Their resistances are 5 Ω, 11 Ω and 8 Ω. What is the total resistance?

$$R_T = R_1 + R_2 + R_3 = 5\,\Omega + 11\,\Omega + 8\,\Omega = 24\,\Omega$$

A What is the total resistance of three resistors with values 8 Ω, 10 Ω, and 7 Ω when they are connected in series?

Potential divider

In a series circuit, the current flowing in the circuit is the same everywhere. The total voltage is shared between all the components, in proportion to their resistances. The voltage across a component is also known as the potential difference.

A **potential divider** circuit is shown in the diagram on the left. The same current flows through both resistors, R_1 and R_2. When the two resistors have the same value, the voltage across each resistor is the same – it is divided between the two resistors. If the resistance of R_2 is double that of R_1, the voltage across R_2 will be double the voltage across R_1.

The voltage across either resistor can be used as an output for other circuits.

If R_2 is replaced with a variable resistor, the output voltage, V_{out}, can be easily changed as required.

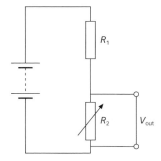

▲ Potential divider circuit where V_{out} can be varied

Output from a potential divider

The circuit for a potential divider is often drawn as shown in the diagram. The power supply is not shown. There is a line that is shown as 0 V and the voltages are shown relative to this.

You can calculate V_{out} using ratios. If the resistance of R_2 is twice the resistance of R_1 then the voltage across R_2 (V_{out}) will be double that across R_1. For example if V_{in} = 30 V and R_1 = 4 Ω and R_2 8 Ω, V_{out} will be 20 V.

When R_2 is smaller than R_1, V_{out} will be smaller than the voltage across R_1. For example, if R_2 is ten times smaller than R_2 then V_{out} will be ten times smaller than the voltage across R_1.

The larger R_2 gets compared with R_1, the higher V_{out} becomes. When R_2 is much greater than R_1, the value of V_{out} is approximately equal to V_{in}. When R_2 is much less than R_1, the value of V_{out} is approximately zero.

Worked example 2

Calculate V_{out} when V_{in} is 12 V, R_1 is 6 Ω and R_2 is 18 Ω.

The resistance of R_2 is 18/6 = 3 times larger than the resistance of R_1, so V_{out} will be 3 times bigger than the voltage across R_1.
So V_{out} = 9 V (and the voltage across R_1 is 3 V).

R_1 and R_2 can be replaced with two variable resistors. This means that you can change the threshold of the output voltage. This is the point at which V_{out} becomes significantly higher than zero, high enough to perform a specific task (eg sound an alarm).

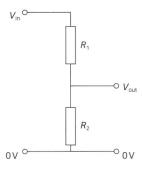

▲ How a potential divider circuit is usually shown

C Calculate V_{out} when V_{in} is 24 V, R_1 is 600 Ω, and R_2 is 2 Ω.

Questions

1 Three resistors with resistances of 20 Ω, 6 Ω, and 9 Ω are connected in series. What is the total resistance? ↓ E

2 Explain how the output voltage can be varied using a variable resistor in a potential divider circuit. ↓ C

3 What values of R_1 and R_2 could you use so that V_{out} is approximately equal to V_{in}?

4 Calculate V_{out} when V_{in} is 18 V, R_1 is 1.2 kΩ, and R_2 is 300 Ω. ↓ A*

Learning objectives

After studying this topic, you should be able to:

- ✔ explain how the resistances of LDRs (light-dependent resistors) and thermistors change with light level and temperature
- ✔ recall that when resistors are connected in parallel, total resistance is reduced
- ✔ calculate the total resistance of resistors connected in parallel

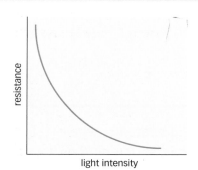

▲ How the resistance of an LDR (light-dependent resistor) changes with intensity of light

Key words

light-dependent resistor, thermistor, parallel

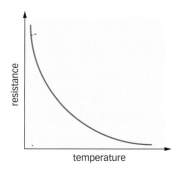

▲ How the resistance of a thermistor varies with temperature

Light-dependent resistors

A **light-dependent resistor** (LDR) is a special type of resistor. Its resistance changes as the intensity of the light falling on it changes.

When light levels are low, the resistance of an LDR is high. When bright light shines on an LDR, the resistance is much lower.

This change in resistance according to the intensity of light means that LDRs can be used as switches. For example, they can be used to switch on security lights when it gets dark.

▲ An LDR (light-dependent resistor) and its circuit symbol

Thermistors

A **thermistor** is another special type of resistor. Its resistance changes as its temperature changes.

When the temperature of the thermistor is low, its resistance is high. As the temperature increases, the resistance of the thermistor decreases. (Thermistors are not made of metal and don't behave like the wire filaments we met earlier.)

▲ A thermistor and its circuit symbol

> **A** What happens to the resistance of a thermistor as the temperature increases?

LDRs and thermistors in potential dividers

You can replace R_2 in the potential divider circuit with an LDR or a thermistor. This provides an output signal that depends on light or temperature conditions.

In low light the resistance of the LDR is higher in comparison with R_1, and the voltage across it is higher. The output voltage is higher. As light gets brighter, the resistance of the LDR goes down compared with R_1 and the output voltage from it also goes down.

For a thermistor, when the temperature is low, its resistance is higher and the output voltage across it is higher. As the temperature increases, the resistance of the thermistor decreases compared with R_1, and the output voltage goes down.

Resistors in parallel

Components can be connected in **parallel** in a circuit. This means that there is more than one way for the current to flow round the circuit, as shown in the diagram.

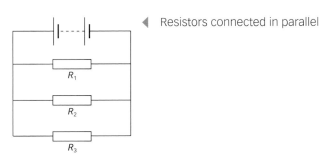

◀ Resistors connected in parallel

Connecting resistors in parallel reduces the total resistance of a circuit.

Calculating total resistance for resistors in parallel

You can calculate the total resistance, R_T for three resistors in parallel with resistances of R_1, R_2, and R_3, using the equation:

$$\frac{1}{R_T} = \frac{1}{R_1} + \frac{1}{R_2} + \frac{1}{R_3}$$

This equation is true for any number of resistors connected in parallel.

Worked example

Three resistors are connected in parallel. Their resistances are 2 Ω, 2 Ω, and 6 Ω. What is the total resistance? Use the equation above.

$$\frac{1}{R_T} = \frac{1}{2\,\Omega} + \frac{1}{2\,\Omega} + \frac{1}{6\,\Omega}$$

$$= \frac{3 + 3 + 1}{6\,\Omega}$$

$$= \frac{7}{6\,\Omega}$$

$$R_T = \frac{6}{7}\ \Omega \text{ or } 0.86\ \Omega.$$

Questions

1 (a) What is a thermistor?   (b) What is an LDR?

2 What happens to the total resistance when resistors are connected in parallel?

3 Three resistors of values 3 Ω, 9 Ω, and 15 Ω are connected in parallel. What is their total resistance?

4 Explain how you would design a potential divider circuit so that it provided an output when the temperature dropped below a certain level.

Learning objectives

After studying this topic, you should be able to:

✔ explain what a transistor is

✔ describe base, emitter, and collector currents

✔ explain how a transistor can be used as a switch for an LED

Key words

transistor, base, collector, emitter, light-emitting diode

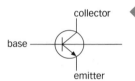

◀ The circuit symbol for an npn transistor

◀ Types of transistor. Each has three terminals.

Did you know...?

As transistors get smaller and smaller, issues arise about the possible dangers of new technologies. Should scientists develop machines with greater artificial intelligence? Are our personal freedoms under threat with increasing facial recognition and tracking? Who owns information (especially biometric data) about you?

How a transistor works

Transistors are the main building block of electronic components. There are probably billions of them in your school or house. A computer will have millions of transistors.

The circuit symbol for an npn transistor is shown in the diagram. There are three terminals – the **base**, the **collector** and the **emitter**.

Advantages of miniaturisation	Disadvantages of miniaturisation
Computer chips can contain more transistors, making them more powerful.	Smaller components are more complex to manufacture, making them initially more expensive.
Smaller components are more energy efficient.	
Smaller components have a wider range of applications.	
Smaller components mean that the products containing them can be made smaller.	

A transistor is an electronic switch – it is either on or off. In the circuit shown below, when the voltage between the base and the emitter is low, or zero, no current flows in the base and emitter part of the circuit. In a transistor, when no current flows through the base–emitter circuit, no current can flow between the collector and emitter either. So the lamp in the circuit will not light up.

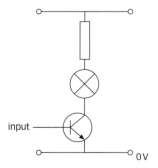

◀ A small current between the base and the emitter 'switches on' a much bigger current between the collector and emitter

When the voltage between the base and the emitter is high, a small current flows through the base, and this allows a much larger current to flow between the collector and emitter. The lamp lights up.

The very small current in the base–emitter part acts like a switch that turns on the much bigger current in the collector–emitter part of the circuit.

In the npn transistor, the current at the emitter is the sum of the currents from the base and the collector:

current through emitter = current through base + current through collector

$$I_e = I_b + I_c$$

A What is the main function of a transistor?

B The current through the collector of a transistor is 0.1896 A and the current through the emitter is 0.19 A. What is the current (in milliamperes, mA) through the base?

Worked example

The current through the base of a transistor is 0.5 mA, and the current through the emitter is 0.2 A. What is the current through the collector?

$$I_e = I_b + I_c$$
$$0.2\ A = 0.5\ mA + I_c$$
Rearranging, $I_c = 0.2\ A - 0.5\ mA$
$$= 200\ mA - 0.5\ mA$$
$$= 199.5\ mA.$$

An npn transistor can be used as a switch for a **light-emitting diode (LED)**, as shown in the diagram.

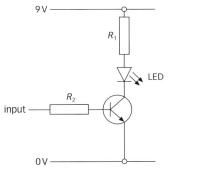

◀ Circuit to control an LED

Using a transistor as a switch for an LED

When there is a current into the base the transistor is turned on. This allows a current to pass through R_1 and the LED, turning it on. If there is no current into the base the LED remains off.

The base of the transistor would be damaged if a large current flowed through it, so a resistor, R_2, is connected in series with it to limit the size of any current in the base–emitter circuit.

Questions

1 Draw the circuit symbol for an npn transistor and label its terminals.

2 What happens when a small current flows through the base of a transistor?

3 What are the two states of a transistor?

4 Look at the LED switch circuit. Explain why R_2 has a high resistance.

5 What do you think the resistor R_3 does in the LED circuit?

Learning objectives

After studying this topic, you should be able to:

- ✔ explain what a logic gate does
- ✔ explain what a truth table is
- ✔ describe truth tables for AND, OR, and NOT gates
- ✔ describe truth tables for NAND and NOR gates

Inputs		Output
A	**B**	
low	low	low
low	high	low
high	low	low
high	high	high

▲ Truth table for an AND gate

A What do logic gates do?

B An AND gate has a low input at A and the input at B is high. What is the output?

C An OR gate has inputs A and B. The input at A is low and the input at B is low. What is the output?

Inputs		Output
A	**B**	
low	low	low
low	high	high
high	low	high
high	high	high

▲ Truth table for an OR gate

An industrial heating boiler must only start up if its pilot light is lit AND if its chimney (flue) is not blocked. It should start if the timer is on OR if someone presses the 'override' button OR if the temperature of the building falls to near freezing.

The boiler is attached to electronic circuits that use logic gates to control how it works. The output (turning the heating on or off) depends on the inputs, for example from sensors such as thermistors, or from other circuits. **Logic gates** are the basis of electronic circuits.

The AND gate

Transistors can be connected together to make logic gates. Here two transistors are used to make an **AND gate**. Each input is connected to the base of one transistor. The input signal for a logic gate is either low (about 0 V) or high. When the input is 0 V, no base current will flow and the transistor is switched off. When the input is high, there is a base current and the transistor is switched on. In an AND gate, both inputs have to be high for the output to be high.

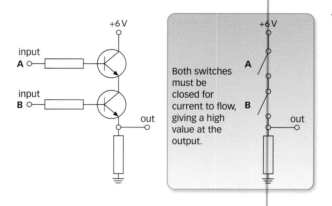

◀ The circuit for an AND gate. The inputs at A AND at B must be high for a high output. (You might think of the two transistors acting like two switches in series.)

A **truth table** for a logic gate (see margin) shows the outputs for all the possible different combinations of inputs.

The OR gate

In an **OR gate**, the output is high when either or both of the inputs are high.

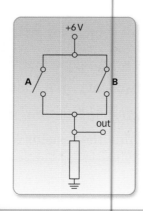

◀ You can think of an OR gate as like two switches connected in parallel. If either A OR B is closed, a current will flow. If both are closed, a current will flow too.

The NOT gate

A **NOT gate** has only one input. The output is the opposite of the input, so the truth table is very simple.

Input	Output
low	high
high	low

▲ Truth table for a NOT gate

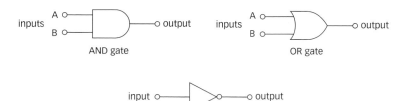

▲ Circuit symbols for the AND, OR, and NOT logic gates

NAND and NOR logic gates

Logic gates can be combined. A **NAND gate** is an AND gate with a NOT gate connected to the output. Its outputs are the opposite to those of an AND gate.

An OR gate combined with a NOT gate makes a **NOR gate**. Its outputs are the opposite of those of an OR gate.

▲ Circuit symbols for NAND and NOR gates

Inputs		Output
A	B	
low	low	high
low	high	high
high	low	high
high	high	low

▲ Truth table for a NAND gate

Inputs		Output
A	B	
low	low	high
low	high	low
high	low	low
high	high	low

▲ Truth table for a NOR gate

Questions

1 Explain what a NOT gate does in terms of its inputs and outputs.

2 Explain what an OR gate does in terms of its inputs and outputs.

3 For a new car to start, the key card should be in its slot and the brake pedal needs to be pressed. What type of logic gate should be used?

4 The sensors in a greenhouse give a high output when the greenhouse is hot and the windows are open. A heater should switch on when it is cold and the windows are closed. Explain why a NOR gate could be used.

Key words

logic gate, AND gate, truth table, OR gate, NOT gate, NAND gate, NOR gate

Learning objectives

After studying this topic, you should be able to:

- ✔ complete a truth table with inputs from three logic gates
- ✔ complete a truth table with inputs from four logic gates

A What are the types of gates shown in the diagram?

B What is the output of an OR gate when one input is high and the other is low?

C What inputs to an AND gate will give a low output?

Exam tip   OCR

- ✔ In an exam, you will be given the truth table to complete – you will not have to draw one up yourself.

When you open a car door, a courtesy light comes on inside the car. The light comes on when you open the driver's door OR the passenger's door OR when you switch the light on.

You can use a logic gate diagram to show this and to show how to provide the output to turn the light on. Two OR gates are needed as shown in the diagram below.

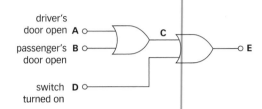

▲ Logic circuit for courtesy light in car

The truth table for this circuit looks like this:

A	B	C	D	E
low	low	low	low	low
low	low	low	high	high
low	high	high	low	high
low	high	high	high	high
high	low	high	low	high
high	low	high	high	high
high	high	high	low	high
high	high	high	high	high

Worked example

Complete the truth table for the logic system shown in the diagram.

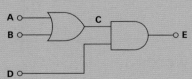

Step 1. Identify the logic gates. A and B are inputs to an OR gate. This gives an output at C. This signal at C and the input at D are inputs to an AND gate, giving an output at E.

Input A	Input B	C	Input D	Output E

Step 2. Find all of the possible combinations of inputs. The inputs from outside the circuit are at A, B, and D.

A	B	C	D	E
low	low		low	
low	low		high	
low	high		low	
low	high		high	
high	low		low	
high	low		high	
high	high		low	
high	high		high	

In the first row, start with all the inputs as low.

In the next row, change input D to high.

Next, change input B to high. This means two new rows. Can you see why?

Next, change input A to high. This means four new rows, to cover all the combinations of B and D that you have already.

Now you have all the possible combinations of inputs at A, B, and D.

Step 3. Work out the outputs. For example, looking at the first row, the output at C will be low, and the output at E will also be low. Looking at the sixth row, the OR gate for inputs A and B will give an output of high at C; the input to the AND gate is high from C and high from D, so the output at E is high. The completed truth table looks like this:

A	B	C	D	E
low	low	low	low	low
low	low	low	high	low
low	high	high	low	low
low	high	high	high	high
high	low	high	low	low
high	low	high	high	high
high	high	high	low	low
high	high	high	high	high

Questions

1 What is the output of a NOT gate when the input is low?

2 For a fire alarm to go off, both the smoke detector and the heat detector need to have high inputs. In addition, there is a button that can be pressed to test the fire alarm. The logic circuit is shown in the diagram.
 (a) Identify each of the gates in the diagram.
 (b) Copy and complete the truth table. You will need 12 rows in your table.

A	B	C	D	E	F
low	low		low		

3 (a) Identify each of the gates in the diagram.
 (b) Copy and complete the truth table. You will need 16 rows in your table.

A	B	C	D	E	F	G	H
low		low		low	low		

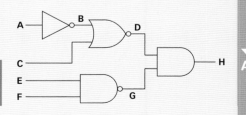

Learning objectives

After studying this topic, you should be able to:

- ✔ describe how to use switches, LDRs, and thermistors to provide input signals for logic gates
- ✔ describe how to use an LED as an output for a logic gate
- ✔ describe what a relay does

Key words

relay

A What can be used as inputs for logic gates?

Did you know...?

Thermistors are used as temperature sensors. They are often used in car engines to monitor the temperature of the cooling system. If the cooling system goes above a certain temperature, the fan is switched on. They can also warn the driver if the cooling system is about to overheat. Thermistors are typically used to measure temperatures in the range −90 °C to 200 °C.

Logic gate inputs

Input signals for logic gates can be provided by switches, LDRs, and thermistors. A fixed resistor is connected in series with the switch, thermistor, or LDR, as shown in the diagram. The two components work as a potential divider.

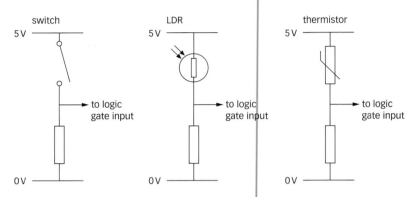

▲ Using different inputs for a logic gate

Controlling the input

By using a thermistor with a fixed resistor, you can generate an input for a logic gate that depends on temperature. As the temperature increases, the resistance of the thermistor drops. So the voltage across the thermistor decreases and the voltage across the resistor increases. When the temperature goes above a certain level, the thermistor resistance becomes so small that the voltage across the resistor provides a high enough input for the logic gate.

With an LDR, as light levels increase, its resistance decreases and the voltage across the resistor increases. When the light increases above a certain level, the resistance of the LDR will have dropped sufficiently to provide a voltage across the resistor that is a high input to the logic gate.

If you use a variable resistor in place of the fixed resistor, you can change the point at which the resistance of the LDR or thermistor has decreased enough to provide a high input. This means that for a thermistor, you could change the temperature at which you get a high input. For an LDR you could change the light level.

Logic gate outputs

LEDs can be connected to the output of a logic gate, as shown in the diagram. When the output is high, the LED will emit light. When the output is low, the LED will not emit any light. LEDs are often used like this to show that something is switched on.

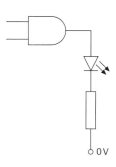

▲ Using an LED to show that the output of a logic gate is high

> When the output of the logic gate is high, there is a voltage across the LED and resistor, so a current will flow through them. The resistor limits the size of the current that can flow through the LED. Without the resistor, the current flowing through the LED would be too high and it would burn out.

Relays

A **relay** is a device that uses a small current flowing through a coil to switch on a circuit where a much bigger current is flowing. Typically, these are used where there is an output from a logic gate that is used to switch something on. For example, an LDR may be used to switch security lights on when the light level drops below a certain level. The high output from the logic gate causes a current to flow through the coil of wire, producing a magnetic field. The iron switch in the main circuit is attracted towards the coil, closing the switch and completing the circuit with the security light in it. The light switches on.

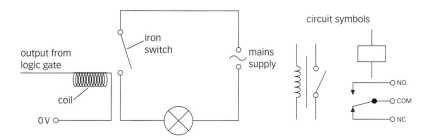

▲ A relay circuit and symbol

Why use relays?

Logic gates are low-power devices. The mains circuit uses a much larger voltage that would damage the logic gate. The relay isolates the logic gate from the mains power. Similarly it isolates the low-voltage sensor circuit of say, a thermistor or LDR, from the mains supply.

> **B** How is an LED used in a logic gate circuit?
>
> **C** What is a relay?

Questions

1 Draw the circuit symbol for a relay.

2 How is a thermistor used to provide an input for a logic gate?

3 Describe what happens in the relay circuit shown on the left when the output from the logic gate is high.

4 (a) Explain how you could use a thermistor as part of the logic gate input to adjust the temperature at which a central heating systems switches on.

   (b) How could you show that the central heating system is switched on?

5 Explain why relays are needed to switch circuits on and off.

Learning objectives

After studying this topic, you should be able to:

- ✔ describe the magnetic fields around a current-carrying wire and a solenoid
- ✔ understand why a current-carrying wire experiences a force when placed inside a magnetic field, and describe the effect of reversing the current
- ✔ use Fleming's left-hand rule to determine the direction of the force on a current-carrying wire inside a magnetic field

Key words

magnetic field, motor effect, Fleming's left-hand rule

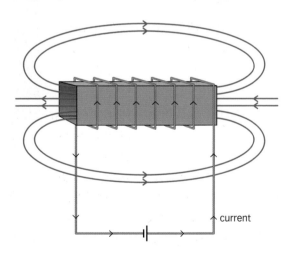

▲ The magnetic field around a rectangular coil carrying a current is the same shape as the field around a cylindrical solenoid and a simple bar magnet

Current and magnetic fields

When an electric current flows in a wire it creates a **magnetic field** around the wire. This magnetic field is only there when there is a current. If the current stops, the magnetic field collapses. It is a bit like the wake from a moving boat. When the boat is moving, a wake is created behind it. When the boat is not moving, there is no wake.

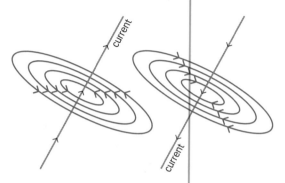

▲ The magnetic field lines around a wire that is carrying a current are shaped like concentric circles. Reversing the direction of the current reverses the direction of the field.

The shape of the magnetic field around a single wire is a series of concentric circles. However, if the wire is looped into a coil (or solenoid) the shape resembles a bar magnet.

> **A** Describe the shape of the magnetic field around a coil of wire.

If the current is reversed then the direction of the magnetic fields is also reversed, but in both cases it stays the same shape.

> **B** What happens to the magnetic field around a current-carrying wire if the current reverses direction?

The motor effect

If a current-carrying wire is placed inside another magnetic field (for example in between the poles of two other magnets), the two magnetic fields interact. The magnetic field from the current and the magnetic field from the magnets push on each other, creating a force on the wire. This often makes the wire kick or move.

This is called the **motor effect**. The force on the wire is always at right angles to the magnetic field.

> **C** What will happen to a current-carrying wire placed inside a magnetic field?

If you reverse the direction of the current, the wire kicks in the opposite direction. Changing the direction of the magnetic field, by swapping the poles of the magnets around, also reverses the direction of the force on the wire.

Predicting the force direction

The direction of the force acting on the wire can be predicted by using **Fleming's left-hand rule**:
If the **F**orefinger points in the direction of the **F**ield and the se**C**ond finger points in the direction of the **C**urrent, then the thu**M**b points in the direction of the **M**ovement.

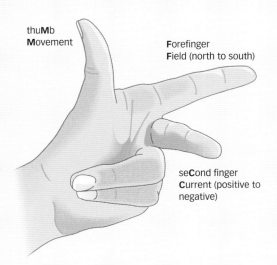

thu**M**b
Movement

Forefinger
Field (north to south)

se**C**ond finger
Current (positive to negative)

▲ Fleming's left-hand rule. The thumb shows the direction that the wire moves in (and therefore the direction of the force).

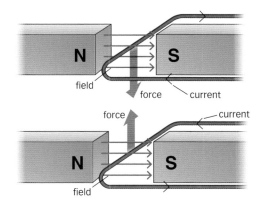

▲ The motor effect. The magnetic field from the current in the wire interacts with the field from the magnets, making a force that pushes the wire, making it move. Reversing the direction of the current flips the direction of the force.

Questions

1 What must pass through a wire in order to create a magnetic field around it?

2 Describe how the motor effect happens.

3 State Fleming's left-hand rule and draw a diagram showing how it might be used.

4 Explain what would happen to the direction of the force acting on a current-carrying wire placed inside a magnetic field if first the current was reversed, and then the poles of the magnets were swapped.

5 In terms of magnetic fields, suggest why reversing the direction of the current reverses the direction of the force on the wire.

Learning objectives

After studying this topic, you should be able to:

- ✔ state some examples of uses of electric motors
- ✔ describe the energy changes in an electric motor
- ✔ explain how an electric motor works and state the factors affecting how fast it turns
- ✔ describe how the current through an electric motor is changed to keep the motor spinning

Key words

electric motor, split-ring commutator, radial field

▲ Electric motors are not just found in small devices. They can be used in large machines, including trains and cars.

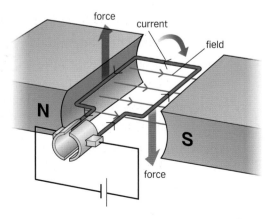

▲ A simple motor spins due to the motor effect

Electric motors

Electric motors are found in a range of things, from washing machines and CD players to food processors and electric drills. They are used to move windscreen wipers on cars, they provide the tiny vibrations in some mobile phones, and they power hybrid cars and even some high-speed trains.

◀ There is a small motor inside an electric drill

Electric motors use the motor effect to transfer electrical energy into kinetic energy. When the motor spins, energy is transferred to a moving load. This results in useful work being done. For example, a motor can be used to lift heavy weights or pull objects along the ground.

No electric motor is 100% efficient. Whenever a motor spins, some energy is transferred to the surroundings. This is usually in the form of waste heat.

> **A** Give one example of a use of an electric motor.
>
> **B** Describe the useful energy changes inside an electric motor.

How motors spin

A simple electric motor consists of a coil of wire inside the magnetic field between two magnets. When there is a current in the wire, the magnetic fields interact. One side of the coil is pushed down and the other side is pushed up. This makes the motor spin.

The size of the current, the strength of the magnetic field from the magnets, and the number of turns in the coil all affect the speed of a motor.

The motor's speed can be increased by:
- increasing the size of the current in the coil
- increasing the number of turns on the coil
- increasing the strength of magnetic field by using stronger magnets

For the motor to continue to spin in the same direction, the current needs to be reversed every half-turn of the coil. This is done using a special switch called a **split-ring commutator**. Each time the coil is vertical, the current inside it reverses. The side of the loop that was pushed up is now pushed down. This allows the motor to continue to spin.

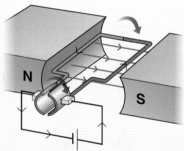

① The blue part of this coil is pushed upwards and the red half downwards. (Check with Fleming's left-hand rule.)

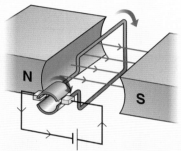

② No current, but the coil continues to turn because of its own momentum.

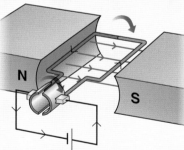

③ The direction of the current in the coil and commutator is reversed. Now the blue part is pushed downwards and the red half upwards.

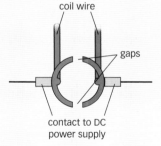

coil wire

gaps

contact to DC power supply

▲ Reversing the current in the wire coil. Look at the direction of the current in the part of the commutator and coil that is shaded blue. The direction of the current changes with each half-turn of the commutator. The same applies to the part shaded red.

Most practical electric motors use curved magnets. This produces a **radial field** so the current remains at right angles to the magnetic field for longer. This provides a more consistent force for longer.

▲ Most motors use curved magnets to create a radial field

Questions

1   What happens to the wasted energy from most electric motors?

2   Describe how the speed of a motor can be increased.

3   Explain why the coil inside a simple motor begins to rotate.

4   Use Fleming's left-hand rule to explain why, inside a simple motor, one side of the coil of wire is pushed down while the other side is pushed up.

5   Describe the purpose of the split-ring commutator found in most simple motors, and explain how it works.

E

C

A*

Learning objectives

After studying this topic, you should be able to:

- ✔ describe the dynamo effect
- ✔ describe the key parts of a simple generator
- ✔ describe how to increase the voltage generated
- ✔ explain the role of slip rings and brushes inside a generator

Key words

dynamo effect, generator, slip rings

▲ Small generators are found in wind-up torches

Did you know...?

You may remember that the mains electricity supply is ac and it has a frequency of 50 Hz. This means the voltage reverses direction 50 times every second (or once every 0.02 s). In the US the frequency of the supply is 60 Hz. Most modern electronic devices such as laptops or mp3 players can run on either 50 Hz or 60 Hz.

The dynamo effect

You might remember that electricity can be generated by:

- moving a wire near a magnet
- moving a magnet near a wire

This is called the **dynamo effect**. When a wire moves through a magnetic field, a voltage is induced. The same thing happens when a wire is inside a changing magnetic field. As long as the field is changing, a voltage is induced across the wire, and this causes a current to flow.

> **A** State two ways in which a voltage can be induced in a wire.

▲ Large industrial generators are used to supply electricity in the event of a power cut

There are many different types of **generator**, but they are all essentially just motors in reverse:

motor: electrical energy → kinetic energy

generator: kinetic energy → electrical energy

> **B** Describe the energy changes inside a generator.

Generating alternating current (AC)

Generating AC rather than DC (direct current) allows energy to be transmitted over long distances. All generators found inside power stations generate alternating current. They use a rotating electromagnet inside a coil of wire. This creates a changing magnetic field inside the coil, inducing a voltage. If the magnetic field is reversed, the voltage is also reversed. Whenever a magnet rotates inside a coil of wire, it induces an alternating voltage and generates alternating current.

The number of turns on the coil of wire inside a generator affects the size of the induced voltage. The greater the number of turns, the higher the voltage. Double the number of turns means the induced voltage is twice as great.

The speed of rotation also affects the induced voltage. Spinnng the coil or electromagnet faster has two effects.

- Spinning the coil faster increases the size of the induced voltage. Spinning it twice as fast will double the size of the voltage.
- Increasing the speed of the coil also affects the frequency of the alternating voltage. Spinning twice as fast doubles the number of rotations each second, doubling the frequency.

If a voltage is induced by a changing magnetic field, the size of this induced voltage depends on the rate at which the magnetic field changes. The faster the field changes, the higher the voltage.

If a voltage is induced by rotating a coil of wire inside a magnetic field, the faster the coil rotates, the greater the size of the induced voltage and the higher the frequency.

If a coil is made to rotate, special connectors called **slip rings** allow the coil to spin without tangling the wires. These slip rings are connected to the circuit through brushes. These provide a good electric electrical contact whilst allowing the coil to rotate.

▲ This generator is in a power station

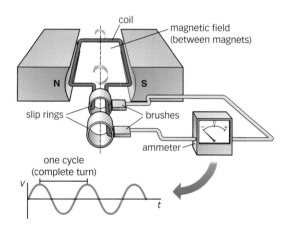
▲ An AC generator and its output

Questions

1. What is the frequency of the main AC supply in the UK?

2. What type of electricity is generated when a magnet rotates inside a coil of wire?

3. Describe the effect on the induced voltage of:
   (a) increasing the number of coils inside the generator
   (b) spinning the magnet faster.

4. Explain the role of slip rings and brushes in a simple AC generator.

Learning objectives

After studying this topic, you should be able to:

✔ describe how transformers change the size of an alternating voltage

✔ describe the structure of step-up and step-down transformers

✔ explain how a transformer works

✔ use the equation linking voltage across the coils and number of turns in the coils

Key words

iron core, primary coil, secondary coil, step-up transformer, number of turns, step-down transformer

A Why does a current not flow from the primary coil to the secondary coil?

B In a step-up transformer which coil has the greater voltage?

C In a step-down transformer which coil has the greater number of turns?

▲ The inside of a transformer

Structure of a transformer

Transformers are used to change the size of an alternating voltage.

A transformer consists of an **iron core** with two coils of wire wound around it – the **primary coil** and the **secondary coil**. The primary coil is connected to a power supply.

The two coils of wire are separate – they are not connected, so current cannot flow from the primary coil to the secondary coil.

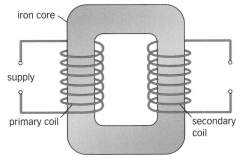

▲ The main parts of a transformer

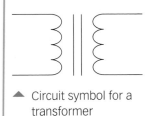

▲ Circuit symbol for a transformer

A transformer only works with an alternating current – it does not work with direct current.

In a **step-up transformer**, the voltage across the secondary coil is greater than the voltage across the primary coil. The **number of turns** on the secondary coil is greater than the number of turns on the primary coil.

In a **step-down transformer** the voltage across the secondary coil is less than the voltage across the primary coil. The number of turns on the secondary coil is less than the number of turns on the primary coil.

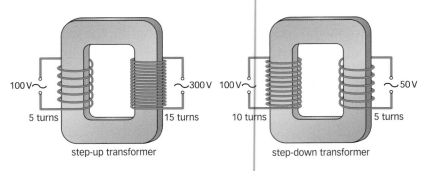

▲ A step-up transformer and a step-down transformer

How a transformer works

When there is an alternating current in the primary coil a constantly changing magnetic field is created. The iron core concentrates the changing magnetic field and this field is transferred throughout the core.

As the current in the primary coil changes direction the magnetic field it creates is reversed. This changing magnetic field continuously magnetises the iron, demagnetises it and then re-magnetises it in the opposite direction.

As the secondary coil is wrapped around the core the changing magnetic field inside the coil acts like a magnet being pushed into and out of the coil. An alternating voltage is induced in the secondary coil. The magnetic field must be changing to induce the voltage, just like a magnet must be moving through a coil to produce a voltage. Using direct current does not create a changing magnetic field and so no voltage would be induced in the secondary coil.

The voltages across the primary and secondary coils of a transformer are related by the equation:

$$\frac{\text{voltage across primary coil}}{\text{voltage across secondary coil}} = \frac{\text{number of turns on primary coil}}{\text{number of turns of secondary coil}}$$

If V_p is the voltage across the primary coil in volts, V, V_s is the voltage across the secondary coil in volts, n_p is the number of turns on the primary coil, and n_s is the number of turns on the secondary coil, then:

$$\frac{V_p}{V_s} = \frac{n_p}{n_s}$$

Worked example

A computer runs off the mains supply, but only needs a voltage of 11.5 V. There are 1000 turns on the secondary coil. How many turns are there on the primary coil?

$$\frac{V_p}{V_s} = \frac{n_p}{n_s}$$

V_p = 230 V (mains voltage), V_s = 11.5 V and n_s = 1000

$$\frac{230\,\text{V}}{11.5\,\text{V}} = \frac{n_p}{1000} \quad n_p = 1000 \times \frac{230\,\text{V}}{11.5\,\text{V}} = 1000 \times 20 = 20\,000 \text{ turns}$$

Exam tip OCR

- ✓ Remember all the parts of a transformer – you may need to identify them in the exam.
- ✓ No current flows between the primary and secondary coils – they are not connected electrically.
- ✓ Transformers do not change alternating current to direct current.

Questions

1 What are the main parts of a transformer?

2 What does a transformer do?

3 What is the difference between a step-up and a step-down transformer?

4 Why will a transformer not work with direct current?

5 A transformer has 20 000 turns on the primary coil and 240 000 turns on the secondary coil. The voltage across the primary coil is 11 kV. What is the voltage across the secondary coil?

6 A transformer has 100 000 turns on the primary coil and 2000 turns on the secondary coil. The voltage across the primary coil is 230 V. What is the voltage across the secondary coil?

Key words

isolating transformer

◀ A shaver socket contains an isolating transformer

◀ An industrial transformer that steps voltage down from 11 kV to 433 V

Applications of transformers

Some electrical devices need a much lower voltage than the 230 V mains supply. Step-down transformers are used in their power supplies to reduce the voltage to what is needed.

▲ The power supplies for all of these devices include a transformer. The laptop needs 19 V, the phone 6.5 V, and the battery charger 4.2 V.

Some electricity circuits use an **isolating transformer**. This means that there is no direct link between the current that flows through the device and the mains supply, so they are safer. They are used for bathroom shaver sockets, because there is an increased chance that water could get into the socket.

> Isolating transformers have equal numbers of turns in the primary and secondary coils. As the link is through the changing magnetic field, it is safer because there is less chance of an earth wire touching live parts.

Transformers in the National Grid

Step-up transformers are used to increase the voltage from the generators at a power station. The power is transmitted at a high voltage over the National Grid.

At electricity substations the voltage is then reduced by step-down transformers for use in homes, shops, and offices.

Some power is wasted as heat. The current flowing through the cables has a heating effect, and the transformers also heat up slightly.

> **A** Give three examples of devices that use step-down transformers?
>
> **B** What are step-down transformers used for in the National Grid?

Why power is transmitted at high voltages

The power loss when electrical energy is transmitted is related to the square of the current in the transmission lines:

$$\text{power loss, } P = (\text{current, } I)^2 \times \text{resistance}$$
$$(\text{watts, W}) \qquad (\text{amperes, A}) \qquad (\text{ohms, } \Omega)$$

Transformers are very efficient. If a transformer is assumed to have an efficiency of 100%, the power input to the primary coil is equal to the power output from the secondary coil. Power is voltage × current.

So we can say:

$$V_p \times I_p = V_s \times I_s$$

If V_p is the voltage across the primary coil in volts (V), I_p is the current in the primary coil in amperes (A), V_s is the voltage across the secondary coil in volts (V), and I_s is the current in the secondary coil in amperes (A).

Worked example

The voltage across the primary coil of a transformer is 11 000 V. The voltage across the secondary coil is 230 V, and the current through the secondary coil is 13 A. What is the current through the primary coil?

$$V_p \times I_p = V_s \times I_s$$

$V_p = 11\,000$ V, $V_s = 230$ V, $I_s = 13$ A

$$11\,000 \text{ V} \times I_p = 230 \text{ V} \times 13 \text{ A}$$

Rearranging the equation:

$$I_p = \frac{230 \text{ V}}{11\,000 \text{ V}} \times 13 \text{ A}$$

$$= 0.27 \text{ A}$$

When the voltage is increased, the current decreases for transmitting the same power. For example, increasing the voltage from 230 V to 11 000 V would reduce the current from 13 A to 0.27 A. The power losses depend on the square of the current.

Questions

1 What are step-up transformers used for in the National Grid?

2 Why is some power lost when electrical energy is transmitted?

3 Why are isolating transformers used for bathroom shaver sockets?

4 Calculate the voltage across the primary coil of a transformer when the current through the primary coil is 0.25 A, the voltage across the secondary coil is 230 V, and the current through the secondary coil is 13 A.

5 Calculate the current in the secondary coil of a transformer when the voltage across the secondary coil is 132 kV, the voltage across the primary coil is 11 kV, and the current in the primary coil is 100 A.

6 How much less is the energy loss when power is transmitted at 230 V rather than 11 000 V?

Learning objectives

After studying this topic, you should be able to:

- ✔ explain that a diode only allows current through it in one direction
- ✔ describe the current–voltage characteristic for a diode
- ✔ describe how diodes are used in half-wave and full-wave rectification
- ✔ explain how a four-diode bridge can produce full-wave rectification

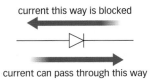

current this way is blocked

current can pass through this way

▲ The symbol for a diode shows which way current can pass through it

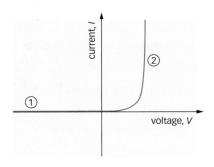

▲ The current–voltage graph (characteristic) for a diode

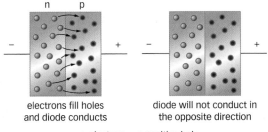

electrons fill holes and diode conducts

diode will not conduct in the opposite direction

● electron   ● positive hole

▲ The diode will only conduct if the electrons are pulled across to fill the positive holes

What is a diode?

Diodes are tiny electronic components. They are an essential part of modern technology. There are hundreds of diodes in most PCs, mobile phones, TVs, and games consoles. Diodes contain two layers of material sandwiched together. These layers have special properties that only allow electric current to pass through the diode in one direction.

The symbol for a diode shows the direction of current through it. Any current in the opposite direction will not pass through the diode.

Plotting the graph of current against voltage for a diode produces an unusual shape (see left). As the current is only allowed through the diode in one direction, any current in the negative (or reverse) direction is blocked by the very high resistance of the diode (this is the part labelled '1' on the graph). When the current is in the positive (or forward) direction, the diode has a low resistance and the current easily passes through the diode (the part labelled '2' on the graph).

The resistance of the diode is different for opposite directions of current because of the materials in the diode. One of the two special layers inside the diode has many extra electrons; this layer is called the 'n' (for 'negative') layer. The other layer (called 'p' for 'positive') is missing electrons; instead there are a series of **positive holes** where the electrons should be.

If the current is in the positive direction through the diode, the extra electrons in the n layer are pulled into the holes in the p layer, allowing a current to pass through the diode. The resistance is very low. However, if the current is in the negative direction, there are no free electrons in the holes and so the diode does not conduct. The resistance is very high.

Converting AC to DC

Nearly all electronic devices use direct current, but the electricity transmitted to homes is alternating current. Conversion of AC to DC is called **rectification**.

There are two types of rectification, and both use diodes to convert the AC into DC. In **half-wave rectification,** a single diode blocks the current in one direction.

Half-wave rectification produces a series of peaks in the current, with gaps in between. The current is always positive, always in the same direction.

Key words

diode, positive hole, rectification, half-wave rectification, full-wave rectification, bridge circuit

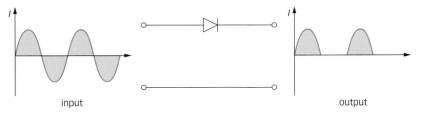

input   output

▲ Half-wave rectification can be achieved using a single diode

Combining four diodes in a bridge circuit produces **full-wave rectification**. Here the diodes are cleverly arranged to convert the negative current (the current in the reverse direction) into a positive one. This produces a series of positive pulses of current. As this output current is only ever in one direction, it is DC. However, as it is a series of pulses it is not very smooth, and further processing is needed before it can be used by some electronic devices.

The **bridge circuit** ensures that current is only allowed through in one direction. As the input is AC, the inputs switch between positive and negative values. If the top input is positive, the current passes through the top diode (diode A) and is blocked by the bottom diode (C). When the input switches and the bottom input becomes positive, the current is blocked on the bottom by diode D but it passes through diode B. This ensures the top output is always positive, so the output current is only in one direction.

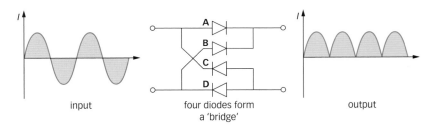

input   four diodes form   output
             a 'bridge'

▲ A four-diode bridge produces full-wave rectification

Questions

1 Draw the circuit symbol for a diode and explain how it shows whether current will pass through it.

2 Draw the voltage–current graph for a diode and explain its key features.

3 Describe the differences between half-wave and full-wave rectification.

4 Explain why diodes only allow current through in one direction.

5 Explain how diodes are used in full-wave rectification.

↓ E

↓ C

↓ A*

▲ The circuit symbol for a capacitor

▲ Capacitors are an essential component in modern electronic devices

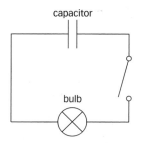

▲ When a capacitor is discharged through a bulb, the bulb lights up

What is a capacitor?

Like a diode, a **capacitor** is a simple electronic component that plays an important role in every electronic device. Without capacitors we would not be able to tune into radios or TV signals, most electronic clocks wouldn't work, and computers would not be possible.

A capacitor is an electrical component that temporarily stores charge. This charge can be discharged later. The simplest capacitor consists of a pair of parallel plates separated by an insulator.

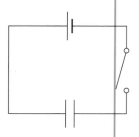

▲ A cell can be used to charge a capacitor

The circuit shown above has an uncharged capacitor. When the switch is closed, charge begins to build up on the plates of the capacitor. The voltage across the capacitor increases.

When the capacitor is fully charged, the voltage across the plates is the same as the voltage from the power supply or cell. The capacitor can now be disconnected and the charge stays on the plates. The capacitor remains charged.

> A Draw the circuit symbol for a capacitor.
> B Name two devices that use capacitors.
> C What happens to the charge on a charged capacitor when it is disconnected from a circuit?

Discharging a capacitor

If you connect a component like a resistor or a bulb across a charged capacitor, then it discharges, providing a current in the circuit.

As the capacitor discharges, the voltage across the plates falls. This has the effect of reducing the current in the circuit.

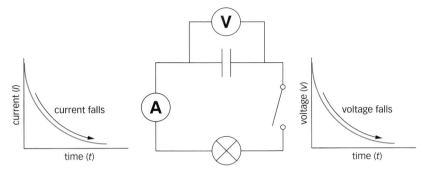

▲ When capacitor discharges through a component, the current and the voltage fall with time

The lower the resistance of the circuit, the faster the capacitor discharges, so the current and voltage fall away much more quickly.

Using capacitors

Capacitors have a number of important uses. They can be used as part of timing circuits and to store small amounts of energy.

One of the most common uses of a capacitor is to help provide a smoother voltage supply. Most electronic devices use DC. A diode is often used to rectify the AC supply, but as we have seen this does not produce a smooth supply – it fluctuates a lot. A constant supply is essential for some electronic devices. A capacitor is used to smooth out the supply.

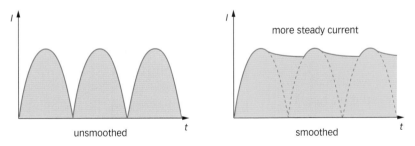

▲ Using a capacitor after full-wave rectification produces a much smoother DC supply

The capacitor is connected as part of the rectification circuit. When the voltage is increasing, the capacitor stores charge. As the voltage begins to fall, the capacitor discharges some of its charge and so keeps the supply more constant. As the voltage begins to rise again, the process is repeated.

Did you know...?

Most large speakers have several different drivers (or speaker cones). They are designed to play different sounds, rather than just having one speaker playing all the frequencies. Capacitors are used to filter the different frequencies of sounds sent to different speakers. Higher frequencies are filtered out of the signal sent to the large bass speaker. The tweeter receives a signal with the lower frequency sounds removed; it just plays the higher frequency notes. This provides a much clearer, much more natural sound.

Questions

1 Describe how a capacitor can be charged.

2 Describe what happens to the current in a circuit and the voltage across the capacitor when a capacitor is discharged.

3 Explain how a capacitor is used to produce a smoother DC supply.

4 Suggest why a charged capacitor takes longer to discharge through a circuit with a higher resistance.

Module summary

Revision checklist

- Resistance (ohms, Ω) = $\dfrac{\text{voltage (volts, V)}}{\text{current (amperes, A)}}$.

- Variable resistors control current. Voltage–current graphs show constant resistance as a straight line. A curved graph shows that resistance is not constant (non-ohmic).

- Resistance in a metal conductor is caused by collision of free electrons in the current with the atoms of the conductor.

- Total resistance in resistors connected in series is cumulative.

- A potential divider shares voltage across components in a circuit. Its output can be varied using a variable resistor.

- The resistance of a light-dependent resistor (LDR) is lower when light levels are high. The resistance of a thermistor is lower when temperature is high.

- Connecting resistors in parallel reduces total resistance.

- Logic gates control how an electrical circuit works. A truth table shows the outputs for all possible input combinations.

- An LED can be used to show that the output of a logic gate is high. A relay is used where an output from a logic gate is used to switch something on.

- The magnetic field around a single wire is a series of concentric circles. The field around a coil of wire (solenoid) is the same as that of a bar magnet.

- The magnetic field from a current-carrying wire placed between two magnets opposes the field from the magnets, creating a force on the wire. This is the motor effect. Fleming's left hand rule predicts the direction of motion.

- Electric motors use the motor effect to convert electrical energy into kinetic energy (some energy is wasted as heat).

- A split ring commutator reverses the current at every half-turn of the coil so the motor continues to spin.

- Electricity is generated by the dynamo effect.

- A transformer is an iron core with two coils of wire around it. Step-down transformers step down voltage supplied to devices that need less than 230 V. Step-up transformers step up voltage from generators at power stations for transmission across the National Grid. Isolating transformers isolate current for safety (eg in bathrooms).

- Diodes allow current through in one direction only.

- Capacitors are used and to smooth DC supply.

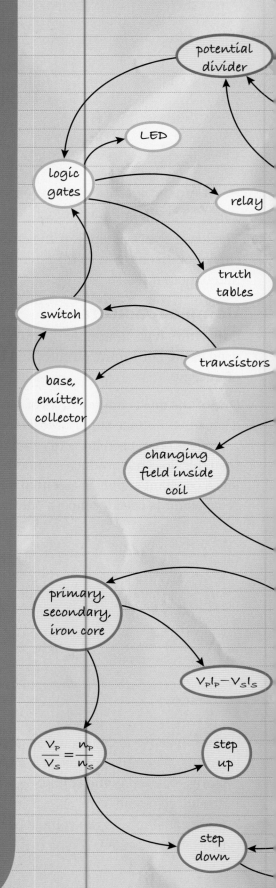

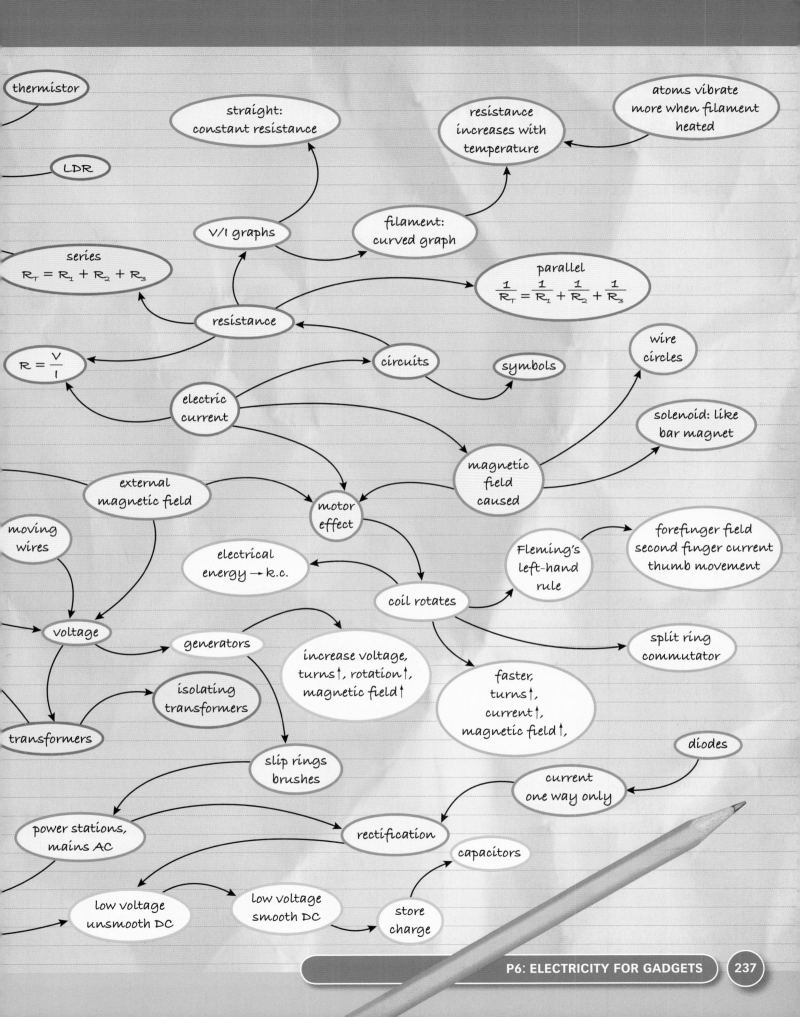

thermistor

straight:
constant resistance

resistance
increases with
temperature

atoms vibrate
more when filament
heated

LDR

V/I graphs

filament:
curved graph

series
$R_T = R_1 + R_2 + R_3$

parallel
$\frac{1}{R_T} = \frac{1}{R_1} + \frac{1}{R_2} + \frac{1}{R_3}$

resistance

$R = \frac{V}{I}$

circuits

symbols

wire
circles

electric
current

magnetic
field
caused

solenoid: like
bar magnet

external
magnetic field

motor
effect

moving
wires

Fleming's
left-hand
rule

forefinger field
second finger current
thumb movement

electrical
energy → k.c.

coil rotates

voltage

generators

increase voltage,
turns↑, rotation↑,
magnetic field↑

split ring
commutator

isolating
transformers

faster,
turns↑,
current↑,
magnetic field↑,

transformers

diodes

slip rings
brushes

current
one way only

power stations,
mains AC

rectification

capacitors

low voltage
unsmooth DC

low voltage
smooth DC

store
charge

OCR gateway Upgrade

Answering Extended Writing questions

Many household appliances include a simple step-down transformer.

Explain how a step-down transformer works, and why one might be used.

The quality of written communication will be assessed in your answer to this question.

A step-down transformer changes the curent so it is safe cos it can kill you the current come into the primry and less current comes out of the secondry it comes in at 230 V and to get less out there must be fewer coils.

↓ E

Examiner: This answer shows only vague understanding of the physics. Some ideas have been half-remembered, but the answer is rambling. Current and voltage are used interchangeably. There is no mention of AC, iron core, or magnetic field; and no explanation of coils or turns ratio. Spelling, punctuation, and grammar are erratic.

There are transformers everywhere, a step-down transformer reduces the voltage, which comes to a house at 230 V and is quite dangrous. There is a primery, a core, and a secondery. Current flows in the primary, and makes a magnetic field, this causes a current in the secondary, for step-down there must be fewer coils on the secondary.

↓ C

Examiner: Most of the described physics is correct. However, the sequence of ideas is not structured well, and there is some rambling and digression. Key points or words are missing: coil, iron, turns, the idea of AC, and changing field. There are occasional errors in spelling, punctuation, and grammar.

A step-down transformer alters the voltage of an electricity supply. In a house the mains comes in at 230 V; an appliance may need a lower voltage, say 12 V. There is a primary coil, an iron core, and a secondary coil. Current in the primary causes a magnetic field in the core; it is AC, so the field changes continuously. This causes AC voltage in the secondary. For step-down there must be fewer turns on the secondary – the same turns ratio as the voltage ratio.

↓ A*

Examiner: This answer is well ordered and accurate. The physics explanations and the use of technical terms are all correct. The sequence explaining how a transformer works is concise and logical. This is a difficult question to answer in a short space, and all the key ideas are there. Spelling, punctuation, and grammar are all good.

Exam-style questions

1 | **A02** Draw a complete circuit with one battery, two bulbs, and a variable resistor. The two bulbs are in parallel with each other. The battery is in series with the two bulbs, and the variable resistor controls the current to them.

2 State which of the following statements are false, and which are true. Rewrite each false statement to make it true.

A02 **a** For resistors in parallel, the total resistance is given by
$$R_T = R_1 + R_2 + R_3.$$

A02 **b** Increasing the light shining on an LDR makes its resistance decrease.

A02 **c** The output of an AND gate is 1 only when both inputs are 1.

A02 **d** If resistors of 1 Ω and 100 Ω are in parallel, the total resistance is just less than 100 Ω.

A01 **e** LED stands for Low Electricity Demand.

A02 **f** The output of a NOT gate is always 0.

3 The diagram below shows the main parts of a simple electric motor.

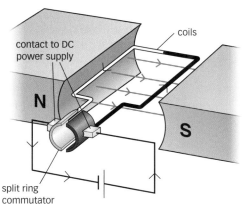

contact to DC power supply

coils

N

S

split ring commutator

A01 **a** Explain why there is a force on the white part of the coil.

A02 **b** Use Fleming's left-hand rule to work out the direction of the force.

A02 **c** What is the direction of the force on the black part of the coil?

A02 **d** What is the combined effect of the forces on the two parts of the coil?

A01 **e** Explain how the split ring commutator allows the motor to work as required.

Extended Writing

4 | **A01** Draw voltage–current graphs for a fixed resistor, a diode, and a filament lamp. Explain what each graph tells you about the component.

5 | **A01** Why do all metals have electrical resistance? Explain what happens to the resistance of a metal wire as it gets hotter.

6 | **A01** Explain the physics of an electricity generator. What changes can be made to the design of a generator to increase the voltage output?

A01 Recall the science
A02 Apply your knowledge
A03 Evaluate and analyse the evidence

P6: ELECTRICITY FOR GADGETS 239

Revising module B5

To help you start your revision, the specification for module B5 has been summarised in the checklist below. Work your way along each row and make sure that you are happy with all the statements for your target grade.

If you are not sure of any of the statements for your target grade, make a note of them as part of your revision plan. You can then work back through the relevant parts of pages 14–45 to fill gaps in your knowledge as a start to your revision.

To aim for a grade G–E	To aim for a grade D–C	To aim for a grade B–A*
B5a **Understand** that different animals have different types of skeletons. **Recall** that an insect's external skeleton is made of chitin. **Describe** different internal skeleton types. **Describe** the different types of fractures of bones. **Recall** that X-rays detect fractures. **Describe** a joint as the place where two or more bones meet. **Recognise** that muscles move bones. **Identify** joints in the human body. **Identify** the main arm bones and muscles.	**Explain** why an internal skeleton is advantageous. **Understand** that cartilage and bone are living. **Describe** the structure of a long bone. **Explain** why hollow long bones are advantageous. **Understand** that, despite being very strong, bones can easily be broken by a sharp knock. **Explain** why the elderly are more to fractures. **Describe** the structure of synovial joints. **Describe** the types and range of movement in a ball and socket joint and a hinge joint. **Describe** how the biceps and triceps operate.	**Understand** that cartilage and bone are susceptible to infection, but can grow and repair themselves. **Describe** how, in humans, the skeleton starts off as cartilage but is later ossified. **Explain** why it can be dangerous to move a person with a suspected fracture **Explain** the functions in a synovial joint of synovial fluid and membrane, cartilage, and ligaments. **Explain** how the arm is an example of a lever.
B5b **Recall** details about different animals' circulatory systems. **Understand** the difference between open and closed circulatory systems. **Recall** that in a closed circulatory system blood will flow in arteries, veins, and capillaries. **Understand** that the heart is a muscle that contracts to cause blood to move. **Describe** the heart as being made of powerful muscles that are supplied with food substances. **Understand** why the heart needs a constant supply of glucose and oxygen. **Describe** the pulse as a measure of heart beat and **recognise** that it can be detected at various places.	**Explain** why many animals need a blood circulatory system. **Describe** a single circulatory system. **Describe** a double circulatory system. **Compare** the circulatory systems of fish and mammals. **Describe** how heart rate is linked to activity. **Understand** that heart muscle contraction is controlled by groups of cells called the pacemakers, and what their function is. **Recognise** that artificial pacemakers are now commonly used to control heart beat. **Recognise** that techniques such as ECG and echocardiograms investigate heart action. **Recall** that heart rate can be increased by the hormone adrenaline.	**Describe** the contribution of Galen and William Harvey towards the understanding of blood circulation. **Explain** why a single circulatory system links to a two-chambered heart. **Explain** why a double circulatory system links to a four-chambered heart. **Explain** that the blood is under a higher pressure in a double circulatory system than in a single circulatory system. **Describe** the cardiac cycle and interpret associated graphs and charts. **Explain** the sequence of contraction of the atria and ventricles, and semilunar and atrio-ventricular valves. **Describe** how the pacemaker cells coordinate heart muscle contraction.
B5c **Recognise** that there are many heart conditions and diseases. **Describe** reasons for blood donation. **Understand** that there are different blood groups. **Describe** the function of blood clots and appreciate that they sometimes occur abnormally. **Recall** that anti-coagulant drugs can be used to reduce clotting.	**Explain** the consequences of a hole in the heart and a blocked coronary artery. **Recognise** that there are heart assist devices as well as heart transplants. **Describe** the processes of blood donation and transfusion. **Recall** haemophilia as an inherited condition in which the blood does not easily clot. **Recognise** that some substances affect clotting. **Recall** that drugs such as warfarin, heparin, and aspirin are used to control clotting.	**Explain** how a hole in the heart results in less oxygen in the blood. **Understand** why a fetus has a hole in the heart and **recall** that it closes at birth. **Explain** the advantages and disadvantages of a heart pacemaker and heart valves (over a heart transplant). **Recall** that unsuccessful blood transfusions cause agglutination (blood clumping). **Explain** how the presence of agglutinins in red blood cells and blood serum determines whether a blood transfusion is successful. **Describe** which blood groups (A, B, AB, O) have which agglutinins. **Explain** which blood groups can be used to donate blood to which other blood groups. **Describe** the process of blood clotting.

To aim for a grade G–E	To aim for a grade D–C	To aim for a grade B–A*	
Understand why most living things need oxygen to release energy from food. **Understand** that small simple organisms take in oxygen through their external surfaces. **Recognise** that larger, more complex animals have special organs for exchange of gases. **Understand** that a large surface area improves exchange of gases. **Describe** the functions of the main parts of the human respiratory system. **Explain** the terms breathing, respiration, inspiration (inhalation), and expiration (exhalation). **Describe** the direction of exchange of carbon dioxide and oxygen at the lungs and in tissues. **Recall** that there are many conditions and diseases of the respiratory system.	**Recognise** that the methods of gaseous exchange of amphibians and fish restrict them to their habitats. **Describe** ventilation in fish. **Explain** the terms tidal air, vital capacity air, and residual air as part of the total lung capacity. **Explain** the process of ventilation (breathing) in humans. **Explain** how gaseous exchange occurs within alveoli by diffusion between air and blood. **Describe** how the respiratory system protects itself from disease. **Recognise** that there are lung diseases with different causes. **Describe** the symptoms of asthma and its treatment.	**Explain** why the methods of gaseous exchange of amphibians and fish restrict them to their habitats. **Describe** how the structure of a fish gill allows efficient gaseous exchange in water. **Explain** how the alveoli are adapted for efficient gaseous exchange. **Explain** why the respiratory system is prone to diseases. **Describe** what happens during an asthma attack.	B5d
Describe the position and function of the parts of the human digestive system. **Describe** the process of physical digestion. **Understand** that in chemical digestion digestive enzymes break down large food molecules. **Recognise** that food enters the blood in the small intestine and leaves in body tissues.	**Explain** the importance of physical digestion. **Explain** how carbohydrates, proteins and fats are digested by specific enzymes in the body. **Recall** that stomach acid aids protease function. **Understand** that large insoluble molecules need to be broken down into small soluble molecules. **Describe** how small digested food molecules are absorbed into the blood plasma or lymph.	**Explain** how bile, from the gall bladder, improves fat digestion. **Explain** why the pH in the stomach is acidic, and the pH in the mouth and small intestine is alkaline. **Understand** that breakdown of starch is a two-step process. **Explain** how the small intestine is adapted for the efficient absorption of food.	B5e
Explain the difference between egestion and excretion. **Name** and locate the main organs of excretion. **Recall** that the kidneys excrete urea, water, and salt in urine. **Understand** what influences the amount and concentration of urine produced. **Understand** that carbon dioxide is removed from the body through the lungs. **Identify** the basic parts of the skin. **Recall** that water and salts are waste products excreted by the skin in sweat.	**Understand** the importance of maintaining a constant concentration of water molecules in blood plasma. **Describe** the gross structure of a kidney and associated blood vessels. **Explain** how kidneys work. **Understand** that urea, produced in the liver, is removed from the blood by the kidneys. **Explain** why the amount and concentration of urine produced is affected by water intake, heat, and exercise. **Explain** why carbon dioxide must be excreted.	**Explain** how the structure of the kidney tubule is related to filtration of the blood and formation of urine. **Explain** the principle of a dialysis machine and how it works in a patient. **Explain** how the concentration of urine is controlled by the anti-diuretic hormone. **Explain** how the body responds to increased carbon dioxide levels in the blood.	B5f
Describe the function of the scrotum. **Describe** the menstrual cycle. **Understand** that fertilisation and pregnancy are not guaranteed for all couples. **Understand** causes of infertility. **Recognise** the use of fertility treatment. **Understand** foetal development checks. **Name** and **locate** human endocrine glands and the hormones produced.	**Describe** the role of hormones in the menstrual cycle. **Recall** that FSH and LH are released by the pituitary gland in the brain. **Explain** treatments for infertility. **Describe** how foetal development can be checked to identify conditions. **Understand** that fertility in humans can be controlled.	**Explain** how negative feedback mechanisms affect hormone production. **Explain** the arguments for and against infertility treatments. **Explain** why foetal screening raises ethical issues. **Explain** how fertility can be reduced. **Explain** how infertility due to lack of eggs can be treated.	B5g
Recall that growth can be measured as an increase in height or mass. **Understand** that a person's final height and mass is determined by a number of factors. **Describe** the main stages of human growth and identify them on a human growth curve. **Understand** that it is sometimes necessary to replace body parts. **Understand** that organs can be donated by living or dead donors.	**Recall** causes of extremes in height. **Describe** how diet and exercise affect growth. **Understand** why babies' length, mass and head size are regularly monitored. **Understand** the use of average growth charts. **Explain** increased life expectancys. **Explain** problems in supply of donor organs, and use of mechanical replacements. **Explain** why donors can be living and what makes a suitable living donor. **Describe** the criteria for a dead donor.	**Recall** that human growth hormone is produced by the pituitary gland. **Describe** possible consequences of more people living longer, on a personal and national level. **Describe** the ethical issues concerning organ donation. **Describe** problems with transplants. **Describe** the advantages and disadvantages of a register of donors.	B5h

Revising module B6

To help you start your revision, the specification for module B6 has been summarised in the checklist below. Work your way along each row and make sure that you are happy with all the statements for your target grade.

If you are not sure of any of the statements for your target grade, make a note of them as part of your revision plan. You can then work back through the relevant parts of pages 52–83 to fill gaps in your knowledge as a start to your revision.

To aim for a grade G–E	To aim for a grade D–C	To aim for a grade B–A*
B6a **Recall** the size of a typical bacterial cell. **Identify** and label parts of a flagellate bacillus as shown by *E. coli*. **Recognise** that bacteria can be classified by their shape. **Describe** how bacteria reproduce. **Understand** that bacteria can reproduce very rapidly in suitable conditions. **Recognise** that bacteria can be grown in large fermenters. **Recall** that yeast is a fungus. **Identify** and label parts of a yeast cell. **Describe** how yeast reproduces asexually. **Understand** that viruses are not living and are smaller than bacteria and fungi.	**Describe** how the parts of bacterial cells relate to their function. **Describe** the main shapes of bacteria as spherical, rod, spiral, and curved rods. **Recall** that bacteria reproduce by a type of asexual reproduction called binary fission. **Describe** aseptic techniques for culturing bacteria on an agar plate. **Describe** how yeast growth rate can be increased, its optimum growth rate being controlled by certain factors. **Describe** the structure of viruses as a protein coat surrounding a strand of genetic material. **Understand** how viruses reproduce and attack.	**Explain** how bacteria survive because some bacteria consume organic nutrients and others can make their own. **Explain** the consequences of very rapid bacterial reproduction in terms of food spoilage and disease. **Explain** reasons for the safe handling of bacteria. **Describe** how yeast growth rate doubles for every 10 °C rise in temperature until the optimum is reached. **Explain** how a virus reproduces.
B6b **Understand** that some microorganisms are pathogens. **Describe** how pathogens can enter the body. **Relate** different types of microorganisms to the disease they can cause. **Recall** that some diseases can be a major problem following a natural disaster. **Recognise** that harmful bacteria can be controlled by antibiotics.	**Describe** the transmission of food poisoning, cholera, athlete's foot, and influenza. **Describe** the stages in an infectious disease. **Explain** why natural disasters cause a rapid spread of diseases. **Describe** the pioneering work of Pasteur, Lister, and Fleming in the treatment of disease. **Describe** use of antiseptics and antibiotics. **Understand** that viruses are unaffected by antibiotics. **Understand** that bacteria can develop resistance to antibiotics.	**Recall** the organisms involved in food poisoning, cholera, and athlete's foot. **Explain** how some strains of bacteria are developing resistance to antibiotics. **Explain** the importance of various procedures in the prevention of antibiotic resistance.
B6c **Recall** that some bacteria are useful in food production, silage, and composting. **Describe** fermentation. **Recall** some of the drinks produced by fermentation and their sources. **Recall** that carbon dioxide is produced during fermentation. **Recall** that some products of fermentation can be further treated to produce spirits.	**Describe** the main stages in making yoghurt. **Recall** and **use** the word equation for fermentation. **Explain** why yeast can be used to deal with water contaminated by sugars. **Explain** the stages in brewing beer or wine. **Recall** the sources of spirits. **Describe** the process of distillation.	**Describe** the action of Lactobacillus bacteria in yoghurt making. **Recall** and **use** the balanced chemical equation for fermentation. **Explain** the implications to the fermentation process of yeast being able to undergo aerobic or anaerobic respiration. **Describe** pasteurisation and explain why this is done in the case of bottled beers. **Understand** how fermentation is limited by the effects of increasing levels of alcohol. **Understand** that different strains of yeast can tolerate different levels of alcohol.
B6d **Explain** how plants produce biomass. **Recognise** examples of fuels from biomass. **Understand** why biogas is an important energy resource in remote parts of the world.	**Describe** different methods of transferring energy from biomass. **Evaluate** different methods of transferring energy from biomass, given data. **Describe** the advantages of using biofuels. **Recall** what biogas contains.	**Explain** why the burning of biofuels does not always cause a net increase in greenhouse gas levels. **Explain** how biofuels production results in habitat loss and extinction of species.

To aim for a grade G–E	To aim for a grade D–C	To aim for a grade B–A*	
Recall how the rotting of organic material occurs and what it produces. **Recall** that biogas can be produced on a large scale using a digester. **Explain** why methane being released from landfill sites is dangerous. **Recall** that alcohol can be made from yeast and can be used as a biofuel.	**Describe** how methane can be produced on a large scale. **Describe** the uses of biogas. **Describe** how biogas production is affected by temperature. **Recall** that a mixture of petrol and alcohol is called gasohol and is used for cars in Brazil.	**Understand** that biogas containing more than 50% methane can be burnt in a controlled way, but lower percentages can be explosive. **Describe** how different types of bacteria are needed to produce biogas. **Understand** that biogas is a cleaner fuel. **Explain** why biogas production is affected by temperature. **Understand** that gasohol is more economically viable in countries that have ample sugar cane and small oil reserves.	B6d
Describe the main components of soil. **Describe** a typical food web in a soil. **Describe** the role of bacteria and fungi as decomposers. **Explain** why soil is important for most plants. **Recognise** that earthworms can improve soil structure and fertility.	**Describe** the difference between a sandy soil and a clay soil. **Recall** what loam soil is. **Recall** what humus is. **Describe** simple experiments to compare soils. **Explain** why some life in soil depends on a supply of oxygen and water. **Explain** the importance of humus in the soil. **Explain** why earthworms are important to soil structure and fertility.	**Explain** how particle size affects the air content and permeability of soils. **Explain** the results of soil experiments in terms of mineral particle size and organic matter content. **Explain** why aerating and draining will improve soils. **Explain** why neutralising acid soils and mixing up soil layers is important. **Recognise** Charles Darwin's work on the importance of earthworms.	B6e
Recognise the wide variety of microorganisms living in water. **Recognise** that plankton are microscopic plants and animals. **Recall** that phytoplankton are capable of photosynthesis and are producers in aquatic food chains and webs. **Understand** that plankton have limited movement and show seasonal variations. **Recall** what affects the variety and numbers of aquatic microorganisms. **Recognise** various pollutants of water. **Analyse** data on water pollution.	**Explain** the advantages of life in water. **Explain** the disadvantages of life in water. **Describe** how factors affecting photosynthesis vary in different conditions. **Explain** how sewage and fertiliser run-off can cause eutrophication. **Describe** how certain species of organisms are used as biological indicators.	**Explain** the problems of water balance caused by osmosis. **Describe** the action of contractile vacuoles in microscopic animals such as amoeba. **Understand** that grazing food webs are most common in the oceans. **Explain** the accumulative long-term effect of PCBs and DDT on animals such as whales.	B6f
Describe everyday uses of enzymes. **Recall** that biological washing powders do not work at high temperature and extremes of pH. **Describe** how people with diabetes test their urine for the presence of glucose **Recall** how some enzymes can be immobilised. **Recall** that immobilised enzymes on reagent sticks can be used to measure glucose levels in blood.	**Describe** the enzymes in washing powders. **Explain** why biological washing powders work best at moderate temperatures. **Describe** how sucrose can be broken down. **Recognise** that, when sucrose is broken down by enzymes, the product is much sweeter. **Describe** how enzymes can be immobilised. **Explain** the advantages of immobilising enzymes.	**Explain** why the products of digestion will easily wash out of clothes. **Explain** why biological washing powders may not work in acidic or alkaline tap water. **Explain** how foods are sweetened using invertase. **Explain** the condition of lactose intolerance. **Explain** the principles behind the production of lactose-free milk.	B6g
Define genetic engineering. **Understand** that genes from one organism can work in another. **Describe** the process of genetic engineering. **Recall** that bacteria can be genetically engineered to produce useful human proteins, **Describe** how these bacteria can be grown in large fermenters to produce proteins. **Recall** that a person's DNA can be used to produce a DNA fingerprint. **Understand** that this can identify a person.	**Recall** that the new type of organism produced by genetic engineering is called a transgenic organism. **Describe** the main stages in genetic engineering. **Recall** that the cutting and inserting of DNA is achieved using enzymes. **Describe** how bacteria can be used in genetic engineering to produce human insulin. **Describe** the arguments for and against the storage of DNA fingerprints.	**Explain** why genes from one organism can work in another. **Explain** how restriction enzymes work. **Recall** that bacteria have loops of DNA called plasmids in their cytoplasm. **Explain** how plasmids can be used as vectors in genetic engineering. **Recall** that assaying techniques are used to check that a new gene has been transferred. **Describe** the stages in the production of a DNA fingerprint.	B6h

Revising module C5

To help you start your revision, the specification for module C5 has been summarised in the checklist below. Work your way along each row and make sure that you are happy with all the statements for your target grade.

If you are not sure of any of the statements for your target grade, make a note of them as part of your revision plan. You can then work back through the relevant parts of pages 90–121 to fill gaps in your knowledge as a start to your revision.

To aim for a grade G–E	To aim for a grade D–C	To aim for a grade B–A*
C5a **Recall** that the unit for the amount of a substance is the mole. **Recall** that the unit for molar mass is g/mol. **Understand** that the molar mass of a substance is its relative formula mass in grams. **Calculate** the molar mass of a substance from its formula. **Understand** that mass is conserved during a chemical reaction. **Use** understanding of conservation of mass to carry out very simple calculations.	**Calculate** the molar mass of a substance from its formula (with brackets) using the appropriate relative atomic masses. **Given** a set of reacting masses, calculate further reacting amounts by simple ratio.	**Recall** and use the relationship between molar mass, number of moles, and mass. **Recall** the relative atomic mass of an element. **Calculate** mass of products and/or reactants using the mole concept.
C5b **Determine** the mass of an element in a known mass of compound, given the masses of the other elements present. **Calculate** the molar mass of a substance from its formula.	**Understand** that an empirical formula gives the simplest whole number ratio of each type of atom in a compound. **Deduce** the empirical formula of a compound, given its chemical formula. **Calculate** the percentage by mass of an element in a compound.	**Determine** the number of moles of an element from the mass of that element. **Calculate** the empirical formula of a compound by looking at the mass.
C5c **Recall** that concentration of solutions may be measured in g/dm³ or mol/dm³. **Recall** that volume is measured in dm³ or cm³. **Recall** that 1000 cm³ equals 1 dm³. **Describe** how to dilute a concentrated solution. **Explain** the need for dilution.	**Understand** that the more concentrated a solution, the more solute particles there are in a given volume. **Convert** volume in cm³ into dm³ or vice versa. **Perform** calculations involving concentration for simple dilutions of solutions.	**Recall** and use the relationship between the amount in moles, concentration in mol/dm³ and volume in dm³. **Understand** that sodium ions may come from several sources.
C5d **Explain** how universal indicator is used. **Identify** the apparatus used in an acid-base titration. **Describe** the procedure for carrying out a simple acid-base titration. **Explain** why it is important to use a pipette filler when using a pipette in an acid-base titration. **Calculate** the titre given appropriate information from tables or diagrams. **Understand** that the titre depends on the concentration of the acid or alkali. **Describe** the colours of some indicators.	**Explain** the need for several consistent titre readings in titrations. **Describe** the difference in colour change during a titration using a single indicator.	**Sketch** a pH titration curve for the titration of an acid or an alkali. **Calculate** the concentration of an acid or alkali from titration results. **Explain** why an acid-base titration should use a single indicator rather than a mixed indicator.
C5e **Identify** apparatus used to collect the volume of a gas produced in a reaction.	**Describe** experimental methods to measure the volume and mass of gas produced in a reaction.	**Explain** why the amount of product formed is directly proportional to the amount of limiting reactant used.

To aim for a grade G–E	To aim for a grade D–C	To aim for a grade B–A*	
Understand that measurement of change of mass may be used to monitor the amount of gas made in a reaction. **Explain** why a reaction stops.	**Understand** that the amount of product formed is directly proportional to the amount of limiting reactant used. **Recall** that the limiting reactant is the reactant that is all used up at the end of the reaction. **Explain** why a reaction stops, in terms of the limiting reactant present.	**Calculate** the volume of a known number of moles of gas. **Calculate** the amount in moles of a volume of gas. **Sketch** a graph to show how the volume of gas produced during the course of a reaction changes.	C5e
Understand that a reversible reaction can proceed both forwards and backwards. **Recall** that the $\rightleftharpoons$ symbol is used to show that a reaction is reversible. **Recognise** reactions that are reversible, given the word or balanced symbol equations. **Recall** the raw materials used to make sulfuric acid by the Contact Process. **Describe** the manufacture of sulfuric acid.	**Recall** that in a reversible reaction at equilibrium the rate of the forward and backward reactions are the same and concentrations do not change. **Understand** that when equilibrium is on the right, the concentration of product is greater than the concentration of reactant and vice versa. **Recall** that a change in temperature, pressure or concentration of reactant or product may change the position of equilibrium. **Understand** that the reaction between sulfur dioxide and oxygen is reversible. **Describe** the conditions used in the Contact Process.	**Explain** why a reversible reaction may reach equilibrium. **Understand** in simple qualitative terms factors that affect the position of equilibrium. **Explain** the effect of changing certain factors on the position of equilibrium. **Explain** the conditions used in the Contact Process.	C5f
Recall that ethanoic acid is a weak acid. **Recall** that hydrochloric, nitric, and sulfuric acids are strong acids. **Understand** that strong acids have a lower pH than weak acids of the same concentration. **Recall** that both ethanoic acid and hydrochloric acid react with magnesium to give hydrogen and with calcium carbonate to give carbon dioxide. **Recall** that magnesium and calcium carbonate react slower with ethanoic acid than with hydrochloric acid. **Understand** that the same amount of hydrochloric and of ethanoic acid produce the same volume of gaseous products in some reactions. **Understand** that ethanoic acid has a lower electrical conductivity than hydrochloric acid. **Recall** that electrolysis of both ethanoic acid and hydrochloric acid makes hydrogen at the negative electrode.	**Understand** that an acid ionises in water to produce H^+ ions. **Understand** that a strong acid completely ionises in water and a weak acid does not fully ionise and forms an equilibrium mixture. **Explain** why ethanoic acid reacts slower than hydrochloric acid of the same concentration. **Explain** why the volume of gaseous products of the reactions of acids is determined by the amounts of reactants present, not the acid strength. **Explain**, in terms of movement of ions, why ethanoic acid is less conductive than hydrochloric acid. **Explain** why hydrogen is produced during the electrolysis of ethanoic acid and of hydrochloric acid.	**Explain** why the pH of a weak acid is much higher than the pH of a strong acid. **Explain** the difference between acid strength and acid concentration. **Construct** equations for the ionisation of weak and strong acids, given the formula of the mono-basic acid. **Explain** why ethanoic acid reacts slower than hydrochloric acid. **Explain**, in terms of transfer of charge, why ethanoic acid is less conductive than hydrochloric acid.	C5g
Describe a precipitation reaction. **Understand** that most precipitation reactions involve ions from one solution reacting with ions from another solution. **Describe** how lead nitrate solution can be used to test for halide ions. **Describe** how barium chloride solution can be used to test for sulfate ions. **Identify** the reactants and the products from an ionic equation. **Recognise** and **use** state symbols. **Label** the apparatus used during the preparation of an insoluble compound by precipitation.	**Understand** that ionic substances contain ions that are in fixed positions but can move. **Understand** that in a precipitation reaction ions must collide with other ions to react to form a precipitate. **Construct** word equations for simple precipitation reactions. **Describe** the stages involved in the preparation of a dry sample of an insoluble compound by precipitation.	**Explain**, in terms of collisions between ions, why most precipitation reactions are extremely fast. **Construct** ionic equations, with state symbols, for simple precipitation reactions. **Explain** the concept of spectator ions.	C5h

Revising module C6

To help you start your revision, the specification for module C6 has been summarised in the checklist below. Work your way along each row and make sure that you are happy with all the statements for your target grade.

If you are not sure of any of the statements for your target grade, make a note of them as part of your revision plan. You can then work back through the relevant parts of pages 128–159 to fill gaps in your knowledge as a start to your revision.

To aim for a grade G–E

C6a

Describe electrolysis as the decomposition of a liquid by passing an electric current through it.
Recall that the anode is positive and the cathode negative.
Recall that cations are positively charged and anions are negatively charged.
Describe the electrolyte.
Recognise anions and cations.
Identify the apparatus needed to electrolyse aqueous solutions.
Recognise that positive ions discharge at the negative electrode and negative ions at the positive electrode.
Describe the chemical tests for hydrogen and oxygen.
Describe the observations of the electrolysis of copper(II) sulfate solution using carbon electrodes.
Predict the products of electrolytic decomposition of the molten electrolytes.

C6b

Understand that the reaction between hydrogen and oxygen is exothermic.
Construct the word equation for the reaction between hydrogen and oxygen.
Describe a fuel cell as a cell supplied with fuel and oxygen, and how it uses the energy to produce electrical energy efficiently.
Recall that hydrogen is the fuel in a hydrogen-oxygen fuel cell.
Recall an important use of fuel cells.
Explain why a hydrogen-oxygen fuel cell does not form a polluting waste product.
Recall that the combustion of fossil fuels has been linked with climate change.

C6c

Understand that redox reactions involve oxidation and reduction.
Recall that rusting of iron and steel requires both oxygen and water.
List methods of preventing rust.
Understand how oil, grease, and paint prevent iron from rusting.
Recall the following order of reactivity (most to least): magnesium, zinc, iron, and tin.
Predict, with a reason, whether a displacement reaction will take place.

To aim for a grade D–C

C6a

Describe electrolysis in terms of flow of charge by moving ions and the discharge of ions at the electrodes.
Recall the products of the electrolysis of NaOH(aq), and H_2SO_4(aq).
Recall the products of the electrolysis of $CuSO_4$(aq) with carbon electrodes.
Understand that the amount of substance produced during electrolysis is directly proportional to the time and to the current.
Explain why an ionic solid cannot be electrolysed, but the molten liquid can.

C6b

Construct the balanced symbol equation for the reaction between hydrogen and oxygen.
Construct the balanced symbol equation for the overall reaction in a hydrogen-oxygen fuel cell.
List some advantages of using a hydrogen-oxygen fuel cell to provide electrical power in a spacecraft.
Explain why the car industry is developing fuel cells.

C6c

Describe oxidation as the addition of oxygen or the reaction of a substance with oxygen.
Describe reduction as the removal of oxygen from a substance.
Understand that rusting is a redox reaction.
Construct the word equation for rusting.
Explain how galvanising protects iron from rusting.
Construct word equations for displacement reactions between metals and metal salt solutions.

To aim for a grade B–A*

C6a

Construct half equations for the electrode processes that happen during the electrolysis of NaOH(aq), or H_2SO_4(aq).
Explain why the electrolysis of NaOH(aq) makes H_2 rather than Na at the cathode.
Construct half equations for electrode processes that happen during the electrolysis of $CuSO_4$(aq) using carbon electrodes.
Perform calculations based on current, time, and the amount of substance produced in electrolysis.
Construct half equations for the electrode processes that happen during the electrolysis of molten binary ionic compounds.

C6b

Draw and **interpret** an energy level diagram for the reaction between hydrogen and oxygen.
Draw and **interpret** energy level diagrams for other reactions given appropriate information.
Explain the changes that take place at each electrode in a hydrogen-oxygen fuel cell.
Explain the advantages of a hydrogen-oxygen fuel cell.
Explain why use of hydrogen-oxygen fuel cells will still produce pollution.

C6c

Understand that oxidation involves loss of electrons and reduction the gain of electrons.
Explain, in terms of oxidation and reduction, the interconversion of certain types of systems.
Explain why rusting is a redox reaction.
Explain how sacrificial protection protects iron from rusting.
Explain the disadvantage of using tin plate as a means of protecting iron from rusting.
Evaluate different means of rust prevention.
Construct symbol equations for displacement reactions between metals and metal salt solutions.
Explain displacement reactions in terms of oxidation and reduction.

To aim for a grade G–E	To aim for a grade D–C	To aim for a grade B–A*	
Explain why alcohols are not hydrocarbons. **Recall** the conditions needed for fermentation. **Recall** the main uses of ethanol. **Recall** that hydration of ethene produces ethanol.	**Recall** the molecular formula and displayed formula of ethanol. **Recall** the word equation for fermentation. **Construct** the balanced symbol equation for fermentation, given all the formulae. **Describe** how ethanol can be made by fermentation. **Explain** why ethanol made by fermentation is a renewable fuel, and why ethanol made by hydration of ethene is not. **Describe** how ethanol is produced for industry. **Construct** the word and balanced symbol equations for the hydration of ethene.	**Recall** the general formula of an alcohol. **Use** the general formula of alcohols to write the molecular formula of an alcohol. **Draw** the displayed formulae of alcohols containing up to five carbon atoms. **Construct** the balanced symbol equation for fermentation (some or no formulae given). **Explain** the conditions used in fermentation. **Evaluate** the merits of the two methods of making ethanol.	C6d
Recall what atoms a chlorofluorocarbon contains. **Recall** the uses of CFCs. **Recall** that ozone is a form of oxygen. **Describe** some properties of CFCs. **Describe** that increased levels of ultraviolet light can lead to medical problems. **Recall** that hydrocarbons can provide safer alternatives to CFCs.	**Explain** why the use of CFCs has been banned in the UK. **Describe** how CFCs deplete the ozone layer. **Construct** an equation to show the formation of chlorine atoms from CFCs. **Recall** that a chlorine radical is a chlorine atom. **Explain** why CFCs are only removed slowly from the stratosphere. **Describe** how depletion of the ozone layer allows more ultraviolet light to reach the Earth. **Recall** that CFCs can be replaced with alkanes or HFCs that will not cause damage.	**Describe** and explain how scientists' attitude to CFCs has changed. **Explain** how a carbon-chlorine bond can break and what it forms. **Explain** why only a small number of chlorine atoms will destroy a large number of ozone molecules. **Explain** why CFCs will continue to deplete ozone a long time after their use has been banned. **Explain** how ozone absorbs ultraviolet light in the stratosphere.	C6e
Recall that hard water does not lather well with soap. **Recall** that both hard and soft water lather well with soapless detergents. **Recall** what causes hard water. **Recall** that boiling destroys temporary hardness. **Describe** how hardness in water can be removed.	**Describe** the origin of temporary hardness. **Construct** the word equation for the reaction between calcium carbonate, water, and carbon dioxide. **Recall** that temporary hardness is caused by dissolved calcium hydrogencarbonate. **Recall** that permanent hardness is caused by dissolved calcium sulphate. **Describe** how boiling removes temporary hardness. **Explain** how an ion-exchange resin works. **Plan** experiments on hardness.	**Construct** the symbol equation for the decomposition of calcium hydrogencarbonate. **Explain** how washing soda can soften hard water.	C6f
Understand that natural fats and oils are important raw materials. **Recall** that vegetable oils can be used to make biodiesel. **Recall** that, at room temperature, oils are liquids and fats are solids. **Describe** an emulsion. **Recall** that milk is an oil-in-water emulsion and butter is a water-in-oil emulsion. **Recall** that a vegetable oil reacts with sodium hydroxide to produce a soap.	**Recall** that animal and vegetable fats and oils are esters. **Explain** whether a fat or oil is saturated or unsaturated, given its displayed formula. **Describe** how unsaturation in fats and oils can be shown using bromine water. **Describe** how margarine is manufactured. **Describe** emulsions and how immiscible liquid can form an emulsion. **Describe** how natural fats and oils can be split up by hot sodium hydroxide solution.	**Explain** why unsaturated fats are healthier as part of a balanced diet. **Explain** why bromine can be used to test for unsaturated fats and oils. **Explain** the saponification of fats and oils.	C6g
Relate ingredients in washing powder and washing-up liquid to their function. **Understand** the terms solvent, solute, solution, soluble, and insoluble. **Recognise** that different solvents will dissolve different substances. **Identify** the correct solvent to remove a stain.	**Explain** the advantages of using low temperature washes. **Describe** detergents as molecules that have a hydrophilic head and a hydrophobic tail. **Describe** dry cleaning as a process used to clean clothes that does not involve water.	**Explain** how detergents can remove fat or oil stains. **Explain**, in terms of intermolecular forces, how a dry cleaning solvent removes stains.	C6h

Revising module P5

To help you start your revision, the specification for module P5 has been summarised in the checklist below. Work your way along each row and make sure that you are happy with all the statements for your target grade.

If you are not sure of any of the statements for your target grade, make a note of them as part of your revision plan. You can then work back through the relevant parts of pages 166–199 to fill gaps in your knowledge as a start to your revision.

To aim for a grade G–E	To aim for a grade D–C	To aim for a grade B–A*
P5a **Recall** what gravity is. **Recognise** that a satellite is an object that orbits a larger object in space. **Describe** the difference between artificial and natural satellites. **Describe** how height above the Earth affects the orbit of an artificial satellite. **Recall** how the height of orbit of an artificial satellite determines its use. **Recall** some uses of artificial satellites.	**Explain** why the Moon remains in orbit around the Earth, and the Earth and other planets in orbit around the Sun. **Describe** the orbit of a geostationary satellite. **Understand** that circular motion requires a centripetal force. **Explain** why different satellite applications require different orbits.	**Describe** the variation of gravitational force with distance (inverse square law). **Explain** the variation in speed of a periodic comet during its orbit around the Sun. **Explain** how the orbital period of a planet depends upon its distance from the Sun. **Understand** that artificial satellites are continually accelerating towards the Earth but they maintain an approximately circular orbit. **Explain** why artificial satellites in lower orbits travel faster than those in higher orbits.
P5b **Recall** that direction is important when describing the motion of an object. **Understand** that the relative speed of two objects is lower if moving in the same direction and higher if moving in opposite directions. **Recall** that speed is a scalar quantity. **Recognise** that distance travelled = average speed × time. **Use** the equation v = u + at.	**Describe** the difference between scalar and vector quantities. **Calculate** the vector sum from vector diagrams of parallel vectors. **Use** the equation v = u + at to calculate v or u. **Use** the equation $s = \frac{(u + v)}{2 \times t}$, including a change of subject.	**Calculate** the resultant of two vectors that are at right angles to each other. **Use** the equation $v^2 = u^2 + 2as$, including a change of subject. **Use** the equation $s = ut + \frac{1}{2}at^2$, including a change of subject.
P5c **Recall** and **identify** that the path of an object projected horizontally in the Earth's gravitational field is curved. **Recall** that the path of a projectile is called the trajectory. **Recognise** examples of projectile motion in a range of contexts. **Recall** that the range of a ball struck in sport depends on the launch angle, with an optimum angle of 45 °C.	**Describe** the trajectory of an object projected in the Earth's gravitational field as parabolic. **Recall** that the horizontal and vertical velocities of a projectile are vectors. **Understand** that an object projected horizontally in the Earth's gravitational field has a steadily increasing vertical velocity. **Understand** that, other than air resistance, the only force acting on a ball in flight is gravity. **Understand** that projectiles have a downward acceleration.	**Understand** that the resultant velocity of a projectile is the vector sum of the horizontal and vertical velocities. **Use** the equations of motion for an object projected horizontally above the Earth's surface where the gravitational field is still uniform. **Explain** how the horizontal velocity of an object projected horizontally is unaffected by gravity. **Explain** how gravity causes the vertical velocity of an object projected horizontally to change. **Understand** that for a projectile there is no acceleration in the horizontal direction.
P5d **Describe** and **recognise** that every action has an equal and opposite reaction. **Describe** and **recognise** the opposite reactions in a simple collision. **Recall** everyday examples of collisions. **Explain**, using a particle model, how a gas exerts a pressure on the walls of its container. **Recall** that in a rocket, the force pushing the particles backwards equals the force pushing the rocket forwards.	**Describe** the opposite reactions in a number of static situations, including examples involving gravity. **Understand** that the equal but opposite forces act in a collision, and use this to **explain** the change in motion of the objects. **Explain**, using a particle model, how a change in volume or temperature produces a change in pressure. **Explain**, using simple kinetic theory, rocket propulsion in terms of fast moving particles colliding with rocket walls, creating a force.	**Understand** that when objects collide or interact, they exert an equal and opposite force on each other. **Understand** that momentum is always conserved, and use this to **explain** explosions, recoil, and rocket propulsion. **Apply** the principle of conservation of momentum to collisions when the colliding objects coalesce. **Explain** pressure in terms of the rate of change of momentum of the particles and the frequency of collisions. **Explain** how sufficient force is created in large rockets used to lift satellites into orbit.

To aim for a grade G–E	To aim for a grade D–C	To aim for a grade B–A*	
Recall that different frequencies are used for low orbit and geostationary satellites. **Recall** that some radio waves are reflected by part of the Earth's upper atmosphere. **Recall** that some radio waves and microwaves pass through the Earth's atmosphere. **Recall** that radio waves have a very long wavelength. **Recognise** that radio waves can spread around large objects. **Describe** a practical example of waves spreading out from a gap.	**Describe** how information can be transmitted to orbiting artificial satellites and then retransmitted to Earth or to other satellites. **Explain** why satellite communication uses digital signals. **Describe** how electromagnetic waves with different frequencies behave in the atmosphere. **Recall** the wave patterns produced by a plane wave passing through different sized gaps. **Explain** why long radio waves have a very long range.	**Describe** how the amount of diffraction depends upon the size of the gap and the wavelength of the wave, including the conditions for maximum diffraction.	P5e
Describe interference as an effect resulting from two overlapping waves. **Recognise** that when waves overlap there are areas where the waves add together or subtract. **Describe** the effect of interference on sound, light, and water waves. **Recall** that light travels in straight lines. **Recognise** that under certain circumstances light can bend. **Recall** that all electromagnetic waves are transverse. **Recall** that explanations of the nature of light have changed over time. **Describe** reflection of light.	**Describe** the interference of two waves in terms of reinforcement and cancellation. **Apply** understanding of interference to describe practical examples of interference effects. **Recall** that coherent wave sources are needed to produce a stable interference pattern. **Understand** that for light the coherent sources are monochromatic light. **Describe** diffraction of light for a single slit or double slits. **Understand** that electromagnetic waves are transverse waves so can be plane polarised. **Explain** why the particle theory of light is not universally accepted.	**Explain** interference patterns in terms of constructive and destructive interference. **Explain** that the number of half wavelengths in the path difference for two waves from the same source is odd for destructive and even for constructive interference. **Describe** the properties of coherent wave sources. **Explain** a diffraction pattern for light in terms of the size of the gap being in the order of the wavelength of light. **Explain** how polarisation is used. **Explain** how the wave theory of light has supplanted the particle theory over time.	P5f
Describe and **recognise** that refraction involves a change in direction of a wave as it passes from one medium into another. **Explain** why a ray of light travelling from air into glass usually has an angle of incidence greater than the angle of refraction. **Describe** and **recognise** that dispersion happens when light is refracted. **Recall** the order of the spectral colours and relate to orders of the wavelengths. **Describe** and **recognise** that some or all of a light ray can be reflected when travelling from glass or water to air. **Recall** the many uses of Total Internal Reflection.	**Explain** why refraction occurs at the boundary between two media. **Describe** refractive index as a measure of the amount of bending after a boundary. **Use** the refractive index equation. **Recall** that the amount of bending increases with greater change of wave speed and refractive index. **Explain** dispersion. **Describe** what happens to light incident on a glass/air surface when the angle of incidence is less than, equal to, or above the critical angle. **Describe** the optical path in devices using Total Internal Reflection. **Recognise** that different media have different critical angles.	**Use** the refractive index equation, including a change of subject. **Explain** dispersion in terms of spectral colours having a different speed in glass and different refractive indices (blue light has a greater refractive index than red). **Explain** the conditions under which Total Internal Reflection can occur. **Explain** that the higher the refractive index of a medium, the lower its critical angle.	P5g
Recall and **identify** the shape of a convex or converging lens. **Describe** what happens to light incident on a convex lens parallel to the axis. **Describe** the focal length of a convex lens. **Recognise** and **recall** that fat lenses have short focal lengths and thin lenses have long focal lengths. **Recognise** and **recall** that convex lenses produce real images on a screen. **Recall** uses of convex lenses.	**Describe** the effect of a convex lens on a diverging and a parallel beam of light. **Recall** and **recognise** the principal axis, focal length, focal point, and optical centre for a convex lens. **Describe** how a convex lens produces a real image on film and on screen. **Describe** the use of a convex lens as a magnifying glass in a camera and projector. **Explain** how the images produced by cameras and projectors are focussed. **Use** the magnification equation.	**Explain** the refraction by a convex lens of rays approaching at different angles. **Explain** how to find the position and size of the real image formed by a convex lens by drawing suitable ray diagrams. **Describe** the properties of real and virtual images. **Use** the magnification equation, including a change of subject.	P5h

Revising module P6

To help you start your revision, the specification for module P6 has been summarised in the checklist below. Work your way along each row and make sure that you are happy with all the statements for your target grade.

If you are not sure of any of the statements for your target grade, make a note of them as part of your revision plan. You can then work back through the relevant parts of pages 206–235 to fill gaps in your knowledge as a start to your revision.

To aim for a grade G–E	To aim for a grade D–C	To aim for a grade B–A*
P6a **Recognise** and draw circuit symbols. **Describe** and **recognise** that a variable resistor can be used to vary the brightness of a lamp. **Recall** the units of voltage, current, and resistance. **Use** the equation resistance = voltage/current. **Recall** and **identify** that for a given ohmic conductor the current increases as the voltage decreases. **Understand** that the current in a wire is a flow of charge carriers called electrons. **Use** models of electronic structure to explain electrical resistance in a metal conductor. **Recall** and **identify** how the resistance changes as a wire becomes hot.	**Explain** the effect of a variable resistor in a circuit. **Use** the equation resistance = voltage/current, including a change of subject. **Use** a voltage-current graph qualitatively to compare the resistances of ohmic conductors. **Use** kinetic theory to explain that for metallic conductors the collision of electrons with atoms makes the atoms vibrate more, increasing collisions and resistance, and increasing the temperature of the conductor. **Describe** and **recognise** how a voltage-current graph shows the changing resistance of a non-ohmic device, such as a bulb.	**Explain** that resistance is varied by changing the length of the resistance wire in a variable conductor. **Calculate** the resistance of an ohmic conductor from a voltage-current graph. **Explain** the shape of a voltage-current graph for a non-ohmic conductor (such as the filament in a lamp) in terms of increasing resistance and temperature.
P6b **Recall** that a potential divider is used to produce a required voltage in a circuit. **Understand** that two or more resistors in series increase the resistance of the circuit. **Calculate** the total resistance for resistors in series. **Recognise** and **draw** the symbol for an LDR and a thermistor. **Recall** and **identify** that an LDR responds to a change in light level and a thermistor responds to changes in temperature.	**Explain** how two fixed resistors can be used as a potential divider. **Understand** that the output voltage depends on the relative values of the resistors R_1 and R_2. **Explain** how one fixed resistor and one variable resistor in a potential divider allow variation of the output voltage. **Describe** how the resistance of an LDR varies with light level and the resistance of a thermistor varies with temperature. **Recall** that resistors in parallel can reduce the total resistance of the circuit.	**Calculate** the value of V_{out} when R_1 and R_2 are in a simple ratio. **Understand** that when R_2 is very much greater than R_1, the value of V_{out} is approximately V_{in}. **Understand** that when R_2 is very much less than R_1, the value of V_{out} is approximately zero. **Explain** how two variable resistors can provide an output voltage with an adjustable threshold. **Explain** why an LDR or a thermistor can be used to provide an output signal dependent on light or temperature conditions. **Calculate** the total resistance for resistors in parallel.
P6c **Understand** that the transistor is an electronic switch. **Recognise** and **draw** the symbol for an npn transistor and label its terminals. **Recall** that transistors can be connected together to make logic gates. **Recall** the input signals for a logic gate. **Describe** the truth table for a NOT logic gate.	**Describe** the benefits and drawbacks of increasing miniaturisation. **Describe** how a small base current is needed to switch a greater current flowing through the collector and emitter. **Use** the equation $I_e = I_b + I_c$. **Recall** that other logic gates can be made from a combination of two transistors. **Describe** truth tables for AND and OR logic gates.	**Explain** how society has to make choices about acceptable uses of new technologies. **Complete** a labelled circuit diagram to show how an npn transistor can be used as a switch. **Explain** why a high resistor is placed in the base circuit. **Complete** a labelled diagram to show how two transistors are connected to make an AND gate. **Describe** truth tables for NAND and NOR logic gates.
P6d **Recall** and **identify** the input and output signals in an electronic system with a combination of logic gates. **Recognise** that the output current from a logic gate is able to light an LED.	**Complete** a truth table for a logic system with up to three inputs made from logic gates. **Describe** how to use switches, LDRs, and thermistors in series with fixed resistors to provide input signals for logic gates.	**Complete** a truth table for a logic system with up to four inputs made from logic gates. **Explain** how a thermistor or an LDR can be used to generate a signal for a logic gate that depends on temperature or light conditions.

To aim for a grade G–E	To aim for a grade D–C	To aim for a grade B–A*	
Recognise and **draw** the symbols for an LED and a relay. **Recall** that a relay can be used as a switch.	**Explain** how an LED and series resistor can be used to indicate the output of a logic gate. **Describe** how a relay uses a small current to switch on a circuit in which a larger current flows.	**Explain** that a thermistor or an LDR can be used to provide a signal with an adjustable threshold voltage for a logic gate. **Explain** why a relay is needed for a logic gate to switch a current in a mains circuit.	P6d
Recall that a current-carrying wire has a circular magnetic field around it. **Describe** and **recognise** that this field is made up of concentric circles. **Explain** why a current-carrying wire placed in a magnetic field can move. **Recall** that motors are found in a variety of everyday applications. **Recall** that electric motors transfer energy to the load (as useful work) and to the surroundings (as waste heat).	**Describe** the shape of magnetic fields. **Understand** that a current-carrying wire at right angles to a magnetic field experiences a force. **Describe** the effect of reversing the current and/or the direction of the magnetic field. **Explain** how the forces on a current-carrying coil in a magnetic field are used in a simple DC electric motor. **Describe** factors influencing the strength of the magnetic field.	**Explain** how Fleming's left-hand rule is used to predict the direction of the force on a current-carrying wire. **Explain** how the direction of the force on the coil in a DC electric motor is maintained. **Describe** how this is achieved using a split-ring commutator in a DC electric motor. **Explain** why practical motors have a radial field produced by curved pole pieces.	P6e
Describe and **recognise** the dynamo effect. **Label** a diagram of an AC generator to show the coil, the magnets, slip rings, and bushes. **Describe** a generator as a motor working in reverse. **Explain** why electricity is useful (enabling long-distance energy transmission and energy storage). **Recall** that in the UK, mains electricity is supplied at 50 Hz.	**Understand** that a voltage is induced across a wire when the wire moves relative to a magnetic field. **Understand** that a voltage is induced across a coil when the magnetic field within it changes. **Describe** the effect of reversing the direction of the changing magnetic field. **Understand** that an alternating current is generated when a magnet rotates inside a coil. **Describe** factors influencing the voltage generated.	**Explain** how the size of the induced voltage depends on the rate at which the magnetic field changes. **Explain** how an AC generator works, including the action of the slip-rings and brushes.	P6f
Understand that transformers are devices that reduce or increase voltage. **Recall** that step-down transformers are used in a variety of everyday applications. **Recognise** and **draw** the symbol for a transformer. **Recall** that an isolating transformer is used in a bathroom shaver socket. **Recall** that step-up transformers are used to increase the voltage to supply the National Grid. **Recall** that step-down transformers are used in sub-stations to reduce the voltage for domestic and commercial use.	**Describe** the construction of a transformer as two coils of wire wound on an iron core. **Describe** the difference in construction of a step-up and a step-down transformer and how this construction changes the size of the output. **Explain** why an isolating transformer is used in some mains circuits. **Recall** and **identify** that some power is lost through heat in the transmission of electrical power in cables and transformers.	**Explain** why the use of transformers requires the use of alternating current. **Describe** how the changing field in the primary coil of a transformer induces an output voltage in the secondary coil. **Explain** how isolating transformers improve safety in some mains circuits. **Understand** that power loss in transmission is related to the square of the current flowing in the transmission lines. **Use** and **manipulate** the equation power loss = current^2 × resistance. **Explain** why power is transmitted at high voltages.	P6g
Recognise and **draw** the symbol for a diode. **Recall** that a diode only allows a current to pass in one direction (shown by diode symbol). **Recognise** half-wave rectification and full-wave rectification from a voltage–time graph. **Recognise** and **draw** the capacitor symbol. **Understand** that a capacitor stores charge. **Recall** and **identify** that a capacitor will produce a more constant (smoothed) output. **Explain** why many devices need a more constant voltage supply.	**Recognise** the current–voltage characteristics for a silicon diode. **Explain** that a diode only allows current to flow in one direction. **Recall** and **identify** that a single diode produces half-wave rectification. **Recall** that four diodes in a bridge circuit obtain full-wave rectification. **Understand** that charge is stored and the voltage across the capacitor increases. **Describe** how the flow of current changes with time when a conductor is connected across a capacitor.	**Explain** the current–voltage graph for a silicon diode. **Describe** the action of a silicon diode in terms of the movement of holes and electrons. **Explain** how four diodes in a bridge circuit can produce full-wave rectification. **Describe** the flow of current and reduction in voltage across a capacitor when a conductor is connected across it. **Explain** the action of a capacitor in a simple smoothing circuit.	P6h

Glossary

acid Substance that ionises when dissolved in water to produce hydrogen ions, H^+, in solution.

action Force that acts on an object.

addition reaction Reaction in which two reactants combine to make only one product.

adolescence 11–15 years of age.

aerial Piece of metal that absorbs radio waves to produce an alternating electrical current.

afferent arteriole Blood vessel that carries blood into the glomerulus.

agglutinins Antigens (proteins) on the surface of red blood cells, that determine your blood group.

alcohol Organic compound that contains the –OH functional group.

alkali Soluble base.

amniocentesis Test that may be carried out on pregnant women to test for fetal abnormality (problems with the fetus).

amplitude The maximum displacement of a wave or oscillation (the maximum height of a wave from the crest to the middle).

AND gate Logic gate whose output is high when both inputs are high.

anion Negatively charged ion.

anode Positively charged electrode.

anomalous Measurement that is significantly different from others obtained in a series of runs of the same experiment.

antibiotic Chemical, usually made by fungi and bacteria, that can be used as medicines to kill other fungi or bacteria in an infected person or animal.

antiseptic Solution that kills microbes.

artificial satellite Man-made object in orbit around the Earth or other planets.

atmosphere Thin layer of gases between the solid surface of the Earth and empty space.

atria Top chambers of the heart that receive blood from veins.

AVN Atrioventricular node, part of the pacemaker in the heart that transmits electrical impulses to the central part of the heart.

bacteria Single-celled microorganism, 1–5 μm in length. The DNA is not enclosed in a nucleus. Bacterial cells have cytoplasm, a cell membrane, and a cell wall.

base One of the terminals of a transistor.

battery Scientific name for two or more cells connected together.

biofuel Fuel such as wood or ethanol, derived from biological materials that absorb carbon dioxide while they are growing, so their use is less harmful to the environment than burning fossil fuels.

biological washing powders Soap powders containing enzymes.

biotechnology An industry developing ways of using microorganisms for industrial processes.

blood vessels Tube-like structures that carry blood throughout the body. Blood vessels include arteries, veins, and capillaries.

bone Living tissue that makes up most of the skeleton; bone is rigid.

breathing Movements of the rib cage and diaphragm that cause air to enter and leave the lungs.

brewing Production of alcoholic drinks by the process of fermentation.

bridge circuit Full-wave rectifier made from four diodes.

burette Glass tube with a tap at the bottom that is used to measure how much liquid has passed through the tap.

bypass surgery Operation in which a piece of blood vessel is taken from elsewhere in the body and transplanted to bypass blocked coronary arteries, supplying the heart muscle with blood.

capacitor Component that stores charge, usually on a pair of parallel plates separated by an insulator.

carbohydrase Enzyme that digests carbohydrates to simple sugars.

cartilage Living tissue that occurs in the skeleton; cartilage is tough and elastic.

cathode Negatively charged electrode.

cation Positively charged ion.

cell A device that transfers chemical energy into electrical energy.

centripetal force Force acting on an object that allows it to follow a circular path. The force must act towards the centre of the circle.

chain reaction Reaction in which radicals take part. At each stage one of the products is a new radical.

childhood 2–11 years of age.

chlorine radical Chlorine atom that is not combined in a molecule.

chlorofluorocarbon (CFC) Compound with molecules that contain the elements carbon, chlorine, and fluorine only.

closed system System in which no material can enter or leave.

coalesce Join together.

coherent Describes different waves that have the same frequency and velocity.

collector One of the terminals of a transistor.

concentration Quantity of solute contained in a given amount of solution, usually measured in g/dm^3 or mol/dm^3.

conception Formation of a fertilised egg; the start of pregnancy.

conservation of mass The principle that the total mass of the products of a reaction is the same as the total mass of the reactants.

constrict Get narrower.

constructive interference Where overlapping waves are in step and make a wave with a bigger amplitude.

Contact Process Industrial method for making sulfuric acid by reacting sulfur dioxide with oxygen.

contamination Process by which microbes infect a host.

contraception Preventing conception (preventing pregnancy).

converging Describes a lens that changes the direction of parallel rays of light so that they meet at a focus once they have passed through the lens.

convex Describes a lens whose thickness decreases with increasing distance from its centre.

critical angle Smallest angle of incidence for which Total Internal Reflection takes place.

denatured State of proteins that have had their structure altered by heating or by chemical treatment.

destructive interference Where overlapping waves are out of step and cancel each other out to leave no wave at all.

detergent Compound with molecules that have one end soluble in oil and one end soluble in water. This means that it will lift grease from clothes.

diffraction Spreading out of waves when they pass through a gap or around an obstacle.

diode Component that only allows charge to flow through it in one direction.

direction Where a vector quantity points to.

directly proportional When one variable changes in the same ratio as another, they are described as being directly proportional.

discharged Ion that has had its charge removed by gain or loss of electrons.

disease Condition caused by part of the body not functioning properly.

dispersion The splitting of white light into its component colours (ROYGBIV).

displacement reaction Reaction in which one element replaces another in a compound.

displayed formula Description of a covalently bonded compound or element that uses symbols for atoms and that also shows the covalent bonds between the atoms.

distillation Process by which alcohol from the fermentation process is made more concentrated by heating and cooling.

DNA fingerprint Analysis of parts of the DNA of an individual for comparison with that of other individuals/DNA samples to find out whether someone committed a crime, or to establish whether individuals are related.

DNA ligase Enzyme used to repair DNA strands in genetic engineering, incorporating a new gene.

donor Someone who donates (gives) something, such as an organ in an organ transplant.

dry cleaning Process of removing dirt from clothes using solvents other than water.

dynamo effect Where changes of magnetic field around conductors result in the generation of electricity.

ECG Electrocardiogram, a trace measured by doctors that shows the electrical activity in the heart.

efferent arteriole Blood vessel that carries blood away from the glomerulus.

electric motor Device with a rotating shaft powered by electric current interacting with a magnet.

electrical conductivity Measure of the ability of a substance to allow an electric current to pass through it.

electrode Conductor through which an electric current enters or leaves a melted or dissolved ionic compound in electrolysis.

electrolysis Process by which melted or dissolved ionic compounds are broken down by passing an electric current through them.

electrolyte Liquid that will conduct an electric current and decompose.

electromagnetic wave Wave that has oscillating electric and magnetic fields at right angles to its direction of motion.

emitter One of the terminals of a transistor.

empirical formula Simplest formula that shows the relative number of each kind of atom present in a compound.

emulsion System that contains small droplets of one liquid dispersed through a second liquid.

end point Point in a titration at which the chemical being added has exactly reacted with the chemical in the flask or beaker.

energy level diagram Diagram that shows the relative energy contents of the reactants and products in a chemical reaction.

enzyme technology Use of enzymes as catalysts in industry.

equilibrium Point in a reversible reaction when the forward and backward reactions are occurring at the same rate.

ester Compound formed when an acid reacts with an alcohol.

ethanol Alcohol with the molecular formula CH_3CH_2OH.

eutrophication Excessive growth of plants and algae in water contaminated with nitrates.

excess A reactant that is not all used up in a reaction that uses all of another reactant is said to be in excess.

exothermic reaction Reaction in which energy is transferred to the surroundings, in the form of heat, light, and sound, for example.

fatty acid An organic acid that has a –COOH functional group attached to a long hydrocarbon chain. The chain may contain both single and double carbon–carbon bonds.

fermentation Process by which a substance is broken down chemically through the action of yeast or bacteria. Used in production of yoghurt and alcoholic drinks.

fermentation Process in which sugars are converted to alcohols and carbon dioxide by the action of enzymes in yeast.

fibrin Insoluble protein that forms a blood clot when you cut yourself.

Fleming's left-hand rule Uses thumb and first two fingers of left hand to show directions of force, current, and magnetic field in a motor.

focal length Distance from the centre of a lens to the principal focus.

focus To aim something at one point, or the single point to which rays of light are focussed by a lens.

fractional distillation Separation of a mixture into fractions that boil at different temperatures.

fuel cell Device that transforms chemical energy directly into electrical energy but does not involve combustion.

full-wave rectification Process of using both positive and negative parts of alternating current to make direct current.

fungi Organisms with cells containing a membrane, cytoplasm, nucleus, and a cell wall.

The fungal cell wall is made of chitin rather than the cellulose of a plant cell wall.

galvanising Coating iron with a layer of zinc to protect the iron from corrosion.

gas syringe Piece of equipment used to collect and measure the volume of a gas.

generator Machine that rotates to generate electricity.

genetic engineering Also called recombinant DNA technology. Permanently changing the genetic make-up of an organism by inserting gene(s) into its DNA.

genitals Primary sexual characteristics – the external features that show the sex of an individual.

geostationary orbit An orbit where the satellite orbits at the same speed that the planet rotates.

global warming Effect caused by greenhouse gases building up in the atmosphere and causing a rise in the global temperature.

glomerulus Knot of capillaries in the nephron of the kidney, where filtration occurs.

glycerol Organic compound with molecular formula $CH_2OHCHOHCH_2OH$.

gravitational attraction The force pulling two objects together because of their mass.

gravity A force that pulls one object towards another, depending on their mass and separation.

greenhouse gas Gas in the atmosphere that absorbs infrared radiation from the Earth's surface and so reduces the loss of energy from the Earth into Space. This has the effect of warming the Earth.

guideline daily amount (GDA) Amount of energy or foodstuff to be consumed each day that should be sufficient to maintain health.

gullet Another name for oesophagus; in the digestive system, a tube that leads from the mouth to the stomach.

half equation Equation that shows the loss or gain of electrons by an atom or ion in a redox reaction.

half-wave rectification Process of allowing only the positive parts of alternating current to pass through.

hard water Water that does not readily form a lather with soap.

heart Muscular organ that pumps blood around the body.

HFC Abbreviation for hydrofluorocarbon, a compound containing carbon, hydrogen, and fluorine only.

host An organism that has been invaded by a virus or parasite.

humus Component of soil formed by decomposition of dead organic material.

hydration reaction Reaction in which water is chemically added to a compound to form new molecules.

hydrogen ion Hydrogen atom that has lost one electron, H^+.

hydrolysis reaction Reaction of a compound with water so that it splits into two products.

hydrophilic The part of a molecule that interacts well with water.

hydrophobic The part of a molecule that does not interact well with water but does interact well with oil.

immiscible Description of liquids that form separate layers when they are in the same container.

immobilised Describes enzymes that are attached to an inert substance to make them more stable and easier to use.

immunosuppressant drugs Drugs that suppress the immune system, given to recipients of a transplanted organ to reduce the risk of rejection.

indicator Substance that changes colour in solutions with different pH values.

indicator species Species that survive best at a certain level of pollution, and give an idea of the level of pollution.

infancy First 2 years of life.

insoluble Describes a substance that will not dissolve in a liquid.

interference What happens when waves overlap and reinforce or cancel each other out.

inverse square law Any relationship where if one variable increases by a factor of x the other falls by x^2. For example, if one doubles the other falls by 4 (2 squared).

ion-exchange resin Substance with molecules that contain ions that can be exchanged with others in a solution that is passed through the resin.

ionic equation Equation that summarises a reaction between ions by showing only the ions that take part in the reaction.

ionise Breaking a molecule into two charged particles (ions), one with a positive charge and one with a negative charge.

ionosphere Layer of ionised particles in the upper atmosphere, on the edge of space.

iron core Central part of a transformer around which the primary and secondary coils are wrapped.

isolating transformer Transformer with the same number of turns on the primary and secondary coils.

IVF In vitro fertilisation – method to help achieve pregnancy in women who cannot become pregnant naturally.

large intestine Part of the digestive system where water and some minerals are absorbed into the blood.

law of conservation of momentum Law that states that momentum is conserved in collisions. Total momentum of a system before a collision or explosion is the same as the total momentum of the system after a collision or explosion.

life expectancy Number of years people might normally be expected to live.

ligament Tissue that holds bones together at a joint.

light-dependent resistor Special type of resistor whose resistance decreases when the intensity of light falling on it increases.

light-emitting diode Diode that emits light when an electric current flows through it.

limescale Deposit of calcium carbonate that builds up in pipes carrying hard water or in kettles and other containers in which hard water is heated.

limiting reactant Reactant that is completely used up in a reaction and so determines how much product can be made.

lipase Enzyme that digests fats to fatty acids and glycerol.

logic gate Circuit that has two levels of input and output, low and high. The output depends on the input(s).

lung capacity Total volume of the lungs, made up of vital capacity plus residual air.

macrophage White blood cell that ingests foreign particles and pathogens.

magnetic field Region of space around a magnet where magnetic forces act on objects.

magnification How much larger the image is than the object.

maturity Having reached full adult height; usually occurs at around 18–20 years for males and 16 years for females.

medium Any substance that a wave passes through, eg air, water, metal.

micron Unit of measurement representing a few thousandths of a millimetre.

microwave Wave that fits between radio waves and infrared in the electromagnetic spectrum.

miscarriage Early ending of pregnancy, when the fetus dies.

mixed indicator Indicator that contains more than one substance and so shows more than one colour change during a titration.

modulation Process of attaching information to a radio wave or other electrical signal.

molar mass Mass in grams of one mole of substance.

molar volume Volume occupied by one mole of a gas.

mole Amount of substance that contains the same number of particles (about 6×10^{23}) as exactly 12 grams of the isotope carbon-12.

molecular formula Description of a compound or an element that uses symbols for atoms. It shows the relative number of atoms of each type in the substance.

monochromatic Describes a wave that has just one value for its wavelength. Monochromatic light waves contain only one colour.

motor effect The push on an electric current placed in a magnetic field.

mouth First part of the digestive system, where food enters; contains salivary glands.

NAND gate Logic gate that is the reverse of an AND gate.

natural satellite A satellite that is there because of natural causes, eg the Moon.

neutral Solution with pH of 7, with equal concentrations of hydrogen ions and hydroxide ions.

neutralisation reaction Reaction in which an acid reacts with a base to leave no excess of acid or base.

non-ohmic conductor Conductor that produces a current-voltage graph that is not a straight line.

non-renewable resource Resource, such as a fuel, that was made a long time ago and is being used up faster than it is being made now.

NOR gate Logic gate that is the reverse of an OR gate.

NOT gate Logic gate with one input that reverses it.

number of turns Number of times a wire is wrapped around in a transformer to make a coil.

oesophagus Another name for gullet; in the digestive system, a tube that leads from the mouth to the stomach.

oil-in-water emulsion Emulsion in which droplets of oil are dispersed through water.

old age Over about 60–65 years of age.

optical centre Point where the principal axis passes through the plane of a lens.

optimum angle Describes the launch angle that gives a projectile maximum range.

OR gate Logic gate whose output is high when either or both inputs are high.

orbit Path followed by a planet or satellite around a more massive object due to a gravitational attraction.

ovulation Release of a mature egg from an ovary.

oxidation Chemical reaction in which an element or compound gains oxygen, or an atom or ion loses electrons.

oxidising agent Chemical that causes oxidation in a redox reaction and is itself reduced.

ozone Form of oxygen in which each molecule contains three atoms, O_3.

ozone layer Layer in the atmosphere that is rich in ozone. It shields the Earth's surface from ultraviolet radiation from the Sun.

parabolic Describes the shape of the path followed by a projectile.

parallel Describes circuit components connected side by side so that there is more than one route around the circuit.

path difference Extra distance travelled by one wave compared to another from the same source before they overlap at the detector.

pathogen Organism that can cause infectious disease.

permanent hardness Water hardness that cannot be removed by boiling the water.

permeable Allows substances to pass through it freely.

pH Measure of the concentration of hydrogen ions in a solution.

pH curve Graph that shows the change in the pH of a solution as acid is added to alkali or vice versa.

pipette Piece of apparatus that delivers accurately a fixed volume of liquid.

pipette filler Safety device for filling a pipette.

pituitary gland Gland in the brain that secretes hormones, including antidiuretic hormone (ADH).

plankton Microscopic organism living in water.

plasmid Loop of bacterial DNA used in the process of genetic engineering.

platelets Small structures in the blood that are involved in blood clotting.

polar orbit An orbit that goes over the north and south poles of a planet.

polarisation Limiting the vibrations of a transverse wave to one plane only (side-to-side, or up and down).

Polaroid filter Sheet of plastic that only transmits light with a particular polarisation.

position of equilibrium Description of the relative amounts of reactants and products in a reaction at equilibrium.

positive hole Point in a semiconductor where an electron has been freed.

potential divider Circuit that can be used to produce an output voltage that is less than the input voltage.

power supply Source of electrical energy.

precipitate Small particles of an insoluble substance formed throughout a liquid.

precipitation reaction Reaction in which a precipitate forms.

primary coil Coil in a transformer where the input is applied.

principal axis Line through the centre of a lens, at right angles to its plane.

prism Block of glass with triangular cross-section.

projectile Object that travels horizontally or at an angle to the Earth's surface.

propellant Chemical used in an aerosol can to eject the useful contents.

protease Enzyme that digests proteins to fatty amino acids.

pulse Expansion and recoil of the arteries as blood is pumped into them from the heart. The pulse gives a measure of the heart rate.

radial field Magnetic field whose lines of force appear to come from a single point.

range How far a projectile will travel when it is in the air.

reaction Force that acts against an action.

reactivity series List of metals in decreasing order of reactivity.

real image Image that can be displayed on a screen.

recoil Backward movement induced by a force exerted on an object.

rectification Process of converting alternating current into direct current.

redox reaction Chemical reaction that involves oxidation of one substance and reduction of another.

reducing agent Chemical that causes reduction in a redox reaction and is itself oxidised.

reduction Chemical reaction in which oxygen is removed from a compound, or an atom or ion gains electrons.

refraction Change of speed and direction of a wave when it passes from one medium to another.

refractive index Sine of the angle of incidence of light divided by the sine of the angle of refraction; a measure of the speed of light in a transparent material.

refrigerant Chemical used to transport heat energy in a refrigerator.

rejection Attack on a transplanted organ by the immune system within a recipient's body.

relative atomic mass The relative atomic mass of an element compares the mass of atoms of the element with the mass of atoms of the ^{12}C isotope. It is the average value of the isotopes of the element. Its symbol is A_r.

relative formula mass The relative formula mass of a substance is the mass of a unit of that substance compared to the mass of a ^{12}C carbon atom. It is worked out by adding together all the A_r values for the atoms in the formula. Its symbol is M_r.

relay Switch that uses a small current flowing through an electromagnet to turn on a larger current.

residual air Air that remains in the lungs after you have breathed out fully.

resistance Ability of a microorganism to withstand the effects of antibiotics and not be killed by them.

resistance How much a component is able to slow down the flow of electrons through it.

resistor Circuit component that reduces the current flowing in a circuit.

respiration Process by which living things release energy from carbohydrates, also producing water and carbon dioxide.

restriction enzymes Enzymes used to make very specific cuts through DNA in the process of genetic engineering.

resultant Describes the sum of two or more quantities.

reversible reaction Reaction that can go either way so that the products of one reaction act as the reactants of the opposite reaction.

rocket Vehicle used to place objects in orbit, usually propelled by ejecting high speed gas.

rtp Abbreviation for 'room temperature and pressure'. At rtp one mole of any gas has a volume of 24 dm³.

SAN Sinoatrial node, part of the pacemaker in the heart that produces electrical impulses which cause the atria to contract.

saponification Process of treating an oil or fat with an alkali to produce the salt of a fatty acid and glycerol.

satellite An object that orbits a planet.

saturated Compound that contains no double bonds in its molecules.

scalar Quantity where direction is not relevant.

secondary coil Coil in a transformer from where the output is taken.

selective reabsorption Absorption of useful substances such as glucose from the kidney tubule back into the blood.

series Describes circuit components connected end-to-end – there is only one way around the circuit.

sex hormones Hormones that control sexual features; oestrogen and progesterone in females, and testosterone in males.

single indicator Indicator that shows only one colour change at the end point of a titration.

size How much space something occupies.

slip rings These rotate with the coil of a motor or generator, pushing against the brushes, allowing current in and out of the coil.

small intestine Part of the digestive system where chemical digestion is completed and absorption occurs.

soft water Water that readily forms a lather with soap.

soluble Describes a substance that will dissolve in a liquid.

solute Substance dissolved in a liquid to form a solution.

solution Mixture of a substance (solute) dissolved in a liquid (solvent).

solvent Liquid that dissolves a substance to form a solution.

spectator ions Ions that are present in a reaction mixture but not involved in the reaction.

split-ring commutator Rotary switch in an electric motor that reverses current in the coil every half revolution.

state symbol Symbol used to represent the physical state of a substance taking part in a chemical reaction (aq, dissolved in water; g, gas; l, liquid; s, solid).

step-down transformer Device that reduces the voltage of an electricity supply.

step-up transformer Device that increases the voltage of an electricity supply.

sterile Free of microbes.

sticky end Cut end of a DNA strand produced by the action of a restriction enzyme, which makes a staggered cut through a DNA strand leaving a few unpaired bases exposed.

stomach Part of the digestive system where physical and chemical digestion occur.

strong acid Acid that has only some of its molecules ionised when in solution.

switch Circuit component that can be used to switch the circuit on or off by creating a gap in the circuit.

symptom How you feel when you have a disease, eg headache, feeling sick. Do not confuse symptoms with signs – signs are the measurable changes when you have a disease, such as increased temperature or a rash.

synovial joint Joint in the body that is lubricated by synovial fluid, such as the knee, hip, and elbow. The joint also has a synovial membrane, ligaments, and cartilage.

temporary hardness Water hardness that can be removed by boiling the water.

tendon Tissue that connects muscles to bones; tendons are tough and do not stretch.

thermal decomposition Process of breaking a compound down into simpler substances by heating it.

thermistor Special type of resistor whose resistance decreases as temperature increases.

tidal volume Volume of air breathed in during one breath.

time period Time taken to complete one full cycle. For example, one orbit or one full oscillation.

tissue match Matching the tissues of donor and recipient in a transplant operation, so that their antigens are similar and there is less chance of rejection.

titration Procedure in which one solution is added to a known volume of another to measure the volume of the first solution required to react with the second.

titre The measured volume of the solution added during a titration to reach the end point.

Total Internal Reflection When a wave travelling inside a denser medium reflects off the boundary with another medium, and so stays inside the original material.

toxin Poison.

trajectory Path followed by a projectile due to gravity.

transgenic Describes bacteria that have taken up an engineered plasmid (carrying a new gene) in the process of genetic engineering.

transistor Electronic device that can act as a switch.

transmission Process by which microbes are spread.

transverse wave Wave whose vibrations are at right angles to the direction of wave motion.

traumatic Physically damaging.

truth table Table summarising all the possible outputs from all the different combinations of inputs to a system of logic gates.

unsaturated Compound that contains at least one double bond in its molecules.

upward displacement Method of collecting a gas by displacing a liquid in a closed inverted tube.

urea Substance produced in the liver from the breakdown of amino acids, and removed by the kidneys in the urine.

variable resistor Resistor whose resistance can be changed.

vector Quantity that includes direction.

velocity How fast something is moving in a certain direction.

ventilation Movement of air into and out of the lungs, brought about by inhaling and exhaling.

ventricles Lower chambers of the heart that contract and force blood out of the heart into the arteries.

virtual image Image that cannot be displayed on a screen.

viruses Extremely small infectious agents that can only be seen with an electron microscope and can only live or reproduce inside a host cell.

visible spectrum Range of colours present in light.

vital capacity Maximum volume of air you can breathe out after taking a big breath in.

washing soda The compound sodium carbonate, Na_2CO_3.

water-in-oil emulsion Emulsion in which droplets of water are dispersed through oil.

weak acid Acid that has all its molecules ionised when in solution.

weight Force on an object due to the force of gravity on a planet.

yeast Name given to single-celled fungi that cause fermentation.

Index

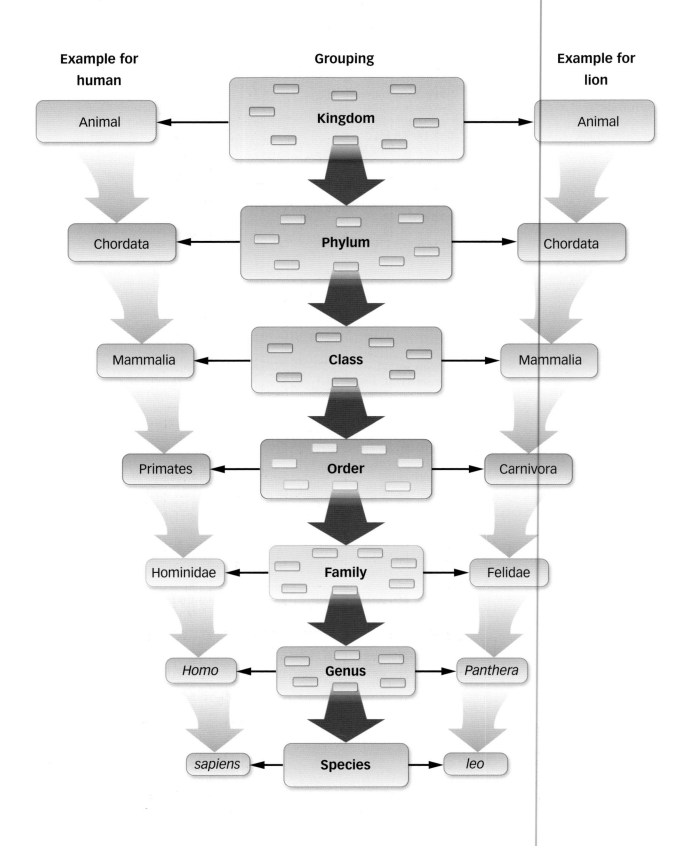

Example for human | Grouping | Example for lion

Animal ← Kingdom → Animal

Chordata ← Phylum → Chordata

Mammalia ← Class → Mammalia

Primates ← Order → Carnivora

Hominidae ← Family → Felidae

Homo ← Genus → *Panthera*

sapiens ← Species → *leo*

Periodic table

Key

relative atomic mass
atomic symbol
name
atomic (proton) number

Example:
1
H
hydrogen
1

1	2											3	4	5	6	7	0
																	4 **He** helium 2
7 **Li** lithium 3	9 **Be** beryllium 4											11 **B** boron 5	12 **C** carbon 6	14 **N** nitrogen 7	16 **O** oxygen 8	19 **F** fluorine 9	20 **Ne** neon 10
23 **Na** sodium 11	24 **Mg** magnesium 12											27 **Al** aluminium 13	28 **Si** silicon 14	31 **P** phosphorus 15	32 **S** sulfur 16	35.5 **Cl** chlorine 17	40 **Ar** argon 18
39 **K** potassium 19	40 **Ca** calcium 20	45 **Sc** scandium 21	48 **Ti** titanium 22	51 **V** vanadium 23	52 **Cr** chromium 24	55 **Mn** manganese 25	56 **Fe** iron 26	59 **Co** cobalt 27	59 **Ni** nickel 28	63.5 **Cu** copper 29	65 **Zn** zinc 30	70 **Ga** gallium 31	73 **Ge** germanium 32	75 **As** arsenic 33	79 **Se** selenium 34	80 **Br** bromine 35	84 **Kr** krypton 36
85 **Rb** rubidium 37	88 **Sr** strontium 38	89 **Y** yttrium 39	91 **Zr** zirconium 40	93 **Nb** niobium 41	96 **Mo** molybdenum 42	[98] **Tc** technetium 43	101 **Ru** ruthenium 44	103 **Rh** rhodium 45	106 **Pd** palladium 46	108 **Ag** silver 47	112 **Cd** cadmium 48	115 **In** indium 49	119 **Sn** tin 50	122 **Sb** antimony 51	128 **Te** tellurium 52	127 **I** iodine 53	131 **Xe** xenon 54
133 **Cs** caesium 55	137 **Ba** barium 56	139 **La*** lanthanum 57	178 **Hf** hafnium 72	181 **Ta** tantalum 73	184 **W** tungsten 74	186 **Re** rhenium 75	190 **Os** osmium 76	192 **Ir** iridium 77	195 **Pt** platinum 78	197 **Au** gold 79	201 **Hg** mercury 80	204 **Tl** thallium 81	207 **Pb** lead 82	209 **Bi** bismuth 83	[209] **Po** polonium 84	[210] **At** astatine 85	[222] **Rn** radon 86
[223] **Fr** francium 87	[226] **Ra** radium 88	[227] **Ac*** actinium 89	[261] **Rf** rutherfordium 104	[262] **Db** dubnium 105	[266] **Sg** seaborgium 106	[264] **Bh** bohrium 107	[277] **Hs** hassium 108	[268] **Mt** meitnerium 109	[271] **Ds** darmstadtium 110	[272] **Rg** roentgenium 111							

Elements with atomic numbers 112–116 have been reported but not fully authenticated

* The lanthanoids (atomic numbers 58–71) and the actinoids (atomic numbers 90–103) have been omitted.

Fundamental physical quantities

Physical quantity	Unit(s)
length	metre (m) kilometre (km) centimetre (cm) millimetre (mm)
mass	kilogram (kg) gram (g) milligram (mg)
time	second (s) millisecond (ms)
temperature	degree Celsius (°C) kelvin (K)
current	ampere (A) milliampere (mA)
voltage	volt (V) millivolt (mV)

Derived quantities and units

Physical quantity	Unit(s)
area	cm^2; m^2
volume	cm^3; dm^3; m^3; litre (l); millilitre (ml)
density	kg/m^3; g/cm^3
force	newton (N)
speed	m/s; km/h
energy	joule (J); kilojoule (kJ); megajoule (MJ)
power	watt (W); kilowatt (kW); megawatt (MW)
frequency	hertz (Hz); kilohertz (kHz)
gravitational field strength	N/kg
radioactivity	becquerel (Bq)
acceleration	m/s^2; km/h^2
specific heat capacity	J/kg°C
specific latent heat	J/kg

Electrical symbols

junction of conductors	ammeter	diode	capacitor
switch	voltmeter	electrolytic capacitor	relay
primary or secondary cell	indicator or light source	LDR	LED
battery of cells		thermistor	NOT gate
power supply	motor	AND gate	OR gate
fuse	generator	NOR gate	NAND gate
fixed resistor	variable resistor		

Acknowledgements

The publisher and authors would like to thank the following for their permission to reproduce photographs and other copyright material:

p6 Mauro Fermariello/SPL; **p8** Laurence Gough/Istockphoto; **p9** 81a/Alamy; **p10B** 81a/Alamy; **p10T** Gordon Scammell/Alamy; **p11** Laurence Gough/Istockphoto; **p13** Tek Image/SPL; **p14** Michael Patrick O'Neill/SPL; **p17** Living Art Enterprises, LLC/SPL; **p21T** Gary Carlson/SPL; **p21B** D. Varty, Ism/SPL; **p22T** Gustoimages/SPL; **p22B** BSIP, Raguet H/SPL; **p24** SPL; **p26** David Aubrey/SPL; **p27** Claude Nuridsany & Marie Perennou/SPL; **p30** Steve Gschmeissner/SPL; **p31T** Moredun Animal Health Ltd/SPL; **p31B** Medical RF.com/SPL; **p33** Eye Of Science/SPL; **p39** Medical RF.com/SPL; **p40T** AJ Photo/SPL; **p40B** CC Studio/SPL; **p43** Jacob Wackerhausen/Istockphoto; **p44L** Hank Morgan/SPL; **p44R** Life In View/SPL; **p51** Patrick Landmann/SPL; **p52T** Eye Of Science/SPL; **p52MT** Scimat/SPL; **p52MB** London School Of Hygiene & Tropical Medicine/SPL; **p52B** SPL; **p54T** Science VU, Visuals Unlimited/SPL; **p54B** David M. Phillips/SPL; **p55L** Pasieka/SPL; **p55R** Cavallini James/SPL; **p56** Mark Clarke/SPL; **p57T** Tim Vernon, LTH NHS Trust/SPL; **p57BL** Adam Hart-Davis/SPL; **p57M** Dr H.C. Robinson/SPL; **p57BR** Adam Hart-Davis/SPL; **p58** Lowell Georgia/SPL; **p60TL** Custom Medical Stock Photo/SPL; **p60TR** Science Source/SPL; **p60B** Chris Ware/Stringer/Hulton Archive/Getty Images; **p62L** BSIP Chassenet/SPL; **p62R** Trevor Clifford Photography/SPL; **p63T** Robert Brook/SPL; **p63BL** Rosenfeld Images Ltd/SPL; **p63BR** Mark Sykes/SPL; **p65** Mike Bentley/Istockphoto; **p72** Julie Dermansky/SPL; **p73** BSIP Martin Pl./SPL; **p74MB** Saturn Stills/SPL; **p74T** Rosenfeld Images Ltd/SPL; **p74MT** Veronique Leplat/SPL; **p74M** BSIP Chassenet/SPL; **p74B** Heike Brauer/Istockphoto; **p75** Jonathan Hordle/Rex Features; **p76** Saturn Stills/SPL; **p77** Jim Amos/SPL; **p79R** Maximilian Stock Ltd/SPL; **p79L** ISM/Photolibrary; **p82T** Pasieka/SPL; **p82B** Dra Schwartz/Istockphoto; **p83** Martin Shields/SPL; **p89** Ted Clutter/SPL; **p90** Andrew Lambert Photography/SPL; **p92** Dirk Wiersma/SPL; **p94** Carlos Neto/Shutterstock; **p96** Martyn F. Chillmaid/SPL; **p97** Andrew Lambert Photography/SPL; **p98** Ian Hooton/SPL; **p100** Andrew Brookes, National Physical Laboratory/SPL; **p101** Paul Rapson/SPL; **p102** Andrew Lambert Photography/SPL; **p104TL** Jerry Mason/SPL; **p104R** Andrew Lambert Photography/SPL; **p104BL** Charles D. Winters/SPL; **p106L** American Honda Motor Co., Inc.; **p106** Andrew Lambert Photography/SPL; **p107** Andrew Lambert Photography/SPL; **p108** Charles D. Winters/SPL; **p110** Kuttig/Alamy; **p112T** Photo Researchers/SPL; **p112B** Andrew Lambert Photography/SPL; **p114** Betty Finney/Alamy; **p115** Andrew Lambert Photography/SPL; **p116L** Christopher Nash/Alamy; **p116R** Martyn F. Chillmaid/SPL; **p118L** Andrew Lambert Photography/SPL; **p118R** SPL; **p120T** Sovereign, Ism/SPL; **p120B** Andrew Lambert Photography/SPL; **p121** Charles D. Winters/SPL; **p129** NASA/SPL; **p128** Trevor Clifford Photography/SPL; **p129** Sheila Terry/SPL; **p130T** Andrew Lambert Photography/SPL; **p130B** Trevor Clifford Photography/SPL; **p134T** NASA/SPL; **p134B** NASA; **p135** Martin Bond/SPL; **p136** Charles D. Winters/SPL; **p138** John Mole Photography/Alamy; **p139T** Photos.com; **p139B** Photos.com; **p140** Charles D. Winters/SPL; **p141** Peter Menzel/SPL; **p142** Peter Bowater/SPL; **p144** George Steinmetz/SPL; **p145** Sue Ford/SPL; **p146L** Photos.com; **p146R** NASA/SPL; **p148** Matthew Benoit/Shutterstock; **p149** Sheila Terry/SPL; **p150** Pink Sun Media/Alamy; **p151** DWD-photo/Alamy; **p152** Cordelia Molloy/SPL; **p154** Charles D. Winters/SPL; **p155** CC Studio/SPL; **p155** BigPileStock/Alamy; **p156** Andrew Lambert Photography/SPL; **p157** Klaus Guldbrandsen/SPL; **p158T** Photos.com; **p158B** Ted Foxx/Alamy; **p165** NASA/SPL; **p166** NASA/SPL; **p166** Parameter/Istockphoto; **p168** NASA; **p169** NASA; **p172** Marcus Lindstrom/Istockphoto; **p173** Bjorn Kindler/Istockphoto; **p174T** Technotr/Istockphoto; **p174B** Albo/Dreamstime; **p177** Drbueller/Istockphoto; **p178B** Lisa Davis/Istockphoto; **p178T** 1 design/Istockphoto; **p179** NASA/SPL; **p180** swissmacky/Shutterstock; **p182** David J. Green/Alamy; **p185** James Scott/Dreamstime; **p186** Andres Rodriguez/Bigstock; **p187R** Mehmet Fatih Kocyildir/Dreamstime; **p187L** Andrew Lambert Photography/SPL; **p188TL** American Institute of Physics/SPL; **p188TR** SPL; **p188B** Laurent Laveder/SPL; **p189** Giphotostock/SPL; **p190** Erich Schrempp/SPL; **p192R** Stewyphoto/Shutterstock; **p192L** Lawrence Lawry/SPL; **p194** Giphotostock/SPL; **p195** Mark Bourdillon/Alamy; **p196R** Jeffrey L. Rotman/Photolibrary; **p196L** Phil Degginger/Alamy; **p198** Imagemore Co., Ltd./Alamy; **p199** Diego Cervo/Shutterstock; **p205** Dr Jeremy Burgess/SPL; **p206T1** Andrew Lambert Photography/SPL; **p206T2** Paul Reid/Shutterstock; **p206T3** Chris Hutchison/Istockphoto; **p206T4** Andrew Lambert Photography/SPL; **p206T5** Trevor Clifford Photography/SPL; **p206T6** Doug Martin/SPL; **p206T7** Trevor Clifford Photography/SPL; **p209** Pali Rao/Istockphoto; **p212B** Andrew Lambert Photography/SPL; **p212T** Martyn F. Chillmaid/SPL; **p214** Alexander Khromtsov/Istockphoto; **p224L** ZCW/Shutterstock; **p224R** Lisa F. Young/Istockphoto; **p225L** Sciencephotos/Alamy; **p226R** U.S. Nuclear Regulatory Commission; **p226L** Awe Inspiring Images/Shutterstock; **p227** Vydrin/Shutterstock; **p228** Jeronimo Create/Istockphoto; **p230BL** Sheila Terry/SPL; **p230TMR** Edhar/Shutterstock; **p230TML** Mark Goble/Alamy; **p230TR** Judith Collins/Alamy; **p230TL** Sheila Terry/SPL; **p234** Vydrin/Shutterstock

Cover image courtesy of DR ARTHUR TUCKER/SCIENCE PHOTO LIBRARY.

Illustrations by Wearset Ltd, and HL Studios.

Although we have made every effort to trace and contact all copyright holders before publication this has not been possible in all cases. If notified, the publisher will rectify any errors or omissions at the earliest opportunity.

OXFORD
UNIVERSITY PRESS

Great Clarendon Street, Oxford OX2 6DP

Oxford University Press is a department of the University of Oxford.
It furthers the University's objective of excellence in research,
scholarship, and education by publishing worldwide in

Oxford   New York

Auckland   Cape Town   Dar es Salaam   Hong Kong   Karachi
Kuala Lumpur   Madrid   Melbourne   Mexico City   Nairobi
New Delhi   Shanghai   Taipei   Toronto

With offices in
Argentina   Austria   Brazil   Chile   Czech Republic   France   Greece
Guatemala   Hungary   Italy   Japan   Poland   Portugal   Singapore
South Korea   Switzerland   Thailand   Turkey   Ukraine   Vietnam

Oxford is a registered trade mark of Oxford University Press
in the UK and in certain other countries.

British Library Cataloguing in Publication Data

Data available

ISBN 978-0-19-9913563-9

10 9 8 7 6 5 4 3 2 1

Printed in Great Britain by Bell and Bain, Glasgow

Paper used in the production of this book is a natural, recyclable product
made from wood grown in sustainable forests. The manufacturing process
conforms to the environmental regulations of the country of origin.

Mixed Sources
Product group from well-managed
forests and other controlled sources
www.fsc.org Cert no. TT-COC-002769
© 1996 Forest Stewardship Council

FSC